UNIVERSITY PHYSICS SERIES

A Group of Textbooks for Intermediate and
Advanced Courses.

Introduction to Optics. FOURTH EDITION. *By* John K.
Robertson, *Formerly, Professor of Physics, Queen's University.*

Principles of Electricity. SECOND EDITION. *By* Leigh Page,
Late Professor of Mathematical Physics, Yale University; and
Norman Ilsley Adams, Jr., *Professor of Physics, Yale University.*

Physical Mechanics. SECOND EDITION. *By* Robert B. Lindsay, *Dean of the Graduate School, Brown University.*

TEXTBOOKS ON PHYSICS

By

JOHN KELLOCK ROBERTSON

INTRODUCTION TO OPTICS: GEOMETRICAL AND PHYSICAL
Fourth Edition.

> Among the up-to-date topics treated at length are nonreflecting glass surfaces, interference filters, the phase contrast microscope, and the use of light from mercury 198 as the ultimate standard of length.
>
> This latest edition is an integration of geometrical and physical optics, showing how, in the treatment of such topics as lenses, the telescope, the microscope, and the phase contrast microscope, both branches of optics are necessary and fit into each other. New units in photometry are explained with reference to the primary standard of luminosity.

ATOMIC ARTILLERY AND THE ATOMIC BOMB
Second Edition.

> Recent and authentic information about the great discoveries of recent years in atomic physics is fully presented by a distinguished scientist. Presenting his subject in a logical, clear-cut scientific fashion, the author has contributed a book that is welcomed by scientists and laymen alike.

RADIOLOGY PHYSICS
Second Edition.

> An Introductory Course for Medical or Premedical Students and for all Radiologists.

PUBLISHED BY

D. VAN NOSTRAND COMPANY, INC.
NEW YORK

PLATE I. FABRY-PEROT INTERFERENCE PATTERN FOR MERCURY
WAVELENGTH 5461 A

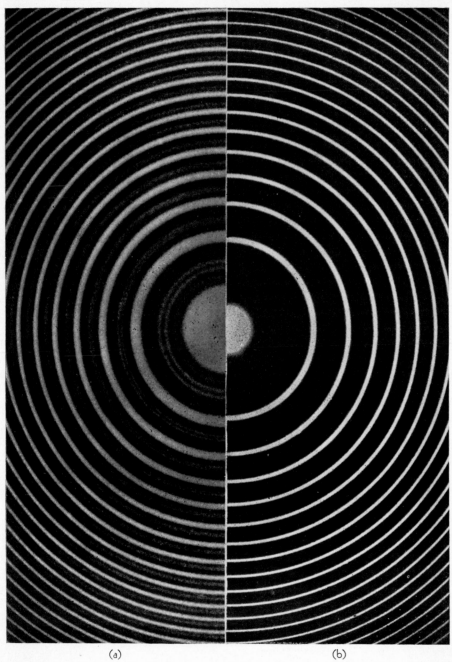

(a)   (b)

(a) Source, ordinary mercury.   (b) Source, mercury 198.   (Courtesy of Director, National Physical Laboratory.   Photograph by Barrell)

INTRODUCTION TO OPTICS
GEOMETRICAL AND PHYSICAL

by

JOHN K. ROBERTSON, M.A., LL.D., F.R.S.C., M.R.I.

Emeritus Professor of Physics, Queen's University
Kingston, Canada

FOURTH EDITION, SECOND PRINTING

D. VAN NOSTRAND COMPANY, INC.

TORONTO   NEW YORK   LONDON

NEW YORK

D. Van Nostrand Company, Inc., 250 Fourth Avenue, New York 3

TORONTO

D. Van Nostrand Company (Canada), Ltd., 25 Hollinger Rd., Toronto

LONDON

Macmillan & Company, Ltd., St. Martin's Street, London, W.C. 2

———

Library of Congress Catalogue Card No. 54–6281

———

First Edition 1929
Second Edition 1935
Third Edition 1941
Nine Reprintings
Fourth Edition April 1954
Reprinted April 1955

TO

DIANA

Preface

Although recent advances in optics have not been as spectacular as in nuclear physics, their importance more than justifies a new edition of this book. A revision is desirable also because of the application of newer optical ideas and optical instruments in other fields.

In revising the book to include a discussion of such topics as nonreflecting glass surfaces, interference filters, the phase contrast microscope, the use of light from mercury 198 as the ultimate standard of length, and other topics, the author has made a complete overhauling of the text in this fourth edition. Numerous minor alterations have been made and, as a result of his own experience or of suggestions from others, a change has been made in the order of some of the material. For example, the chapter on wave motion has been moved forward to appear just before the work on interference for which it is a natural prelude. Again, the empirical work on spectral series now appears in the same chapter as Bohr's theory of the origin of spectra. So much new work relating to the velocity of light has appeared in the last decade that a special chapter has been given to this important subject. In the chapter on radiation a brief reference to the common link between radiation and photometry in the black body standard has provided an opportunity of explaining recently adopted units in photometry. The sets of problems—in the author's opinion one of the most important features in any basic book in physics—are almost completely new, for a large number of new ones appear and, where old ones have been used, new data are given.

The author has adhered consistently to his original aim of writing a comprehensive intermediate text to serve the needs of two classes of students: (1) those who, at the outset of an intensive study of physics, are laying a thorough foundation for subsequent work in the theory of optics; (2) those specializing in other branches of science, for whom a general knowledge of optics is desirable and, indeed, frequently indispensable. Developments in the use of microwaves and radar, for example, have emphasized the necessity of a knowledge of optics in other fields. It is hoped, too, that the treatment is such that an appeal will be made to the general reader who desires to have some acquaintance with the fascinating problems of modern physics—problems some of which are most directly approached through the study of light.

In developing his subject the author has tried to steer a middle course between the Scylla of extreme conservatism and the Charybdis of radicalism. The almost perfect agreement between so many facts and the predictions of a wave theory, the constant necessity in light of speaking of wavelengths, the manner in which frequencies are so intimately connected with quanta—these things and many others demand a thorough discussion of wave motion and its ramifications in light. A large part of the book, therefore, is devoted to such a study. On the other hand, an important place has been given to quantum ideas, although, except for a brief reference at the end of Chapter I, this work does not appear until a discussion of the origin of spectra, of the spectrum of an incandescent solid, and of spectral series has provided the necessary background.

Since the first edition, much material which is primarily geometrical optics has been added. The treatment of such topics as the telescope, the microscope, the phase contrast microscope, involves the use of both geometrical and physical optics. Even the elementary formulae in reflection and refraction are derived in this book by a combination of geometrical and physical ideas.

Although the author makes no claim to any striking originality of method, in his opinion the book is characterized by a continuity which gives the subject a desirable unity, by its clarity of explanation, and by the stress laid on a quantitative discussion of many questions. Thus the somewhat extended discussion of wave motion in Chapter VII, with its numerous numerical examples, is justified on two grounds: (a) that this work is a necessary preparation for the following chapters on Interference and Diffraction; and (b) that hazy ideas are best avoided by quantitative methods. Much use has also been made of graphical methods by means of which physical ideas are kept uppermost in the student's mind.

In previous editions the author has expressed his indebtedness to many individuals and a number of corporations. For courtesies in connection with the preparation of this fourth edition, grateful thanks are due to Philips Electrical; the Polaroid Corporation; Bausch and Lomb Optical Company; to Director Sir Edward Bullard and Mr. H. Barrell of the National Physical Laboratory (London) for permission to use two illustrations; to Professor G. I. Finch for a photograph of an electron microscope; and to Professor S. Tolansky for a photograph of Newton's Rings with transmitted light. Mr. L. J. Collier of the N.P.L. kindly provided information about the most accurate value of the mechanical equivalent of light. The author is also grateful to Professor B. K. Johnson of the Department of Technical Optics, Imperial College, London, for reading and discussing the section on the phase contrast microscope and for information about reflecting microscopes.

It is a pleasure also to thank all fellow physicists who have made suggestions or pointed out errors—in particular, to Professor L. G. Abernathy, Professor E. Scott Barr, Professor Rollo Cook, Dr. H. H. Hopkins, Professor J. E. Kennedy, Professor E. J. Knapp, Dr. W. G. Nixon, Professor Waldemar Noll, Professor B. W. Sargent, Professor G. K. Schoepfle, Dr. D. Smith, Mr. Roy Waters and Mr. C. B. Wright.

February, 1954

J.K.R.

Contents

CHAPTER   PAGE

I. WHY WE STUDY WAVE MOTION   1
Two Theories of Light . . . Corpuscular *versus* Wave Theory . . . Quantum Theory.

II. THE VELOCITY OF LIGHT   10
Galileo's Attempt . . . Römer's Astronomical Method . . . Bradley's Aberration Method . . . Fizeau's Toothed-Wheel Method . . . Rotating Mirror. Displaced Image . . . Rotating Mirror. Null Method . . . The Tunnel Experiment . . . Anderson's Method . . . Bergstrand's Method . . . Essen's Method . . . Method of Hansen and Bol . . . Houston's Method . . . Present Accepted Value . . . Problems.

III. REFLECTION AND REFRACTION BY HUYGENS' PRINCIPLE   21
Meaning of Wave-front . . . Huygens' Principle . . . Plane Waves Striking a Plane Reflecting Surface Obliquely . . Plane Waves Striking a Refracting Surface Obliquely . . . Deduction of the Sine Law . . . Total Reflection . . . Spherical Waves Reflected at a Plane Surface . . . Spherical Waves Refracted at a Plane Surface . . . Plane Waves at a Spherical Surface . . . Spherical Waves Reflected from a Spherical Surface . . . Spherical Waves Reflected from a Convex Mirror . . . Refraction at a Spherical Surface . . . The Sine Condition . . . Lenses . . . Plane Waves Incident on a Lens Thicker at the Center . . . Spherical Waves Incident on a Thin Lens . . . Spherical Aberration . . . Coma . . . Astigmatism . . . Curvature of Field . . . Distortion . . . Chromatic Aberrations . . . Problems.

IV. FURTHER STUDY OF LENSES   56
Distant Point Source and Parallel Rays . . . Combination of Thin Lenses . . . Thick Lens . . . Nodal Points . . . Equivalent Focal Length of Two Thin Lenses Not in Contact . . . Linear Magnification . . . Problems.

CHAPTER   PAGE

V. VISION THROUGH AN INSTRUMENT. THE TELE-
   SCOPE AND THE MICROSCOPE   71
   Accommodation . . . Magnifying Power . . . The Simple Tel-
   escope . . . Magnifying Power of Telescope . . . The Eye
   Ring. Eye Point . . . Diameter of Eye Ring . . . Position
   of Eye Point . . . Field of View . . . The Eyepiece . . .
   Ramsden Eyepiece . . . Huygens' Eyepiece . . . Crosshair
   Lines . . . The Microscope . . . Numerical Aperture . . .
   Normal Magnifying Power . . . Radius of Exit Pupil . . .
   Problems.

VI. DISPERSION   95
    Refraction Through a Prism . . . Angle of Minimum Devia-
    tion . . . Small-angled Prisms . . . The Spectrometer . . .
    Dispersion . . . White Light . . . The Angstrom . . . Disper-
    sion Formulae . . . Irrational Dispersion . . . Spectrometer,
    Spectroscope, Spectrograph . . . Dispersion of an Instrument
    . . . Achromatism . . . Achromatic Lens . . . Dispersive
    Power . . . Condition for Achromatic Combination of Two
    Lenses . . . Direct Vision Spectroscope . . . Problems.

VII. STUDY OF WAVE MOTION   115
     The Cause of a Train of Waves . . . The Fundamental Wave
     Equation . . . The Form of a Train of Waves . . . Simple
     Harmonic Motion . . . Graphical Representation of a S.H.M.
     . . . More General Equation of a S.H.M. . . . Phase Angle
     . . . Composition of S.H.M. in Same Straight Line . . . Re-
     sultant Amplitude for S.H.M. of the Same Period . . . Equa-
     tion of Resultant S.H.M. . . . Composition of Two S.H.M.
     in Lines at Right Angles . . . Fourier's Theorem . . . Equa-
     tion of a Plane Wave . . . Phase Difference and Path Dif-
     ference . . . Plane and Spherical Waves . . . Change of
     Amplitude with Distance for Spherical Waves . . . Shape of
     a Train of Waves . . . Stationary Waves . . . Analytical
     Proof of Nodes and Loops . . . Problems.

VIII. INTERFERENCE   144
      Realization of Interference . . . Double Slit . . . The Bi-
      prism . . . The Fresnel Mirrors . . . Wavelength and Double-
      Slit . . . Rayleigh's Refractometer . . . Index of Refraction
      of a Gas and its Measurement.

CHAPTER   PAGE

IX. INTERFERENCE (CONTINUED): THIN FILMS AND
     PLANE PARALLEL SURFACES 162
     Fringes of Equal Thickness . . . Phase Change on Reflection
     . . . Nonreflecting Glass . . . Newton's Rings . . . Fringes
     of Equal Inclination . . . Newton's Rings with Multiple Re-
     flections . . . Interference Filters . . . Comparison of Two
     Wavelengths . . . Structure of a Single Spectral Line . . .
     Lummer Plate . . . Michelson's Interferometer . . . Mer-
     cury 198 as Standard Source . . . Difference in the Wave-
     lengths of Sodium D_1 and D_2 . . . Problems.

  X. DIFFRACTION 187
     Half-Period Elements . . . Circular Aperture . . . Zone Plate
     . . . More General Treatment . . . Cornu's Spiral . . . Fres-
     nel and Fraunhofer Diffraction.

 XI. FRAUNHOFER DIFFRACTION 207
     Single Rectangular Aperture . . . Rectilinear Propagation
     . . . Limit of Resolution and Resolving Power of a Telescope
     . . . Reflecting Telescopes . . . Resolving Power of a Micro-
     scope . . . Reflecting Microscopes . . . Microscope Conden-
     densers . . . Magnifying Power and Resolving Power . . .
     Electron Microscope . . . Two Narrow Apertures (The Dou-
     ble Slit) . . . Many Apertures (The Transmission Grating)
     . . . Width of Maxima . . . Measurement of Wavelength
     . . . Number of Orders . . . Phase Contrast Microscope . . .
     Dispersion and Resolving Power of a Grating . . . Reflection
     Grating . . . Echelon, Echelette and Echelle Gratings . . .
     Concave Grating . . . Scattering by Small Particles . . . The
     Blue of the Sky . . . Problems.

XII. DOUBLE REFRACTION 247
     The Fact of Double Refraction . . . Uniaxial and Biaxial
     Crystals . . . Huygens' Explanation . . . Determination of
     Refractive Indices . . . The Nicol Prism . . . Principle Plane
     . . . Foucault Prism . . . Polaroid.

XIII. PLANE POLARIZED LIGHT 259
     The Meaning of Polarization of Light . . . Polarization by
     Scattering . . . O and E Beams Each Polarized . . . Double-
     Image Prism . . . Polarization by Reflection . . . Pile of
     Plates as Analyzer . . . Law of Malus . . . Advantages and
     Disadvantages of Polaroid.

CHAPTER   PAGE

XIV.   INTERFERENCE OF POLARIZED LIGHT   271
       Color with Thin Crystals . . . Complementary Colors . . .
       Interference Phenomena with Scattering Medium as Analyzer
       . . . Elliptically and Circularly Polarized Light . . . Analysis
       of a Beam of Light . . . Photoelastic Test of Strain in Glass
       . . . Interference with Highly Convergent Light.

XV.   ROTATORY POLARIZATION   285
       Rotation of the Vibration Plane . . . Tint of Passage . . .
       Analysis of Optically Active Substances . . . Specific Rota-
       tion . . . Rotation by Magnetic Field . . . Explanation of
       Rotation of Vibration Plane . . . Problems.

XVI.   THE ELECTROMAGNETIC THEORY OF LIGHT . .   298
       Early Work . . . Electromagnetic Theory . . . Work of
       Hertz . . . Range of Electromagnetic Waves . . . Electric
       Vector the Light Vector . . . Theory of Dispersion . . .
       Anomalous Dispersion.

XVII. THE ORIGIN OF SPECTRA   311
       Light Sources . . . Emission Spectra . . . Plurality of Spectra
       . . . Absorption Spectra . . . Doppler Effect . . . Zeeman
       Effect . . . Stark Effect . . . Origin of Spectra.

XVIII. RADIATION AND THE QUANTUM THEORY . . .   329
       Birth of the Quantum Theory . . . Black Body . . . Photom-
       etry . . . The Candela . . . Mechanical Equivalent of Light
       . . . Color Temperature . . . Illumination . . . Luminous
       Emittance . . . Radiation   Laws . . . Wien's . . . Ray-
       leigh's . . . Planck's Radiation Formula . . . Photoelectric
       Effect and Quantum Theory . . . Quantum Theory and Emis-
       sion of a Single Spectral Line.

XIX.   SPECTRAL SERIES AND ORIGIN OF SPECTRA . .   340
       Spectral Series . . . Graphical Representation of Hydrogen
       Series . . . General Series Relations . . . Doublet, Triplet
       and Multiplet Series . . . Quantum Defect . . . Bohr's The-
       ory and Origin of Spectra . . . Heavy Hydrogen and Bohr
       Theory . . . Ionized Helium . . . A Vector Model of the
       Atom and Interpretation of Spectral Series . . . First Selec-
       tion Principle . . . Doublet Fine Structure . . . Second
       Selection Principle . . . Triplet and Associated Singlet Sys-
       tem . . . Hyperfine Structure.

CHAPTER   PAGE

XX.   RADIATION POTENTIALS; ABSORPTION AND BAND
      SPECTRA 367
      Radiating Potentials . . . Ionization Potential . . . Energy
      Diagrams . . . Resonance Radiation . . . Absorption Spec-
      tra . . . Band Spectra . . . Isotope Effect . . . Sequences
      and Progressions . . . Problems.

XXI. THE DILEMMA 379
      Duality Problem . . . The Compton Effect . . . Electron
      Waves . . . Wave Mechanics . . . Electron Diffraction.

XXII. CAN THE EXISTENCE OF AN ETHER BE DETECTED? 387
      Aberration of Light . . . Airy's Experiment . . . Michelson-
      Morley Experiment . . . Fitzgerald-Lorentz Contraction . . .
      Relativity . . . Is There an Ether?

      TABLE XX.   Some Useful Wavelengths 401

      TABLE XXI.   Term Values for Lithium Series 402

      ANSWERS TO PROBLEMS 403

      INDEX 405

List of Plates

PLATE

I. FABRY-PEROT INTERFERENCE PATTERNS FOR MER-
CURY WAVELENGTH 5461 A . . . . *Frontispiece*

TO FACE PAGE

II. SPECTRA OF HYDROGEN, HELIUM, TIN, AND MER-
CURY 96

III. SPECTRA OF MAGNESIUM, MERCURY, AND EXAMPLES
OF BAND SPECTRA 97

IV. EXAMPLES OF INTERFERENCE FRINGES 153

V. NEWTON'S RINGS; RINGS AND BRUSH INTERFERENCE
PATTERN 168

VI. EXAMPLES OF DIFFRACTION PATTERNS 209

VII. ELECTRON MICROSCOPE, STARK EFFECT, AND PHO-
TOELASTIC STRAIN TEST 224

VIII. DOPPLER EFFECT, ZEEMAN EFFECT, AND ANOMA-
LOUS DISPERSION 321

IX. CADMIUM SPECTRUM, ÉTALON FRINGES, AND ELEC-
TRON DIFFRACTION RINGS 352

I

Why We Study Wave Motion

1.1. Light may be provisionally defined as the physical agency by means of which the eye receives the sensation of sight. This definition is much too restricted because frequently we are concerned with the invisible ultraviolet and infrared regions. The subject is traditionally divided into two classes: Physical Optics, in which we are concerned primarily with the nature of light, and Geometrical Optics, where we deal with the formation of images by instruments on the assumption that light travels absolutely in straight lines. Neither branch can be understood properly without some knowledge of the other, and in this book work on both branches is included.

In this introductory chapter, which is partly historical, the student is asked to recall a few elementary facts and, in the light of them, to consider tentatively what can be said about the nature of light. The chapter should be read in a general way only, because a detailed consideration of many of the problems raised will be given later in the book. Note, then, the following facts.

(a) *Matter is not necessary* for the propagation of light. While light passes readily through certain kinds of matter which we call transparent, its passage is unobstructed in the vast interstellar spaces, or through a glass vessel from which all the air has been exhausted. Contrast this fact with the case of sound which is not propagated in a vacuum.

(b) Light is *regularly reflected* at a smooth surface such as a mirror, subject to the simple law that the angle of reflection is equal to the angle of incidence. This fact was known as long ago as the time of the Platonic school, which flourished four centuries before the Christian era.

(c) Light is *refracted* at a surface separating two transparent media of unequal density, such as air and water. In the case of a plane surface, the sine of the angle of incidence bears a constant ratio to the sine of the angle of refraction. (Snell's Law.) While the fact of refraction was known, and observations were made as far back as the time of Ptolemy (Greece, 2nd century), the sine law was not discovered until early in the seventeenth century, probably independently by Snell (Holland, 1591–1626) and by the famous philosopher Descartes (France, 1596–1650).

(d) Light may be *simultaneously* reflected and refracted. For example, if a beam of light such as 1, Fig. 1.1, be allowed to strike, at a suitable angle, the under surface AB separating air from water, both a refracted beam 2 and a reflected beam 3 are observed.

(e) For all practical purposes, light travels in straight lines—the fact of rectilinear propagation. This, too, was known to the Greek philosophers. Of its approximate truth, the sharpness of the shadows of obstacles cast by a small source of light and the practical use to which it is put in placing objects in a straight line by "sighting" give ample evidence.

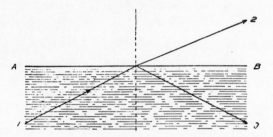

Fig. 1.1   Simultaneous reflection and refraction.

It may here be noted that under special circumstances which we shall later consider, it may be shown that light does not always travel in straight lines, a fact to which attention was first drawn by Grimaldi (Italy, 1618–1663).

(f) Light travels in free space at a very definite velocity, which, within 0.06 per cent, is equal to 3×10^{10} cm per sec. In Chapter II a detailed description will be given of some of the methods used for determining this important constant. Here we merely wish to call attention to this very important fact.

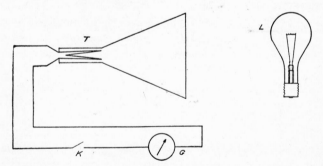

Fig. 1.2.   Arrangement with thermocouple T and galvanometer G to demonstrate radiation of energy from lamp L.

(g) The velocity of light in a medium such as water is *less* than the velocity in air. This important fact was first experimentally shown by Foucault (France, 1819–1868) about 1862 by a method to be described in Chapter II. Some years later, in 1883, Michelson (United States, 1852–1931) showed that the ratio of the velocities for these two media was 1.33.

(*h*) Energy is carried by a beam of light. The student, who scarcely needs to be reminded of this fact, will at once recall the rise in temperature which results from the absorption of the sun's rays, as well as other manifestations of energy due to the same cause. The fact may be demonstrated otherwise by a simple experiment such as is represented in Fig. 1.2, where T is a thermopile, G a galvanometer, K a knife-key, and L an incandescent lamp so placed that rays from it may fall on one juncture of the thermopile. On closing the key K, the galvanometer indicates an electric current which continues as long as the lamp is lighted. Energy, therefore, passes from the lamp to the thermopile.

1.2. Two Theories of Light. These facts may be supplemented by many others. Those we have given, however, are outstanding and, for that reason, form a good basis for a preliminary discussion concerning the nature of light. If we take the last statement first, it will readily be evident that only two general theories are possible, because energy can be transmitted from one place to another by only one of two general means. A window pane may be broken from a distance either by being struck by some moving object or by the concussion resulting from a disturbance which has traveled through the atmosphere from the region of an explosion. We hear a distant source of sound because of the impact on the ear of waves which have traveled through the air from the source to the ear. We detect an odor from an object at some distance away by the motion of particles which have emanated from the object. In general, energy can be propagated either by moving matter or by a wave disturbance traveling through a medium which does not itself move as a whole. In light, therefore, two general theories have been formulated. According to the one, *the wave theory*, a disturbance travels from a light source through a surrounding medium, differences in color corresponding to differences in wavelength; according to the other, *the emission or corpuscular theory*, light consists of a flight of invisible rapidly moving particles whose size varies with the color, projected from the luminous source. One important difference between the two theories may here be noted. On the wave theory, at all points on a surface through which an ordinary beam of light is passing, energy is *uniformly and continuously* distributed; whereas, on the other, the energy distribution is *discontinuous*, being concentrated at points. In the seventeenth and eighteenth centuries, when the pioneers of modern science were laying the foundations of the structure which today is so elaborate, each of these theories received strong support. We find a wave theory upheld by such men as Hooke (England, 1635–1703), Huygens (Holland, 1629–1695), Descartes (France, 1596–1650), and Euler (Switzerland, 1707–1783); while the corpuscular theory was defended by such intellectual giants as Newton (England, 1642–1727) and Laplace (France, 1749–1827). Which, then, is the better?

1.3. Corpuscular *versus* Wave Theory. A theory is satisfactory only in so far as it provides an explanation of facts. A single fact for which a satisfactory explanation cannot be given, or which goes contrary to a deduction which may reasonably be made from the theory, weakens it. If many such facts come to light, the theory has to be discarded or at least radically altered. In testing two rival theories, therefore, we must examine carefully as many facts as we can to see which provides the more satisfactory explanation. We begin naturally with the list of facts which has been enumerated. In the light of these, is it possible to give a decided preference to one theory rather than the other? Let us consider the facts one by one.

(*a*) As it is impossible for most minds to think of waves without a medium to carry the wave motion, and as matter is not necessary for light propagation, a hypothetical luminiferous ether has to be postulated. Although no such postulate is necessary on the corpuscular theory, this was never considered an objection to the wave theory. As will be seen presently, the assumption of an ether in which vibrations may be set up played an important part in the corpuscular explanation given by Newton for more than one fact. To quote from Newton's writings, "It is to be supposed that there is an ethereal medium, much of the same constitution with air, but far rarer, subtiler, and more strongly elastic."

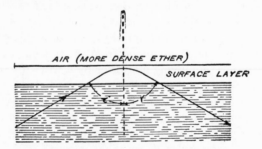

Fig. 1.3.   A surface layer reverses the direction of light corpuscles at sufficiently oblique incidence.

(*b*) and (*c*) As the explanation of both reflection and refraction on the wave theory will be given in some detail in Chapter III, we shall here consider only that given by Newton on a corpuscular theory. In this the supposition of an ether of variable density, *more* dense in free space than in solids, and of decreasing density at the surface of a body, plays an important part. When a corpuscle strikes a surface separating two media, therefore, it encounters a region of variable density—of "graduated rarity," as Newton put it. The explanation involves the further assumption that the speed of the corpuscle is accelerated in passing from more dense ether (*e.g.* air) to less dense (*e.g.* glass), and retarded when traveling in the opposite direction. In the case of *total* reflection, the retardation is sufficient to turn gradually ("incurve") the particle in its passage through the surface layer, somewhat as illustrated in Fig. 1.3, so that it emerges in a direction making the angle of reflection equal to the angle of incidence. In refraction, on the other hand, "if the differing densities of the mediums be not so great, nor the incidence of the ray so oblique as to make it parallel to that surface (superficies) before it gets through, then it goes through and is refracted"—somewhat as shown in Fig. 1.4. *It is important to note that this explanation of refraction involves the assumption that a ray of light is retarded, that is, travels at a less rate in air than in a medium like water.*

Ordinary reflection, such as at a surface separating air from glass, is accounted for by assuming (apparently because of the peculiar surface effects which we now study under surface tension) that "ether in the confine of two mediums is less pliant and yielding than in other places," in consequence of which, "a ray finds more than ordinary difficulty to get through," and has its direction reversed just as when a corpuscle encounters denser ether.

To the twentieth century student such explanations may seem very artificial, but if he considers how readily a beam of invisible cathode rays may nowadays be deflected from a straight line path by an electric or a magnetic field, he will recognize that something is to be said for the corpuscular viewpoint.

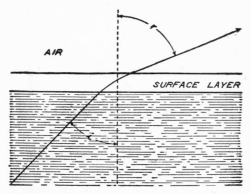

Fig. 1.4. At small angles of incidence light corpuscles emerge into air.

(*d*) The exponents of the corpuscular theory were by no means unaware that reflection and refraction may take place simultaneously at the same surface. On the wave theory this is to be expected (see Chapter III). In the light of the corpuscular explanation which has just been given, how can some particles be sent back from the surface while others are transmitted? To that question Newton gave an ingenious answer by means of his theory of "fits of easy reflection and easy transmission." According to this, "the rays when they impinge on the rigid resisting ethereal superficies . . . cause vibrations in it, as stones thrown in water do in its surface; and these vibrations . . . *alternately contract and dilate the ether in that physical superficies.*" In consequence of this, the surface layer of ether, when contracted, is sufficiently dense to cause reflection of the ray, whereas, when dilated, it is sufficiently rarefied to allow transmission, that is, to give rise to refraction.

It will be seen, then, that the corpuscular theory involved the idea of waves in an ether, even if rays themselves were considered corpuscular. It would seem, therefore, that preference should be given the simpler wave theory, provided it gives at least an equally satisfactory explanation of other facts.

(e) There was one important fact, however, the explanation of which on the wave theory was long delayed, and that was the fact of approximate rectilinear propagation. This was the big stumbling-block to those early scientists who were unable to accept the wave theory. How can waves travel in straight lines, they said? A whistle can easily be heard around the corner of an obstacle; a candle certainly cannot be seen from behind it. The one is undoubtedly a wave phenomenon, how can the other be? And so we have the objection given in the following words of Newton: "If it (light) consisted in pression or motion . . . it would bend into the shadow. For pression or motion cannot be propagated in a fluid in right lines, beyond an obstacle which stops part of the motion, but will bend and spread every way into the quiescent medium which lies beyond the obstacle. . . ."

S •

S_1

S_2

Fig. 1.5. An eye viewing a narrow source of light S through a double slit S_1S_2 sees interference fringes.

On the other hand, the emission theory provided a ready explanation of rectilinear propagation. This fact, combined probably with the weight given to the opinion of such an intellectual giant as Sir Isaac Newton, was largely responsible for the preference given the corpuscular theory until the early part of the nineteenth century. That there was a slight deviation from the straight line path when, for example, a beam emerging from a small hole passed by the edge of an obstacle, was known in Newton's time. But this bending was slight and at that time a satisfactory explanation of the phenomenon on the wave theory was not forthcoming, although both Hooke and Grimaldi were on the verge of discovering the principle which more than a century later was to clarify the whole question.

The satisfactory explanation of rectilinear propagation on the wave theory is largely the result of the work of Thos. Young (England, 1773–1829), and of Fresnel (France, 1788–1827), both of whom demonstrated the phenomenon of interference of light, and showed its implications. In Chapters VIII and IX this subject will be discussed in detail. In view, however, of the question now under discussion—the relative merits of the corpuscular and the wave theories —it is necessary at this stage to consider briefly its significance. This can perhaps best be done by reference to a simple experiment which the student should try for himself.

If two narrow slits, S_1 and S_2 (Fig. 1.5), about 0.5 mm apart, are cut in a piece of dark paper, or scratched on a bit of old photographic negative, and an observer views through them a narrow source of light S, such as a straight filament lamp, placed two or three meters away, a series of alternately dark and light narrow bands is seen in the center of a tolerably wide band of light. Should a red glass be interposed between the source S and the slits, a series of red and black narrow bands is observed. Some idea of their appearance will be obtained from Fig. 1, Plate IV (facing p. 153), a reproduction of an actual photograph taken with an ordinary lens replacing the eye lens, and a sensitive plate, the retina. Now what is the significance of these alternately light and dark bands? A wave theory of light, combined with the principle of interference, gives the answer.

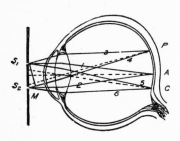

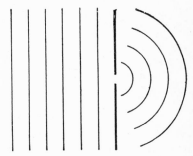

Fig. 1.6. At points on the retina, such as P, A and C, beams originating at the slit openings S_1 and S_2 are superimposed.

Fig. 1.7. Spherical waves spread out from a narrow opening.

If light is a wave phenomenon, then it is reasonable to assume (what indeed can experimentally be shown) that rays spread out to some extent from each slit S_1, S_2 (Fig. 1.6) just as water waves spread out from a narrow opening, somewhat as represented in Fig. 1.7. The eye lens then collects these rays, and, since the retina is approximately at its focal distance from the lens (when a distant source is viewed), parallel pairs of rays are brought together at different points on the retina. For example, if the student recalls the simple lens law, that a ray goes through the center unchanged in direction, he will see that rays 1 and 2 will meet at A, rays 3 and 4 at P, rays 5 and 6 at C and so on. Now, if rays are corpuscles, wherever they strike a surface, whether there are two bundles or only one, there must be light. But what if rays are waves?

Consider the point P. The path S_2 to P is longer than the path S_1 to P by the distance S_2M, where S_1M is perpendicular to S_2M. On the wave theory we have to do with what are analogous to crests and troughs in water waves. If, therefore, S_2M is half a wavelength (distance crest to trough), or any odd number of half wavelengths, it is evident that at P crests from S_1 always meet troughs from S_2, and vice versa, whereas if S_2M is one, two, three or any whole number of wavelengths, crests always meet crests, troughs, troughs.   Now, according to the principle of interference, "when two undulations from different origins coincide . . . their joint effect is a combination of the motions belonging to each."   If we accept this, the joint effect of a crest and a trough is zero, or, in other words, there is, in such a case, no disturbance and no light, whereas at places where two crests or two troughs meet, the joint effect produces a maximum disturbance, that is, bright light.   The explanation, therefore, of the alternate dark and light bands is simply that, because of the varying difference in the paths from the two slits to successive points on the retina, we have alternately reinforcement and annulment of the two sets of waves.   In Chapter VIII this experiment will be discussed quantitatively, and it will then be seen that with the aid of simple linear measurements it provides us with a means of evaluating the actual lengths of light waves.

The principle of interference when first published about 1801 by Young did not receive general acceptance.   Indeed, in some quarters it was almost ridiculed. When a few years later, however, Fresnel showed how by means of it a ready explanation could be given of approximate rectilinear propagation, as well as of the observed slight bending to which reference has been made, the wave theory gradually came into great favor.   It was seen to provide a much simpler explanation of optical facts than the corpuscular.

Acceptance of the wave theory became almost universal when Foucault and Michelson showed experimentally that the speed of light is less in water than in air.   This was a fact which provided a crucial test of the relative merits of the two theories, for the explanation of refraction on the corpuscular theory involved, as we have already noted, the assumption of a greater velocity in water than in air, whereas the wave theory postulated a less velocity.   In the light of this experimental fact, the corpuscular theory could not be accepted, at any rate without radical revision, and the wave theory took complete possession of the field.   By means of it, throughout the last half of the nineteenth century tremendous advances were made in the interpretation of light phenomena.   The form of the theory was not always the same, the conception of vibrations in an elastic solid ether, for example, giving way to Maxwell's electromagnetic theory (Chapter XVI), but it was always a wave theory.   Indeed, so perfect was the agreement between fact and theory that in 1889 we find Hertz (Germany, 1857–1894) making the statement, "The wave theory of light is from the point of view of human beings, a certainty."

1.4. That, however, was a rash statement for any scientist to make, and this chapter would not be complete without a brief reference to some work of the twentieth century which should warn us against the too hasty acceptance of any theory.   For a generation the attention of physicists has been directed to problems connected with the emission and the absorption of light.   This work has shown that there are many facts for which an adequate explanation cannot be given in terms of a simple wave theory.   One of the most important of these facts, strangely enough, was discovered by Hertz in the very year in which the foregoing statement was made—the fact that light when incident on a metal plate may cause an emission of electrons.   When the laws governing this process were later discovered, it was found that a **quantum theory** which postulates the emission of light *discontinuously* in isolated bundles or *quanta* provided an explanation, whereas the continuous wave front of the wave theory failed to do so. A *quantum* is a definite unit of radiant energy equal to the product of h, a certain universal constant about which more will be stated later, and, ν, the frequency of the radiation.

There are certain phenomena, therefore, which can be interpreted only by thinking of light as having a corpuscular nature, or a kind of atomicity, the fundamental unit possessing a quantum of energy.   This unit is frequently called a *photon*.   In many ways this is suggestive of the old corpuscular theory, but it is by no means a return to it.   Photons are not material particles, as Newton's light corpuscles were considered to be.   Moreover, the mere fact that the frequency of radiation is involved in the numerical magnitude of the energy of a photon shows that there is an intimate connection between quantum and wave theories.   We must not forget, too, that other phenomena such as interference and diffraction find a complete and satisfactory explanation by an ordinary wave theory.

The modern position, then, is that light has a dual aspect.   Sometimes we must think in terms of photons, sometimes in terms of waves.   To this whole question we shall return in later chapters, but, at this stage, it should be evident that no intelligent study of light is possible without a clear understanding of wave motion in general.   In Chapter VII this is the subject of discussion.

II

The Velocity of Light

The numerical value of the velocity of light is such an important quantity that its determination has been the subject of many investigations spread over many years. In Chapter XVI it is shown that light waves are electromagnetic in nature and that in free space all such waves travel with the same velocity. A determination of the velocity of light, therefore, gives also the velocity of all electromagnetic waves.

2.1. Galileo's Attempt. The direct method of determining any velocity, either of a particle or of a disturbance, is to observe the time taken to pass over a measured distance. It is not surprising, therefore, to find that Galileo (Italy, 1564–1642) suggested a simple, direct, if crude, way to observe the time taken for a beam of light to travel a distance of a few miles. Two observers, A and B, who had previously practiced uncovering the light from lanterns which they held at close range, until they acquired "such skill . . . . that the instant one sees the light of his companion he will uncover his own," * were subsequently to station themselves a few miles apart at night. A was then to note the time interval which elapsed between the moment he uncovered his lantern and the instant he saw B's light. This interval obviously is the time taken for light to travel from A to B and back again to A.

The experiment was never tried, however, except "only at a short distance, less than a mile, from which I have not been able to ascertain with certainty whether the appearance of the opposite light was instantaneous or not." Even with a distance of many miles it would have failed because the time taken to travel a few miles at a speed of 186,000 miles a second is far too short to be measured in such a crude way. The principle of the experiment, however, is exactly the same as that utilized in the refined methods described below.

2.2. Römer's Astronomical Method. To make measurements of such a high velocity, either the measured distance must be so great that time values can be easily observed or methods of measuring extremely small intervals of time must be devised. Conditions for the first alternative are supplied by astronomical

---

* Quotation from *Dialogues Concerning Two New Sciences*. By Galileo Galilei. Translation by H. Crew and A. de Salvio. The Macmillan Co., N. Y. 1914.

distances, and the earliest determination of the velocity of light was made in this way by Römer (Denmark, 1644–1710), when working in Paris in 1676. To understand his method, it is necessary to recall that the earth and Jupiter are both planets revolving about the sun, the earth with its yearly period, Jupiter with a period just under 12 years. It follows, then, that in a little over half a year (0.545 of a year, to be more exact) the earth will pass from a position of conjunction, where it is nearest Jupiter, as at E_1, Fig. 2.1, to a position of opposition, as at E_2, where the distance between these planets is a maximum. It is also necessary to know that Jupiter has several moons or satellites which, to an observer on the earth, are eclipsed when they get behind the planet. Confining our attention to a single satellite (for example, to one which makes a complete revolution about Jupiter in less than two days), we see that it is a simple matter, by observing the times at which this satellite is eclipsed, to determine its period of revolution. It is then possible to predict the time of future eclipses. In Römer's time this was done and it was noticed that there were unexpected disagreements between the observed and the predicted times of

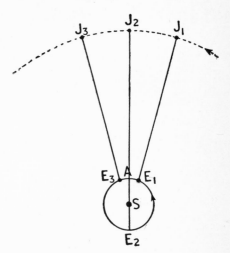

Fig. 2.1. In position E_2 the distance from the earth to Jupiter E_2J_2 exceeds the distance AJ_2 by the diameter of the earth's orbit about the sun.

eclipses. In 1676 Römer reported to the French Academy of Science that a certain eclipse would not occur until ten minutes after the calculated time, and, at the same time, stated that the cause of the disagreement was the fact that light travels with a finite velocity. The calculated results were out, he said, because this factor had been neglected in the calculations. By reference to Fig. 2.1 it will be seen that, when the earth is in position E_2, light has to travel from Jupiter a distance J_2E_2 which is greater than J_1E_1, the distance when the earth is in position E_1, by an amount equal to the diameter of the earth's orbit about the sun, that is, by some 196 million miles. If we take this fact into consideration, the velocity of light can be calculated in the following way.

Let t = the actual time of one revolution of a satellite,
$\quad n$ = the number of revolutions made by the satellite during the time that the earth moves from the position E_1 to E_2, that is, during the interval conjunction to opposition.

Then T_1, the *observed* time for these n revolutions, is given by

$$T_1 = nt + \frac{D}{c},$$

CORRECTION FACTOR.

where D = the diameter of the earth's orbit,
c = the velocity of light in free space.

Similarly, if T_2 is the observed time of the n revolutions which take place during the interval from opposition to conjunction, that is, when the earth moves from E_2 to E_3,

$$T_2 = nt - \frac{D}{c}.$$

Hence
$$T_1 - T_2 = \frac{2D}{c}.$$

Now $T_1 - T_2$ is an observed quantity. Using the value obtained from the observations of his time and the astronomical estimate of the size of the earth's orbit, Römer concluded that light requires less than 1 second to traverse about 3000 leagues. (Now that the value of the velocity of light has been obtained to a high degree of accuracy, the modern value of $T_1 - T_2$, which is 16 min 26 sec, may be used to evaluate the mean diameter of the earth's orbit.)

2.3. Bradley's Aberration Method. The essential ideas underlying this second astronomical method, first noted in 1728 by Bradley (England, 1693–1762), are discussed in another connection in the last chapter of this book.

2.4. Fizeau's Toothed-Wheel Method. It was not until 1849 that the velocity of light was measured by what we might call a laboratory method, due to Fizeau (France, 1819–1896). In this, as in all similar methods, astronomical

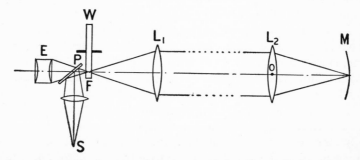

Fig. 2.2.   Fizeau's method for measuring the velocity of light.   The teeth of the rotating wheel W periodically interrupt the passage of the light to the mirror M.

distances are replaced by a length of a few miles and a device is used for measuring an extremely short time interval. The essentials of Fizeau's arrangement are shown in Fig. 2.2. Light from a small source S by means of a lens and reflection from one face of a transparent plate P is focused to form a small spot at F from where it diverges, falling on the lens L_1 which makes the beam parallel. After traversing a distance, which in Fizeau's original experiment was 8633

meters, the parallel beam passes through the lens L_2 which focuses it on the
face of a concave mirror M, so placed that its center of curvature coincides with
O, the center of lens L_2. The beam of light is then reflected back along the
incident path. On striking the transparent plate P, part of the light is transmitted, and thus the spot F can ordinarily be observed in an eyepiece E. W represents a toothed wheel, with 720 projecting teeth, separated by open spaces of
equal width.

Suppose, now, with the wheel in rapid rotation, that at a certain instant the
spot F is exactly between two teeth, somewhat as shown in Fig. 2.3(a). As the
light which leaves the spot at this instant travels to M, the wheel is turning
and, for a particular speed of rotation, the reflected beam, on arriving back at F,
will strike the center of a tooth, as in Fig. 2.3(b). If the wheel is maintained at
this speed, the light which gets through an opening will always arrive back at
the wheel in time to strike a tooth, and so for this speed of the wheel an eclipse

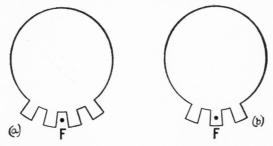

Fig. 2.3. Two positions of the toothed wheel in Fizeau's method with respect to the spot of light F.

is noted by an observer looking through E, Fig. 2.2. At twice this speed of
rotation, the light on its return to F strikes the center of the next opening and,
in this case, is seen as a bright spot. By still further speeding up the wheel,
alternate eclipses and bright spots can be seen. From observations of the value
of these critical speeds, a simple calculation gives the speed of light. For example, in one of Fizeau's experiments, the first eclipse occurred at a speed of
12.6 revolutions per second. Therefore, the time taken to travel twice 8633
meters is equal to $\frac{1}{2} \cdot \frac{1}{720} \cdot \frac{1}{12.6}$ sec, from which the velocity of light is at once
found. As at the end of this chapter, values are given for many of the exact
determinations in recent years, definite values are not given for each of these
earlier methods.

In 1874–1878 Fizeau's method was repeated by Cornu (France, 1841–1902),
with the distance increased to 23,000 meters, with an improved method of
measuring time, and with observations made of the change in speed when the
brightness of F passed from a certain intensity (observed by comparison with a
fixed source) through an eclipse back to this same intensity.

2.5. Rotating Mirror. Displaced Image Method. A method suggested in 1838 by Arago (France, 1786–1853) was planned jointly by Fizeau and Foucault and subsequently carried out independently by Foucault, who reported his results in 1862. The principle of the method can be understood by reference to Fig. 2.4.

Light emerging from a narrow source S passes through a transparent plate P, falls on a lens L, is converged to a plane mirror M, capable of rotation, which reflects the beam to the concave mirror M_1. Here an image of the source S_1 is formed. As the center of curvature of this concave mirror is at C (a point on the axis of rotation of the plane mirror M), the light normally retraces its path back to the source S. By means of the transparent plate P part of the returning beam is reflected to form an image at I. *Even if the position of the plane mirror M is altered* so that the incident beam strikes it at a different angle, the image will

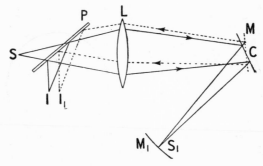

Fig. 2.4. Velocity of light by rotating mirror M. The magnitude of the displacement of the image from I to I_1 depends on the angle of rotation of the mirror during the passage of the light from M to M_1 and back again.

still be formed at I because, although the position of S_1 varies with the inclination of M, the reflected beam between M_1 and M always follows the incident path, and so strikes M at the same angle as it left M. Suppose, however, that the mirror M is rotated so quickly that, during the time it takes for light to go from this mirror to M_1 and back again, M has moved to the position represented by the dotted line. In that case, the return beam strikes the face of the plane mirror at an angle which is not the same as the angle with which the light left this mirror. The reflected beam, therefore, no longer retraces its path back to I but follows a slightly different path, giving rise to a displaced image at I_1. The magnitude of the displacement II_1 evidently depends on the angle through which M is rotated while light travels twice the distance M to M_1. By observing the value of II_1, therefore, this angle can be found, and hence, from the speed of rotation of the mirror, the corresponding small interval of time. From this time value and twice the distance MM_1, the velocity of light is at once obtained.

In Foucault's arrangement MM_1 was an effective length of 20 meters. (The actual length was only 4 meters, but the beam was reflected back and forth five times between fixed mirrors.)   The displacement II_1 was only 0.7 mm, but the images were sharply defined and their positions could be located with precision.

It was by this method that Foucault proved more or less qualitatively the very important result that the velocity of light in water is less than in air.   By the same method Michelson proved that the ratio of these two velocities was 1.33.

In the period 1879–1882 the rotating mirror method was repeated with great care by Michelson and by Newcomb (United States, 1835–1909).   As it is our aim to give principles rather than refined experimental details, we shall simply point out that Michelson, using a path length of 600 meters, obtained an image displacement of 133 mm and that Newcomb, working with a distance of 1200 ft, used a four-sided (cubical) mirror which increased the brightness of the image.

2.6. Rotating Mirror.   Null Method.   In the rotating mirror method the angle through which the mirror rotates cannot be measured to the same degree of accuracy as the speed of rotation and the length of the optical path.   This difficulty can be overcome by making use of a suggestion made by Newcomb that a many-sided mirror be used and an optical path of such a length that the return

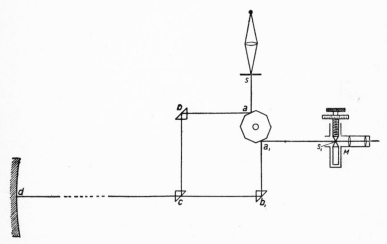

Fig. 2.5.   Velocity of light by rotating multiple-faced mirror.   For critical speeds of the mirror, the image at S_1 of the light source S remains fixed.

beam strikes one face of this mirror *at the same angle* as it left the adjoining face, on its outward journey.   In that case, there is no displaced image.   To avoid practical difficulties, the optical arrangement may be such that the return beam strikes a face when it is *parallel* to the incident face.   Thus, in Fig. 2.5 (to be explained more fully presently), if the octagonal mirror there represented is at rest, the incident beam strikes one face at a and the return beam at a_1 on a parallel face. In applying this method with an octagonal mirror the mirror must be rotated until it is going at such a speed that it turns through 45° during the time that a beam of light has traveled from a to the outward reflector and back again to a_1. For that critical speed the beam is reflected from the last face along exactly the same path as when the mirror is at rest.

This is the principle used in an extremely painstaking investigation carried on under the direction of Michelson, during the years following 1924. One of the arrangements used will be clear from Fig. 2.5 and from the following description, both of which are taken from a paper by Michelson in the *Astrophysical Journal*, 1924. "The light source is a Sperry arc which is focused on the slit s. Falling on the face a of the octagon, the light is reflected to a right-angle prism b, to another at c, whence it proceeds to the concave mirror d, of 24-inch aperture and 30-foot focus. This reflects the pencil as a parallel beam to the distant mirror (also a 24-inch, 30-foot concave), proceeding thence to a small concave reflector at its focus. An image of the slit is formed at the face of this small reflector which necessitates the return of the light to the concave mirror at d, whence it passes *over* the prism c to b_1, whence it is reflected to the face a_1 of the octagon, forming an image at s_1, where it is observed by the micrometer eyepiece M."

In this experiment the light traveled from the observing station on Mt. Wilson to Mt. San Antonio, California, a distance of 22 miles, a length which was measured by the U. S. Coast and Geodetic Survey to an accuracy of nearly one part in seven million. The greatest care was also taken to measure the time with the utmost accuracy. The velocity of the revolving mirror was measured "by stroboscopic comparison with an electric fork" whose rate was obtained "by comparison with a free seconds pendulum, which last is compared with an invar gravity pendulum furnished and rated by the Coast and Geodetic Survey." By observing the slight difference in the positions of the images seen in the eyepiece when the mirror was revolved in opposite directions, a small correction was made for the inability to rotate at such a speed that the second face was *exactly* parallel to the incident face. Some idea of the amazing accuracy attained will be had from the following average results obtained, using not only an octagonal mirror, but others, both of glass and of steel, with 12 and 16 faces.

km per sec *in vacuo*

Glass 8 sides 299,797
Steel 8 sides 299,795
Glass 12 sides 299,796
Steel 12 sides 299,796
Glass 16 sides 299,796

2.7. The Tunnel Experiment. In the years following 1930–1931, the same general method was employed by Michelson in collaboration with G. F. Pease of the Mount Wilson Observatory and F. Pearson of the University of Chicago. After the death of Professor Michelson in 1931 this work was carried on by Pease and Pearson.   In this experiment an attempt was made to increase the accuracy by using a short base line which could be measured without triangulation.   This was done by constructing a tunnel in the form of a galvanized pipe tube, one mile long, three feet in diameter, from which the air was exhausted by powerful vacuum pumps, to a pressure as low as 0.5 mm of mercury.   By working at such a low pressure, errors arising from the dependence of the velocity on the index of refraction of atmospheric air were eliminated, and, moreover, the sharpness of the optical images utilized was greatly increased.   The base line was measured by the U. S. Coast and Geodetic Survey with a probable error of ± 0.47 mm, that is, to an accuracy of about one part in 3,400,000.   With the air of a 32-sided rotating mirror and an optical arrangement similar in principle to the one just described, all housed in evacuated chambers and operated by remote controls, the time taken for a beam of light to travel back and forth sometimes eight, sometimes ten times was measured with even greater care than in the 1925–1926 investigation.   In the final report of this investigation the result given is

$$299,774 \text{ km per sec } in\ vacuo.$$

This value is the simple mean of some 2885 determinations, but it is worth while noting that the averages of smaller numbers of determinations taken during different time intervals gave values differing from this final mean by more than experimental error.   For example, the mean of one set of 55 determinations was 299,780 km per sec, while the mean of another set of 47 (both sets being taken at different intervals in the period March to August, 1932) gave 299,771 km per sec.

Although the tunnel experiment gave results appreciably lower than the San Antonio determination, it is significant that Bergstrand (Sweden) in a critical analysis* of the precision of optical methods for measuring the velocity of light concludes that "from the rotating prism experiments we get a combined value of

$$c = 299,792 \pm 6 \text{ km per sec.}"$$

2.8. Anderson's Method.   In this method a beam of light is divided by reflection at a semi-silvered surface into two beams which are subsequently superimposed in a way that is suggestive of Michelson's Interferometer (section 9.12).   The highly simplified diagram in Fig. 2.6 will make the basic idea clear.   Light from L, a Pointolite lamp, has its intensity altered periodically, f times a second, by means of a modulator M.   The beam falls on a half-silvered mirror S where it is divided into two parts, a reflected one traveling over a short distance to a mirror M_1, a transmitted one over a much longer path to a mirror M_2.   (In the actual arrangement the path is made long by reflections back and forth from several mirrors.)   After reflection from M_1 the first beam passes

---

* Recent Developments and Techniques in the Maintenance of Standards, p. 75, London: H.M. Stationery Office, 1952.

through S and falls on a photoelectric cell P, while the second beam after reflection from M_2 is reflected from S to the cell, where the two beams are superimposed. Because the intensity of the light fluctuates from a maximum to a minimum, the superimposed beams may arrive in step, giving a maximum response of the photoelectric cell, or exactly out of step, with a minimum photoelectric current. By altering the path difference between the two beams, a minimum can be located *exactly*.

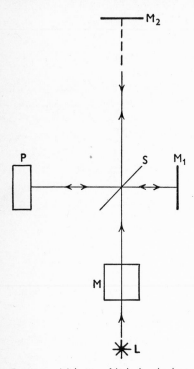

The time to travel the path difference D, therefore, must be $n \cdot (T/2)$, where T is the periodic time between two successive maxima (or minima) of intensity in the original beam and n is an *integral* odd number. Hence, c, the velocity of light $= 2D/nT$, or $2fD/n$, where f, the frequency of modulation $= 1/T$. Since n is integral, its value can be found, using an approximate value of c, without any error.* With n known, the velocity of light can be found to a high degree of accuracy. The value given by Anderson (United States) in 1941 was

$$c = 299{,}776 \pm 14 \text{ km per sec.}$$

Bergstrand in his analysis obtains a systematic error in Anderson's method of 18 km per sec and concludes that "Anderson's result does not contradict that of Michelson."

Fig. 2.6. Velocity of light by Anderson's method. The intensity of light from a source L is altered periodically by a modulator M, from which the emergent light is partially reflected, partially transmitted, by the semi-silvered surface S. After reflection at the mirrors M_1 and M_2 the two beams are superimposed and strike the photoelectric cell P.

2.9. Bergstrand's Method. Some years later E. Bergstrand carried out an investigation in which use was again made of minima observed in the response of a photoelectric cell when a modulated beam of light fell upon it. In Bergstrand's method, a single beam of light was used, because, by means of a crystal-controlled oscillator attached both to the light source and to the photoelectric cell, the intensity of the light and the response of the cell varied in

---

* In Anderson's experiment, $f = 9.6 \times 10^6$ modulations per sec and D (uncorrected) $= 171.8$ meters. Hence, if we take 3×10^8 m per sec as an approximate value of the velocity of light, the time to travel 171.8 m $= \dfrac{171.8}{3 \times 10^8}$ sec. But the time also $= n\dfrac{1}{2 \times 9.6 \times 10^6}$ sec. Equating the two, we find $n = 11$.

synchronism. In consequence, as the path length of the optical beam was altered, the cell gave maximum and minimum readings. From observations of the path lengths for minima readings and of the frequency of modulation of the light source, the velocity of light can readily be calculated.* Details of this method are unnecessary in this text. The final result, published in 1950, was

$$c \; in \; vacuo = 299{,}792.7 \pm 0.25 \; \text{km per sec.}$$

2.10. Essen's Method. This is a nonoptical method to which reference is made because the value obtained agrees with that of Bergstrand and also with his conclusion regarding the best value given by the rotating prism experiments. Essen and Gordon-Smith (Great Britain), working in the National Physical Laboratory in England, made use of microwaves varying in frequency from 3101.25 to 3563.80 Mc per sec (wavelength about 10 cm). In their investigation the velocity of electromagnetic waves was calculated from measurement of the dimensions of an evacuated cavity oscillator in the microwave system and the frequency of resonance. In 1950 Essen published as his final result,

$$c \; in \; vacuo = 299{,}792.5 \pm 3 \; \text{km per sec.}$$

2.11. Method of Hansen and Bol. A resonant microwave method was also used by Hansen and Bol (United States) in work not yet published in detail. In a brief note in the *Physical Review* (1950), however, Bol reports the value

$$c \; in \; vacuo = 299{,}789.3 \pm 0.4 \; \text{km per sec,}$$

and states that due to a possible error arising from tarnish on the silver-plated walls of the cavity, this result may be too low by 0.5 km per sec.

Confirmation of the higher values for c is given by work done by the United States Coast and Geodetic Survey, using airplanes flying across a line between two stations, and triangulation methods. Aslakson (United States) reporting the results of this work in 1949 gives

$$c \; in \; vacuo = 299{,}792.3 \pm 2.4 \; \text{km per sec.}$$

2.12. Houston's Method. A final brief reference is made to still another optical method. In 1949 R. A. Houston (Great Britain) reported briefly on the result obtained using a method (suggested by him in 1938) which was essentially that of Fizeau's toothed wheel experiment, the alternate interruptions of the beam being brought about by replacing the wheel by a piezo-quartz crystal. To quote Houston, "When placed in an alternating field, this has the property of acting as an intermittent diffraction grating. The light in the first order spectrum is then interrupted two hundred times as rapidly as by Fizeau's toothed

---

* Bergstrand originally designed his apparatus, called a geodimeter, for the accurate measurement of distances, using the known value of the velocity of light.

wheel." The greater speed of interruption allows the use of much shorter optical paths. Using a path about 39 meters, Houston obtained,

$$c \; in \; vacuo = 299,795 \text{ km per sec.}$$

2.13. Present Accepted Value. Although in 1944 Dorsey (United States), after a careful analysis of all significant experiments, gave 299,773 as the best mean value for the velocity of light and in 1941 Birge (United States) had given 299,774 as the best value, it will be noted that all the recent nonoptical methods give 299,790 or higher. Moreover, in section 2.7 attention has been directed to Bergstrand's conclusion that the combined value of the rotating mirror experiments is 299,792.

Further evidence that the higher values should be accepted is given in two articles in the *Physical Review* for 1951, both of which deal with the best values of standard atomic constants. In the first, Bearden and Watts (United States) give for the velocity of light

$$c = 299,790.0 \pm 0.7 \text{ km per sec.}$$

In the second, Du Mond and Cohen (United States) give

$$c = 299,790.2 \pm 0.9 \text{ km per sec.}$$

It would seem, therefore, that we can now accept the value 299,790.

PROBLEMS

1. In a Fizeau toothed-wheel experiment for obtaining the velocity of light, an eclipse of the source is first observed when the speed of the disc is rotated at a speed of 1500 rpm. (a) If the distance from the toothed wheel, which has 600 teeth, to the reflecting mirror is 4980 meters, find the velocity of light. (b) At what speed will a second eclipse be observed?

2. In a Fizeau toothed-wheel experiment, if the number of teeth in the wheel is 640 and the distance from wheel to the reflecting mirror is 23,000 meters, calculate 3 speeds for which an eclipse is observed. Take velocity of light $= 2.998 \times 10^8$ m per sec.

3. In the rotating mirror method used to measure the velocity of light which traveled from Mt. Wilson to Mt. San Antonio, no shift of the observed source of light was obtained with an 8-face mirror rotated at a speed of 530 rps. If the measured distance the light traveled (in one direction) was 354.3×10^2 m, calculate the velocity of light.

4. In the experiment to which reference is made in problem 3 find the minimum speeds at which a 12- and a 16-sided mirror would have to be revolved so that no shift of the source is observed. Use velocity of rotation for the 8-face mirror given in problem 3.

5. In Anderson's method for measuring the velocity of light, the response of the photoelectric cell was a minimum when the path difference was 171.8 meters and the frequency of modulation 9.6×10^6 cps. Find the value of the velocity of light (without corrections or refinements). *N.B.* Determine first the value of n, as in section 2.8.

III

Reflection and Refraction
by Huygens' Principle

Before reading this chapter the student who is not thoroughly familiar with the simple laws of reflection and refraction, as well as with the geometrical means of locating images in mirrors and in lenses by the use of principal rays, is strongly advised to review this work with the help of any good elementary text on general physics.

3.1. Meaning of Wave-front. In Chapter I it was stated that a simple explanation of the laws of reflection and of refraction could be given from the viewpoint of waves. Before deriving these laws by the use of what is sometimes called *Huygens' Principle*, but might better be described as Huygens' Construction, the student is asked to recall one or two elementary ideas about waves. In Chapter VII a quantitative discussion of wave motion will be given, but for the work of this chapter all that is necessary is a clear understanding of the term *wave-front*.

Consider the simple case of a line of elastically connected particles, one end of which goes through a periodic motion. For simplicity, suppose that this periodic motion is similar to the to and fro motion of a simple pendulum or of a mass vibrating at the end of a spring. In Fig. 3.1 we have represented the position of successive particles (1) at the instant the end particle marked 0 has reached its position of maximum displacement, as in *a*; (2) one-quarter of a vibration later, when the end particle is back in its normal position, as in *b*; (3) when this particle has reached its position of maximum displacement on the other side of the normal, as in *c*; (4) after one complete vibration, when particle 0 is back to its normal position, as in *d*.

The figures have been drawn on the supposition that, during the time of one-quarter of a vibration, the wave disturbance travels the distance separating six particles. In *a*, Fig. 3.1, therefore, particle 6 is just on the point of being displaced, while intermediate particles are displaced amounts depending on their distances from the source. In *b*, Fig. 3.1, particle 12 is on the point of being displaced; in *c*, Fig. 3.1, particle 18, while it is not difficult to see that after one complete vibration of the source, the first 24 particles occupy positions somewhat as illustrated in *d*, Fig. 3.1.   After two complete vibrations the configuration will be as in *e*, Fig. 3.1, in which case the diagram is drawn on a smaller scale.

In *e*, Fig. 3.1 it is clear that particles marked 0, 24, 48 are all in their normal undisturbed positions, but moving "up"; particles 12 and 36 are also in their normal positions moving "down"; particles 18 and 42 are displaced maximum amounts above their normal positions and are about to move down; particles 6 and 30 are displaced maximum amounts below the normal positions and are about to move up.   Now all particles moving in the same way with respect to their normal positions are said to be in the same *phase.**   Thus particles 0, 24, and 48 are in the same phase; particles 12 and 36; and so on.

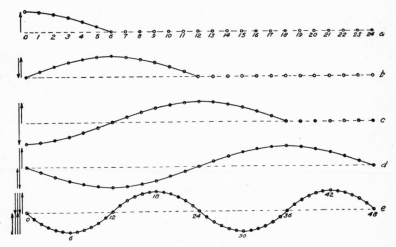

Fig. 3.1.   The positions of displaced particles after: *(a)* one; *(b)* two; *(c)* three; *(d)* four-quarters of a vibration, and *(e)* two complete vibrations, of a vibrating source causing a wave disturbance to travel along a line of particles.

So far we have been considering only a line of particles.   Generally we have to deal with a disturbance traveling through a medium of three dimensions.   In that case we must distinguish between plane and spherical *wave-fronts*.   A *plane* wave-front is a plane surface through which a wave disturbance is passing and in which all vibrating particles are in the same phase.   A *spherical* wave-front is a portion of a spherical surface in which all particles are in the same phase.

3.2. Huygens' Principle.   Huygens, it will be recalled, was one of the supporters of the wave theory at a time long before the phenomenon of interference had been discovered.   Indeed he is generally considered to be the founder of this theory.   It was necessary for him not only to deduce the laws of reflection by means of waves, but also to account for approximate rectilinear propagation.

* In Chapter VII it will be seen that the phase of a particle executing a simple periodic motion can be exactly defined by means of an angle.

To some extent the solution of these questions is found in this principle. According to it, if a wave-front originating in some source S, Fig. 3.2, has reached the position AB, each vibrating particle in this wave-front must be considered as a secondary source from which spherical wavelets spread out. After a time t, therefore, there will be a series of "wavelets" with centers 1, 2, 3, 4 . . . each of radius Vt, where V is the velocity of the wave disturbance. The principle states further that the surface which envelops all these wavelets constitutes a new wave-front. It will be evident from Fig. 3.2 and Fig. 3.3 that spherical wave-fronts will be propagated as spherical, plane wave-fronts as plane.

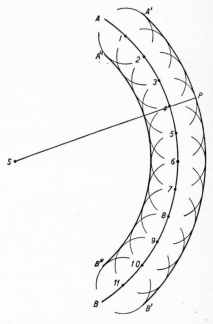

The principle as thus stated tacitly assumes that a wavelet is effective only at the small portion which is tangent to the enveloping surface, and defines a ray as the line joining the center of a wavelet, such as 4, Fig. 3.4, to this small portion at P. Although, in a way, it thus "explains" rectilinear propagation, the principle is open to one or two objections.

(1) Why is a wave-front not propagated backward, giving rise to $A''B''$ (Fig. 3.2) as well as to $A'B'$?

(2) What right has one to neglect the large portion of the wavelet not tangent to the enveloping surface? For example, in Fig. 3.3, why is there no edge effect from the wavelet originating in particle m?

Fig. 3.2. According to Huygens' Principle wavelets originate from particles 1, 2, 3, 4, etc., on a spherical wave-front. The enveloping surface to the wavelets forms a new wave-front.

The answer to these questions involves the study of diffraction which is discussed in some detail in later chapters. At this stage we note that Huygens' Principle as given previously is unable to interpret diffraction phenomena. Later we shall see that, by assuming a wavelet effective over the whole front hemisphere, Fresnel gave a partial explanation of diffraction. It was not, however, until after many years that a satisfactory general treatment of Hugyens' Principle was given by Voigt and Kirchhoff. When this highly mathematical treatment is applied, it can be shown that the contribution of a wavelet in any direction making an angle θ with AP, Fig. 3.4, is proportional to $\dfrac{1 + \cos \theta}{2}$, which, when $\theta = 180°$, is equal to zero.

But in this chapter we are dealing with cases where diffraction effects may be neglected and we wish to show how, by means of Huygens' Principle in its original form, the common laws of reflection and refraction may be deduced.

3.3. Plane Waves Striking a Plane Reflecting Surface Obliquely.

Suppose a set of plane waves is incident in the direction of the arrow I, Fig. 3.5, on the plane reflecting surface XY. Let OM represent the position of a wave-front at a certain instant. After a time, had there been no change of medium, the wave-front would have advanced to the position DO'. Actually, therefore, particles

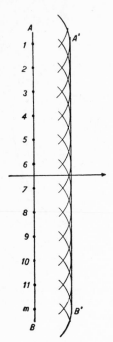

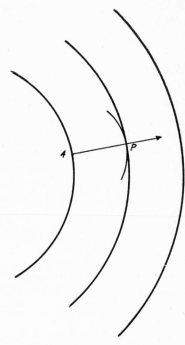

Fig. 3.3. The plane wave-front $A'B'$ is the tangential surface to wavelets originating in particles on the wave-front AB.

Fig. 3.4. The ray AP is the line joining the origin A of a wavelet to the place P where it is tangential to the new wave-front.

in the surface XY between O and D will be *successively* disturbed as the wave-front advances, and each particle becomes the source of a reflected wavelet. In the figure the positions of wavelets originating from particles O, A, B, C are drawn at the instant the particle D is on the point of being disturbed. The wavelet from O, for example, has radius $= OO'$; that from $A = AA'$, and so on for the others.

Now, applying Huygens' Principle we see that these wavelets give rise to a plane reflected wave-front DK, which will continue to propagate itself in the direction of the arrow R. By taking an incident *ray* such as PO and the corre-

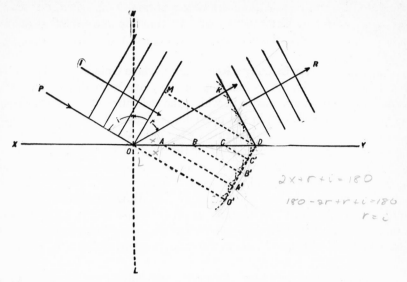

Fig. 3.5. Huygens' construction to show the formation of a reflected wave-front *KD* when an incident wave-front O_1M strikes the plane reflecting surface *XY* obliquely.

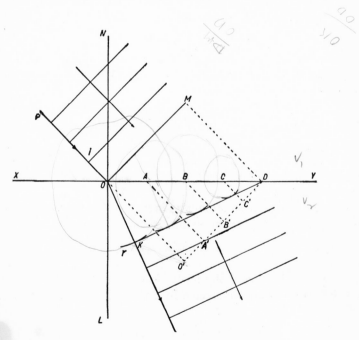

Fig. 3.6. Huygens' construction for the refraction of plane waves at the plane refracting surface *XY*.

sponding reflected ray OK, and drawing a normal to the surface at O, it is not difficult to prove by elementary geometry that the angle NOP = angle NOK; that is, that the angle of incidence = the angle of reflection.

3.4. Plane Waves Striking a Refracting Surface Obliquely.   Suppose a plane wave-front OM, Fig. 3.6, is incident on the plane refracting surface XY separating two transparent media in which the velocities of the wave disturbance are v_1 and v_2, $v_1 > v_2$. As in the previous case, particles in the surface are successively disturbed, and in the figure we have represented the position of several wavelets at the instant the edge M of the original wave-front has reached the point D. Putting it otherwise, the wavelets are drawn at the time that OM would have reached $O'D$ had there been no change in medium. The radius OK of wavelet originating in O will, therefore, equal $OO' \cdot (v_2/v_1)$; the radius of that from A will equal $AA' \cdot (v_2/v_1)$; and so on for other points. Again we see the formation of a plane refracted wave-front DK, traveling in a direction making a smaller angle with the normal to the refracting surface than the incident train.

Deduction of the Sine Law.   Consider an incident ray PO (Fig. 3.6) and the corresponding refracted ray OK.

If i = angle of incidence, and r = angle of refraction, then

$$\frac{\sin i}{\sin r} = \frac{\sin PON}{\sin KOL} = \frac{\sin MOD}{\sin KDO} = \frac{v_1}{v_2} = \text{a constant.}$$

By definition the index of refraction of a medium is the ratio of the velocity of light c in a vacuum* to the velocity in the given medium. Hence, introducing c into the above relation, we may write

$$\frac{\sin i}{\sin r} = \frac{(c/v_2)}{(c/v_1)} = \frac{n_2}{n_1},$$

or

$$n_1 \sin i = n_2 \sin r,$$

where n_1 is the index of the medium in which the velocity is v_1 and n_2 bears a similar relation to v_2.

If, following the notation often used in geometrical optics, we put $i = \theta_1$ and $r = \theta_2$, we obtain the convenient symmetrical form

$$n_1 \sin \theta_1 = n_2 \sin \theta_2. \tag{3.00}$$

3.5. In courses in general physics the index of refraction is usually defined in terms of the empirical law discovered by Snell and by Descartes, that is, by the relation

$$\frac{\sin \theta_1}{\sin \theta_2} = \text{a constant.}$$

---

* In handbooks and tables of constants indices are given with respect to air a 60 mm. pressure and a standard temperature.

Although the treatment in section 3.4 has the great advantage that it explains *why* the ratio is a constant (the velocity of light in isotropic media like glass and water being the same in all directions), the definition given in this text and others has been described as "misleading and artificial." With this opinion the author does not agree for the following reasons.

(a) The ratio of two velocities is a physical idea so simple and so fundamental that it gives rise to no difficulty whatever in the mind of a student.

(b) As explained in Chapter XII, in crystalline media the Snell-Descartes law does not hold for the extraordinary ray and the use of velocities can scarcely be avoided.

(c) The objection has been made that what is actually measured in any direct determination of the velocity of light in a medium is the *group* velocity and that this is not the same (except in free space) as the individual velocities of the component wavelengths. In consequence, it is argued, *direct* determination of velocities leads to an evaluation of the group index only. This is correct, but the fact that in actual practice indices for individual wavelengths are determined by measurement of angles, as in the prism-spectrometer (see Chapter VI), surely in no way invalidates the definition of an index in terms of the ratio of velocities.

(d) The very important idea of the dispersion of a medium (section 6.3) has to do with the change in the velocity of light with changing wavelength.

(e) The relation

$$\frac{\sin \theta_1}{\sin \theta_2} = \frac{v_1}{v_2}$$

is extremely useful in solving problems. (Apply it to problem 6, p. 53.)

3.6. Total Reflection. According to Huygens' Principle no special hypothesis is necessary to explain simultaneous reflection and refraction because if particles such as O, A, B, C, in either Fig. 3.5 or Fig. 3.6, are disturbed, both reflected and refracted wavelets are to be expected. Our problem is rather to explain why, under certain conditions, the refracted wave-front is absent.

The student will recall the phenomenon of total reflection. If a ray traveling in a more dense medium strikes a plane refracting surface sufficiently obliquely, there is no refraction and total reflection occurs. We shall examine, therefore, what explanation can be given of this fact by means of Huygens' Principle. First of all, the student should note that to obtain a refracted wave-front, it is not necessary to draw a large number of wavelets. In either of the cases illustrated in Figs. 3.5 and 3.6, all that is necessary is to draw through D the plane DK which is tangent to the *single* wavelet originating in O. If, then, we wish the refracted wave-front corresponding to a plane wave-front OM, Fig. 3.7, striking a plane surface separating water and air, at nearly normal incidence, we can proceed by (1) drawing a wavelet with center O and radius $OR = 1.33MD$, and (2) drawing through D the plane DK tangent to this wavelet.

Suppose, however, the incident wave-front strikes the surface very obliquely. as in Fig. 3.8.   In that case the radius (OB) of the wavelet originating at O is so large that it is impossible to draw a plane through D tangent to it.   A refracted wave-front is then impossible and we have total reflection.   Obviously, there will be a certain critical obliquity lying between the two cases illustrated in Figs. 3.7 and 3.8.

This limiting case will occur when the wavelet originating in O just reaches D, that is, when its radius = OD, as in Fig. 3.9.   In the case of air-water, we have

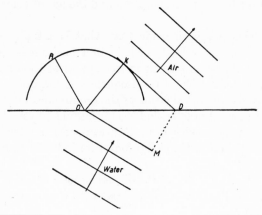

Fig. 3.7.   Plane waves striking a plane refracting surface at small angles of incidence are refracted into the less dense medium above the surface.

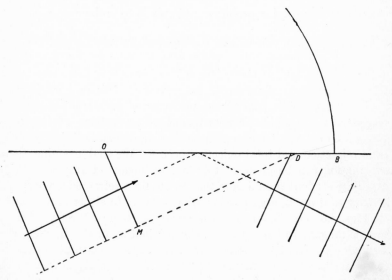

Fig. 3.8.   At large angles of incidence, plane waves striking a plane refracting surface are totally reflected when the medium above the surface is less dense than the lower.

this critical condition when $OD = 1.33MD$, or more generally when OD/MD = $v_\text{air}/v_\text{water} = n$.

But from Fig. 3.9, $1/\sin C = OD/MD$, where C is the critical angle of incidence, since $MOD = C$.

Therefore, we have the relation which the student should recognize:

$$\sin C = \frac{1}{\text{index of refraction}}. \tag{3.01}$$

The question of total reflection may be approached somewhat differently. Suppose *spherical* waves spread out from a source P, Fig. 3.10, strike the plane surface AB separating two media, the velocity of the wave motion in the upper

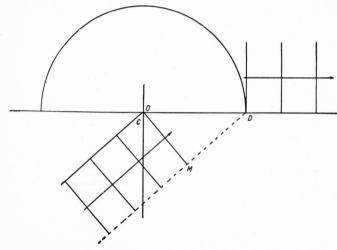

Fig. 3.9. At a critical angle of incidence, plane waves striking a plane refracting surface are refracted into the less dense medium above the surface, with the emergent wave-front at right angles to the surface.

being greater than in the lower. (Fig. 3.10 has been drawn on the supposition that the ratio of velocities = 1.5.) As a wave-front advances from P it will strike the surface first at the point O, causing a secondary wavelet to originate at this point. As time goes on, other wavelets will originate successively at particles 1, 2, 3, 4, 5, etc., so that, by the time the original wave-front has just reached the point 10, the reflected and the refracted wave-fronts may be found by drawing the surfaces tangent to all the wavelets in their positions *at that instant*. The student will readily see that the radius of the refracted wavelet originating in point 4, for example, = $(P10 - P4) \times 1.5$, while that of the corresponding reflected wavelet = $P10 - P4$. In this way wavelets for all the particles from 0 to 10 have been drawn.

A glance at the diagram will show that, while there is an enveloping surface for all the reflected wavelets, and for the refracted wavelets from 0, 1, 2, 3, 4, and 5, *there is no real envelope for wavelets from 6, 7, 8 and 9*. This means that for all particles on the surface beyond a point D somewhere between points 5 and 6, *no refracted wave-front is possible* because the individual wavelets fall within each other. It follows, then, that OPD is the critical angle for these two media. For purposes of reproduction the points 1, 2, 3, 4, etc., have been taken fairly far apart and an exact location of D is not possible. In the figure, the angle $OP5$ is $39° 44'$, $OP6$ is $44° 46'$, while the critical angle as calculated from formula (3.01) is $42°$. It will be noted that not only have we obtained a physical reason for total reflection, but we have been able to make a fair estimate of the critical angle without the use of the sine law of refraction.

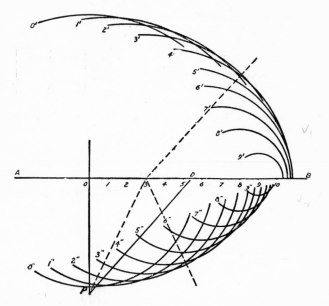

Fig. 3.10. When incident spherical waves strike a plane refracting surface AB separating a lower less dense from an upper more dense medium, it is impossible to draw an enveloping surface to wavelets originating at particles 6, 7, 8 and 9.

3.7. Spherical Waves Reflected at a Plane Surface.

Although in the foregoing discussion of total reflection some consideration of reflection of spherical waves was necessary, this case is so important that we shall now consider it more carefully. Suppose, then, that spherical waves coming from a source S, Fig. 3.11, strike the plane reflecting surface XY. At a certain instant the incident wave-front will have reached the position LAK, and a wavelet will be on the point of spreading out from A. As the wave-front advances, successive particles in the surface XY will become the source of other wavelets. In this figure we have represented the position of such wavelets at the particular instant that the original wave-front would have reached CMD had there been no reflecting surface. The wavelet originating at P, for example, will have a radius = PN. Applying Huygens' Principle, we see the formation of a reflected wave-front CED which will continue to propagate itself in the normal way. The reflected wave-front evidently leaves the reflecting surface *as if* it came from a center S', the *virtual image* of S. Since $AE = AM$, $PN' = PN$, etc., the curvature of CED is equal to that of CMD, and, without any further formal proof, we see that this virtual image is as far behind the reflecting surface as the original source is in front—the second elementary law of reflection.

If the eye is in a position such as E_1, it "sees" the image by means of the disturbance confined within the shaded cone, apparently coming from S', in

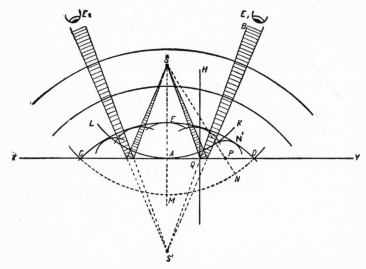

Fig. 3.11. Huygens' construction for spherical waves reflected at the plane surface XY.

reality from the original source along the shaded path. In another position such as E_2, the same image is visible, but by means of the different cone shown in the figure.

If we deal with a ray, such as SQ, it is reflected along the path QB, and it is a simple matter to prove geometrically that the angle of incidence SQH = the angle of reflection HQB, where HQ is normal to the surface at Q.

3.8. Spherical Waves Refracted at a Plane Surface. Here again we consider more in detail the case of the refracted wave-front arising from wavelets originating in particles 0, 1, 2, 3, 4, 5, Fig. 3.10. Suppose spherical waves spreading out from the source S, Fig. 3.12, pass through the plane surface XY into a less dense medium, where the velocity v_1 is greater than v_2, that in the lower. In the figure the positions of the refracted wavelets have been drawn at the instant an incident wave-front LMK would have reached the position ANB, had there been no change of medium. The wavelet from the point M, therefore, has a radius

$$MN' = MN \cdot \frac{v_1}{v_2}.$$

Again Huygens' Principle shows us the existence of a refracted wave-front $AN'B$ spreading out from the surface as if it came from some center S', the virtual image of S. In the case considered, S' is obviously nearer the surface than the original source. How much nearer, we shall find out in section 3.10.

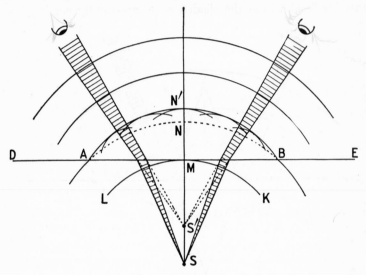

Fig. 3.12. Huygens' construction for spherical waves refracted at the plane surface DE.

As in the previous case of reflection, the eye sees the image in different positions by means of little cones of rays, two of which are shown in Fig. 3.12.

3.9. Before considering this case quantitatively, it is necessary to digress in order to establish an expression for measuring the curvature of a circle or sphere. In Fig. 3.13, DCE is a portion of circle or sphere of radius r; AOC is a diameter, and DBE a chord at right angles to this diameter.

By elementary geometry,

$$BD \cdot BE = AB \cdot BC$$

or
$$y^2 = (2r - x)x$$
$$= 2rx - x^2 \qquad (3.02)$$

where
$$y = BD = BE, \text{ and } x = BC.$$

Now, if x is a small quantity compared with y or r, with little error we may neglect its square, and write

$$y^2 = 2rx,$$

or
$$\frac{1}{r} = \frac{2x}{y^2} \qquad (3.03)$$

Relation (3.03), of which we shall make considerable use, tells us that the curvature (the reciprocal of the radius) of a circle or a sphere is proportional to the distance x, sometimes called the sagitta, *provided x is sufficiently small.*

Many students have a feeling of dissatisfaction in thus dropping quantities, as is so frequently done in physics. Their difficulty lies in their failure to appreciate that physics is a science based on measurement. Now there is a limit of accuracy beyond which it is not possible to go in any measurement. If, for example, a student is measuring the distance of an image from a mirror, he may record 20 cm. That does not mean 20.00000 $\cdots$, for there are many factors which make it impossible for him to go beyond a certain degree of accuracy. He may be using a ruler graduated in millimeters, fractions of which he must estimate; the ruler may be unevenly scaled, the image may not be sharply focused, and, in general, he finds his independent measurements varying somewhat. If asked to consider his measurements and use his judgment, he may finally say that his measurement cannot be relied on to more than 1 mm. His length 20 cm, therefore, is considered correct to about 1 part in 200, or to $\frac{1}{2}$ per cent, and might be written 20.0 ± 0.1 cm.

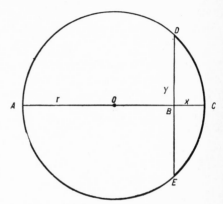

Fig. 3.13.   If BC is sufficiently small, $BD^2 = 2AO \cdot BC$.

Now suppose this number has to be used in making calculations from a formula such as (3.02), which could be simplified by dropping x^2 to the simpler relation (3.03). If the dropping of x^2 means introducing an error considerably less than $\frac{1}{2}$ per cent, the student would be justified—indeed, he would only be using his common sense—in making use of the simpler expression.

The actual error in dropping x^2 may readily be found for special cases. For example, if $r = 60$ cm, $x = 5$ mm,

$$y^2 = 59.75, \text{ from relation } (3.02),$$
$$= 60.00, \text{ from relation } (3.03).$$

It will be seen that the magnitude of the error depends on the value of x compared with the other quantities. Whenever we use relation (3.03), we are assuming that this error may be neglected and it is important to realize that *any*

*relations which are derived from it, such as (3.05), hold only subject to this quali-
fication.*

3.10. We return now to the case of refraction illustrated in Fig. 3.12. Applying relation (3.02) we write

$$MB^2 = 2SN \cdot MN - MN^2,$$

and

$$MB^2 = 2\,S'N' \cdot MN' - (MN')^2,$$

from which

$$2\,SN \cdot MN - MN^2 = 2S'N' \cdot MN' - (MN')^2,$$

or

$$MN(2SN - MN) = MN'(2S'N' - MN'),$$

or

$$MN\,(2\,SM + MN) = MN'(2S'M + MN').$$

Therefore,

$$\frac{2SM + MN}{2S'M + MN'} = \frac{MN'}{MN}$$

$$= \frac{v_1}{v_2} = n,$$

or

$$n = \frac{SM\left(1 + \dfrac{MN}{2SM}\right)}{S'M\left(1 + \dfrac{MN'}{2S'M}\right)}$$

$$= \frac{SM}{S'M},\text{ with slight error,}$$

$$= \frac{\text{object distance}}{\text{image distance}}. \tag{3.04}$$

It is easy to estimate the size of the error in dropping $MN/2SM$ in the foregoing relation, in the case of an eye looking vertically downward at a small
object below the surface of water. Suppose, for example, in Fig. 3.12, the
source S is 2.5 cm below the surface DE and we take the aperture of the eye to
be 3 mm. Then the distance AB is less than 3 mm and MN is less than 0.045 mm.
(Use relation 3.02 or 3.03.) Hence, the value of $MN/2SM$ is 0.0009, and the
error in dropping this term is extremely slight.

The student should derive relation (3.04) also by using rays and the sine
law of refraction. He will note that it holds, provided the angles are sufficiently
small that the error involved in putting the tangent of an angle equal to its sine
may be neglected.

3.11. We pass now to a consideration of curved reflecting and refracting surfaces. In all cases we shall assume that the surfaces are portions of spheres, and

that the portion actually used is such a small fraction of the whole that we may use the approximate relation (3.03) as a measure of the curvature. The relations we deduce will then be applicable only when this restriction holds good. It is well to realize, however, that in our diagrams, for the sake of clearness, the lengths corresponding to x of Fig. 3.13 are all grossly exaggerated. Moreover, we are justified in considering wave-fronts such as $AN'B$, Fig. 3.12, and $A'OC'$, Fig. 3.14, as spherical only when the same restriction applies.

Plane Waves at a Spherical Surface. Let ABC, Fig. 3.14, be a plane wave-front incident on the concave spherical mirror AOC, whose center of curvature is R and radius of curvature $= r = RO$. Proceeding in the same way as has already been done more than once, we have drawn the position of wavelets at the instant the wave-front would have reached the position MON. This means that the radius of the wavelets originating at A and at $C = BO$. Again we see

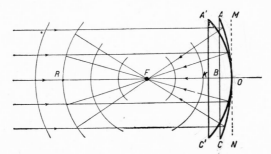

Fig. 3.14. The incident plane wave-front ABC after reflection by the spherical surface AOC gives rise to the reflected wave-front $A'OC'$.

the formation of a reflected wave-front $A'OC'$ which, since we are dealing only with a small portion of a curved surface, may be considered as spherical, making for a center F, the *principal focus* or *focal point*.

The position of F evidently depends on the curvature of the mirror; for the larger BO, the greater the curvature of the reflected wave-front, that is, the shorter the focal length, OF.

Join A' and C', the outer edges of the reflected wave-front. $A'C'$ will then intersect RO at right angles, and $KB = AA'$.

Since the incident disturbance advances from B to O, while the reflected goes from A to A',

$$AA' = BO. *$$

---

* It may be objected that it is not the distance AA' but AP in Fig. 3.15 which is equal to BO. This is quite true, but for sufficiently small apertures the angle $A'AP'$ will be so small that its cosine $= 1$, and with small error $AA' = AP$. Fig. 3.15 is, of course, grossly exaggerated.

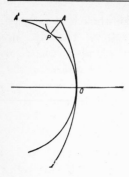

or $KB = BO.$

$$\therefore \quad KO = 2BO$$

$$\therefore \quad \frac{2KO}{y^2} = 2 \cdot \frac{2BO}{y^2},$$

multiplying each side by $\dfrac{2}{y^2}$, where $y = A'K = AB = \dfrac{1}{2}$ the aperture of the mirror.

$$\therefore \quad \frac{1}{OF} = \frac{2}{OR}, \text{ by relation (3.03)}$$

Fig. 3.15. If the angle $A'AP$ is sufficiently small, $AP = AA'$ with slight error. The figure is grossly exaggerated.

or $$f = \frac{r}{2}, \tag{3.05}$$

that is, the focal length is equal to one-half the radius of curvature—subject always to the restriction of small aperture. If the aperture is large, the focal length of the central portion differs somewhat from the outer portions, and plane waves from a distant point give rise not to a point image but to the familiar caustic curve MFN illustrated in Fig. 3.16.

It is left to the student to prove relation (3.05) for a convex mirror.

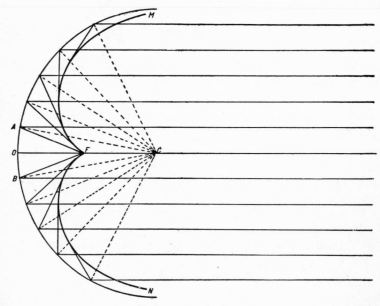

Fig. 3.16. *MFN* is the caustic curve formed when parallel rays are reflected from a concave mirror of wide aperture.

3.12. Spherical Waves Reflected from a Spherical Surface.   Plane waves imply distant sources, and in actual practice we more frequently have to do with sources which are not distant.   Suppose, then, that spherical waves spread out from a point source P, Fig. 3.17, fall on a concave mirror AOC, whose center of curvature is at R.   Let ABC be an incident wave-front, striking the mirror first at A and C.   Without going into details, the student should now be able to see that $A'OC'$ will be a reflected wave-front, with $AA' = BO$.   This reflected

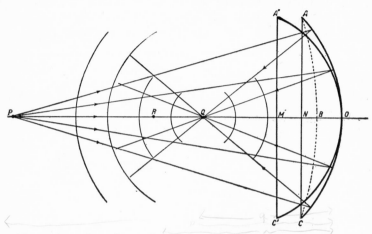

Fig. 3.17.   The incident spherical wave-front ABC after reflection at the concave spherical mirror AOC gives rise to the reflected wave-front $A'OC'$.

wave-front will advance toward a center Q, the real image of P, from which the disturbance will continue to spread out in ever-widening areas.

Let $p = PO$, the distance of object P from the mirror;
$\quad q = OQ$, the corresponding distance of image Q.

We wish to find a relation connecting p, q, and r.

Since $\quad AA' = BO$,
$\quad \therefore \quad MN = BO$,

M and N being points of intersection of $A'C'$ and AC with the axis PQO

$$\therefore \quad MO - NO = NO - NB.$$

This step is taken to introduce only those distances which are proportional to the curvatures $1/p$, $1/q$, and $1/r$.

$$\therefore \quad MO + NB = 2NO$$

or
$$\frac{2MO}{y^2} + \frac{2NB}{y^2} = \frac{2 \cdot 2NO}{y^2}, \text{ where } 2y = \text{aperture.}$$

$$\therefore \quad \frac{1}{q} + \frac{1}{p} = \frac{2}{r}$$

$$= \frac{1}{f}. \tag{3.06}$$

3.13. Spherical Waves Reflected from a Convex Mirror. As in the previous case, AOC, Fig. 3.18, represents the mirror, DOE an incident wave-front from the source P, ANC the reflected wave-front, while DE and AC intersect the

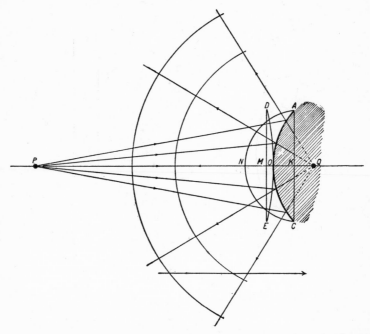

Fig. 3.18. The incident wave-front DOE after reflection at the convex spherical surface AOC gives rise to the reflected wave-front ANC.

axis POQ at M and K. In this case the central portion of the incident wave-front strikes the mirror first, and the reflected wave-front comes off *as if* it came from the image Q, which is therefore virtual.

Since
$$AD = NO,$$

$$\therefore \qquad MK = NO$$

$$\therefore \qquad MO + OK = NK - OK$$

$$\therefore \quad \frac{2MO}{y^2} - \frac{2NK}{y^2} = -2 \cdot \frac{2OK}{y^2}$$

$$\therefore \qquad \frac{1}{p} - \frac{1}{q} = -\frac{1}{f}. \qquad\qquad (3.06a)$$

It will be noticed that the signs in this relation differ from those of (3.06). Since these relations are frequently used, it is desirable, if possible, to have a single relation applicable to both kinds of mirrors. This can be done, provided some sign convention is adopted. The student will find that all writers do not adopt either the same final relation or the same convention. In this book the convention which is used is the same for all cases of reflection and refraction at spherical surfaces, and also for lenses, both converging and diverging, and, moreover, is in agreement with the recently published (1951) recommendation of a committee of the International Commission on Optics. According to it, *distances measured from the mirror or lens or surface in the direction in which the light is traveling are positive; distances measured in the opposite direction, negative.* In other words, if, in a diagram, the light travels from left to right, and the center of the mirror or lens or curved surface is placed at an imaginary origin of coordinates, the axis of the optical system coinciding with the x-axis, distances on the right of the origin are positive, on the left, negative.

Adopting this convention, we then write

$$\frac{2MO}{y^2} = -\frac{1}{p}, \frac{2NK}{y^2} = +\frac{1}{q}, \text{ and } \frac{2OK}{y^2} = \frac{1}{r}.$$

Instead of relation (3.06a) we then have

$$\frac{1}{-p} - \frac{1}{+q} = -\frac{1}{+f}$$

or $\dfrac{1}{q} + \dfrac{1}{p} = \dfrac{1}{f}$, a relation exactly the same as that (3.06) deduced for the concave mirror.

In using relation (3.06) in a numerical problem, *the student must never forget to substitute values subject to the sign convention.* A simple example may not be out of place.

A small object is placed 50 cm from a convex mirror whose radius of curvature is 20 cm. Find where the image is.

We are here given $p = -50, f = +10,$

$\therefore$ since
$$\frac{1}{q} + \frac{1}{p} = \frac{1}{f},$$

we have
$$\frac{1}{q} + \frac{1}{-50} = \frac{1}{+10}$$

or
$$q = +8.3 \text{ cm}.$$

The plus sign means that the image is on the side of the mirror opposite to that from which the light comes, that is, is a virtual image 8.3 cm behind the mirror.

3.14. Refraction at a Spherical Surface.   The same general method may be used to deduce relations connecting object and image distances when refraction takes place at a spherical surface separating two media.   Two such cases will be discussed.

(*a*) *Plane waves incident on a convex surface.*   In Fig. 3.19, $A'BC'$ represents a convex surface, radius of curvature $= r$, separating the less dense medium on the left from the more dense (shaded) on the right, while ABC is an incident plane wave-front.   Since the center of the incident wave-front strikes the surface first at B, a wavelet will begin to spread out from this point, while points

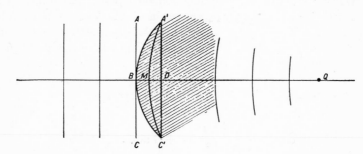

Fig. 3.19.   The incident plane wave-front ABC after refraction at the spherical surface $A'BC'$ separating a less from a more dense medium gives rise to the refracted wave-front $A'MC'$.

between B and A' will be successively disturbed.   To obtain the refracted wave-front, for example, at the instant the outer edges of the plane wave have reached the refracting surface at A' and C', all that is necessary is to draw the position of the wavelet which originated at B.   If BM is the radius of this wavelet at the instant under consideration, then $A'MC'$ is the new refracted wave-front, making for some center Q—the real image.

Because of the slower velocity in the more dense medium, the radius BM will be less than the distance AA' in the ratio of the two velocities, and we may write

$$AA' = n \cdot BM, \qquad\qquad (a)$$

where $n =$ the index of refraction for these two media.

To find the distance of the image from the surface, all that is now necessary is to obtain from this equation a relation involving the distances proportional to the various curvatures.   Thus we now write instead of (*a*),

$$BD = n \cdot BD - n \cdot MD$$

or
$$n \cdot MD = (n - 1) \cdot BD$$

or
$$\frac{2n \cdot MD}{y^2} = (n-1) \cdot \frac{2BD}{y^2}$$

from which
$$\frac{n}{f} = \frac{n-1}{r}$$

or
$$\frac{1}{f} = \frac{n-1}{n} \cdot \frac{1}{r}. \tag{3.07}$$

(b) *Spherical waves emerge from a more dense medium through a spherical surface into a less dense medium.* In Fig. 3.20, ABC is the incident spherical wave-front, $A'BC'$ the spherical refracting surface of radius of curvature r, while $A'DC'$ will be the emergent refracting wave-front if $n \cdot AA' = BD$.

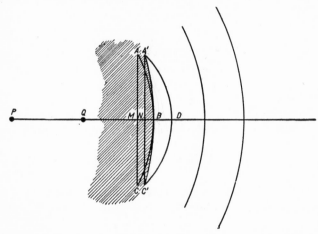

Fig. 3.20. The incident spherical wave-front ABC after refraction at the spherical surface $A'BC'$ separating a more from a less dense medium gives rise to the refracted wave-front $A'DC'$.

We have, therefore,
$$n \cdot MN = BD$$

or
$$n \cdot MB - n \cdot NB = ND - NB$$

or
$$n \cdot MB - ND = (n-1)NB$$

or
$$\frac{n}{-p} - \frac{1}{-q} = \frac{n-1}{-r}$$

or
$$\frac{n}{p} - \frac{1}{q} = \frac{n-1}{r}, \tag{3.08}$$

where p and q stand for object and image distance.

If the curvature of the surface is sufficiently large, and the object at some distance from the surface, the emergent wave-front EBL, Fig. 3.21, may have the opposite curvature to that of the incident ANC. It is left to the student to prove, that, subject always to the sign convention, the same relation holds.

If, using the notation given at the end of section 3.4, we designate the index of the medium in which the object lies by n_1 and the index for the image medium by n_2, relation (3.08) may be put into the more convenient form

$$\frac{n_2}{q} - \frac{n_1}{p} = \frac{n_2 - n_1}{r}. \tag{3.08a}$$

It is left as an exercise for the student to derive this relation by applying exactly the same method as has been used in the derivation of (3.08).

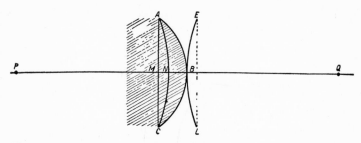

Fig. 3.21. The incident spherical wave-front AMC after refraction at the spherical surface ABC gives rise to the refracted wave-front EBL of opposite curvature.

Relation (3.08a) can be made still more symmetrical by following the method, frequently used in geometrical optics, of designating an object distance by s_1 and an image distance by s_2.* In that case, (3.08a) becomes

$$\frac{n_2}{s_2} - \frac{n_1}{s_1} = \frac{n_2 - n_1}{r}, \tag{3.08b}$$

a relation which is sometimes designated as the paraxial equation for refraction at a single spherical surface.

In this text, however, we shall continue to use the symbols p and q.

3.15. The Sine Condition.   In this section a relation of great importance in geometrical optics is derived.   It is used later, for example, in deriving the resolving power of a microscope.

In Fig. 3.22, let PP_1 represent a small object in a medium of index n_1 and QQ_1 the corresponding image formed in the medium of index n_2 after refraction at the curved surface MBN.   The object distance is then $PB = p$; the image distance is $BQ = q$; and, if C is the center of curvature of the refracting surface, $BC = r$, the radius of curvature.

Since Q is the image of P, then any paraxial ray incident at M must travel

---

* A committee of the International Commission on Optics has recommended the use of still another notation, that is, that all image distances should be "primed." For example, if s is an object distance, s' is the corresponding image distance.

the path MQ in the image medium. Hence, since CMD is perpendicular to the surface at M,

$$\angle PMD = \text{angle of incidence} = \theta_1,$$

and $$\angle QMC = \text{angle of refraction} = \theta_2.$$

As shown in section 3.4, it follows that

$$n_1 \sin \theta_1 = n_2 \sin \theta_2. \tag{a}$$

Moreover, if Q_1 is the image of P_1, then the ray from P_1 to Q_1 through C, the center of curvature, is a straight line, being normal to the refracting surface at N.

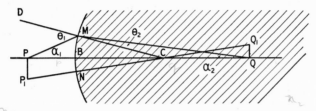

Fig. 3.22. Diagram used in deriving the sine condition.

Since the triangles PCP_1 and QCQ_1 are similar,

$$\frac{QQ_1}{PP_1} = \frac{QC}{PC}$$

or $$\frac{y_2}{y_1} = \frac{q-r}{p+r}, \tag{b}$$

where y_1 and y_2 are symbols for the lateral extensions of object and image.
  From triangle PMC,

$$\frac{\sin MPC}{r} = \frac{\sin PMC}{p+r},$$

or, putting $\angle MPC = \alpha_1$, the *slope angle* of the ray PM in object space,

$$\frac{\sin \alpha_1}{r} = \frac{\sin \theta_1}{p+r},$$

or $$p+r = \frac{r \sin \theta_1}{\sin \alpha_1}. \tag{c}$$

Similarly, from triangle QMC,

$$q-r = \frac{r \sin \theta_2}{\sin \alpha_2}, \tag{d}$$

where $\angle PQM = \alpha_2$, the slope angle of the ray MQ in the image space.
  Combining (c) and (d), we have

$$\frac{q-r}{p+r} = \frac{\sin \theta_2}{\sin \alpha_2} \frac{\sin \alpha_1}{\sin \theta_1}$$

$$= \frac{n_1 \sin \alpha_1}{n_2 \sin \alpha_2}, \text{ from } (a). \tag{e}$$

Finally, combining (*b*) and (*e*), we have

$$\frac{y_2}{y_1} = \frac{n_1 \sin \alpha_1}{n_2 \sin \alpha_2},$$

or $$n_1 y_1 \sin \alpha_1 = n_2 y_2 \sin \alpha_2. \qquad (3.09)$$

This is the *sine condition*.

This proof, it will be noted, applies only to a single refracting surface and hence, because the restriction of small aperture limits the position of M to points near the axis, the angles α_1 and α_2 are small. It is important to note, however, that the sine condition may be applied, even when these angles are not small, to any system of refracting surfaces which has been corrected for defects so that a point image is formed at Q for *all* rays which leave P and pass through the system. For example, it may be applied to the objective lense of a good microscope. (Section 5.8.)

For a single refracting surface of small aperture, the sine condition reduces to

$$n_1 y_1 \alpha_1 = n_2 y_2 \alpha_2. \qquad (3.10)$$

This is a statement of *Lagrange's Theorem*, according to which the product $ny\alpha$ is constant for any number of refractions, if attention is confined to paraxial rays.

Examples of the use of the sine condition will be found in sections 5.8 and 11.4.

3.16. In any problems dealing with refraction at spherical surfaces, it is better to work not from a formula, but from fundamental considerations. When this is done, the sign convention may or may not be used. If it is used, it is important to realize that two steps are necessary: (1) to establish the general relation, (2) to substitute numerical values—both subject to the convention. The following example will make the point clear.

Waves from a point source in air fall on a convex surface separating air from glass (n = 1.5). If the source is 100 cm from the surface, whose radius of curvature is 20 cm, find the position of the image.

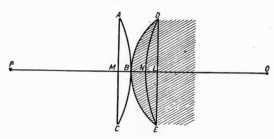

Fig. 3.23.   Diagram used for the solution of problem in section 3.16.

Let ABC, Fig. 3.23, be the incident wave-front,
　　DBE the convex surface,
　　DNE the emergent wave-front, making for the image Q, q cm from the
　　surface.

Since the central portion of the disturbance travels in glass from B to N,
while the outer portions go in air from A to D, or C to E,

$$AD = 1.5BN$$

∴　　　　　　$ML = 1.5BN$

∴　　$MB + BL = 1.5BL - 1.5NL$

∴　$1.5NL + MB = (1.5 - 1)BL.$

Without the sign convention we may write at once, since the student should
now be able to multiply each side by $2/y^2$ mentally,

$$\frac{1.5}{q} + \frac{1}{100} = \frac{0.5}{20},$$

from which $q = 100$ cm.

With the sign convention, we must first establish the general formula; thus

$$\frac{1.5}{+q} + \frac{1}{-p} = \frac{0.5}{+r}. \qquad (a)$$

We now use this formula (a) by substituting for $p = -100$, $r = +20$, and we
then have

$$\frac{1.5}{+q} + \frac{1}{100} = \frac{0.5}{+20},$$

from which $q = +100$ cm.

The numerical answer in each case is, of course, the same. In the second
case the plus sign tells us that the image is on the positive side of the surface.

It may seem to the student that the two steps taken in the second solution
annul each other, and in one sense this is quite true. On the other hand, the
final answer must always bear a plus or a minus sign, and this enables us to say
at once on which side of the surface the image is to be found.

3.17. Lenses. In dealing with the passage of waves through lenses, we shall
confine our attention to problems dealing with those whose surfaces are either
plane or spherical, and whose thickness can be neglected in comparison with
object and image distances. (See, however, section 4.5.) Only paraxial rays
will be considered and, unless otherwise stated, we shall assume that the medium
on both sides of the lens is always the same.

Although a variety of shapes is possible, it is well to note that all thin lenses
may be divided into two groups, according as their thickness at the center is
greater or less than at the edges.

Plane Waves Incident on a Lens Thicker at the Center. (*a*) *Medium of lens denser than that of its surroundings.* In Fig. 3.24, *HBK* and *HEK* represent the two spherical surfaces of such a lens, radii of curvature = r_1 and r_2; *ABC* is an incident wave-front; *DEL* the emergent wave-front making for a center *F*, the *principal focus* or *focal point*. To find the value of *f*, the focal length, we follow the same method as in the case of mirrors and refracting surfaces. Thus, since

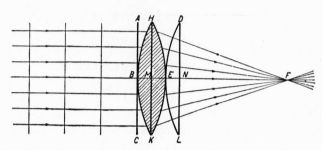

Fig. 3.24.   The incident plane wave-front *ABC* after passage through a double-convex lens of more dense material than the surroundings gives rise to the convergent wave-front *DEL*.

the central portion of the disturbance travels in the lens from *B* to *E*, while the edges go from *A* to *D* (or *C* to *L*) in the surrounding medium, we have

$$AH + HD = n \cdot BE$$

$$\therefore \qquad BM + MN = n \cdot BM + n \cdot ME$$

$$\therefore \quad BM + ME + EN = n \cdot BM + n \cdot ME$$

$$\therefore \qquad EN = (n - 1)(BM + ME)$$

$$\therefore \qquad \frac{1}{f} = (n - 1)\left(\frac{1}{r_1} + \frac{1}{-r_2}\right)$$

$$\therefore \qquad \frac{1}{f} = (n - 1)\left(\frac{1}{r_1} - \frac{1}{r_2}\right). \qquad (3.11)$$

This is an important fundamental thin lens relation.

(*b*) *Lens medium less dense than that of the surroundings.* In this case, since the velocity in the lens medium is greater than in the surroundings, the central portion of the disturbance will get ahead of the edges, and a plane wave-front such as *ABC*, Fig. 3.25, will give rise to an emergent wave-front *HNK*, which apparently comes from the virtual principal focus *F*. This is exactly what happens if a parallel beam of light is allowed to fall on an air lens of this shape (bounded by two thin glass walls) immersed in a tank of water.

It is left to the student to prove for himself that relation (3.11) holds for this case, as well as when a lens thinner at the center is used, *provided n is always considered the index of the lens material with respect to the surrounding medium.*

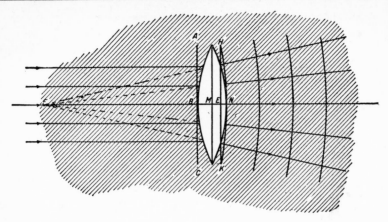

Fig. 3.25.   The incident plane wave-front *ABC* after passage through a double-convex lens of less
dense material than the surroundings gives rise to the divergent wave-front *HNK*.

3.18. Spherical Waves Incident on a Thin Lens.   Fig. 3.26 represents the
case of a more dense double-convex lens on which a wave-front ANB is incident.
EHF is the emergent wave-front making for the real image Q, while CND and
CHD are the lens surfaces with radii of curvature equal to r_1 and r_2 respectively.

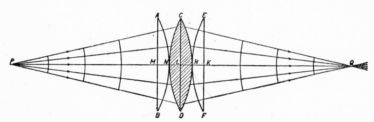

Fig. 3.26.   The convergent lens reverses the curvature of the incident spherical wave-front *ANB*
giving rise to the emergent wave-front *EHF*.

We have then

$$AC + CE = n \cdot NH$$

$$\therefore \qquad ML + LK = n \cdot NH$$

$$\therefore \quad MN + NL + LH + HK = n \cdot NL + n \cdot LH$$

$$\therefore \qquad MN + HK = (n-1)(NL + LH)$$

$$\therefore \qquad \frac{1}{-p} + \frac{1}{+q} = (n-1)\left(\frac{1}{r_1} + \frac{1}{-r_2}\right)$$

or

$$\frac{1}{q} - \frac{1}{p} = (n-1)\left(\frac{1}{r_1} - \frac{1}{r_2}\right)$$

$$= \frac{1}{f}, \qquad (3.12)$$

where p and q are object and image distances.

Relation (3.12) will be found to apply to any case of spherical waves, falling on any kind of thin lens. For example, in Fig. 3.27 we have given the diagram when the source P is so near a double-convex lens that the curvature of the emergent wave-front is lessened but not reversed (as in Fig. 3.26), and the image is, in consequence, virtual.

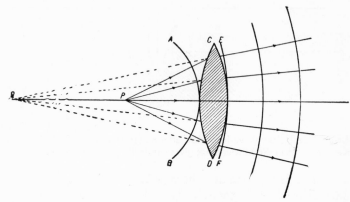

Fig. 3.27.   When the curvature of the incident wave-front AB is sufficiently great, the curvature of the emergent wave-front EF is lessened, not reversed.

Again, Fig. 3.28 is the diagram for a dense lens thinner at the center, in which case the curvature of the incident wave-front ABC is increased so that the emergent wave-front DEF comes off as if from the virtual image O.

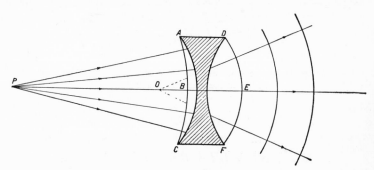

Fig. 3.28.   The incident spherical wave-front ABC after passage through a diverging lens gives rise to the wave-front DEF of increased curvature.

3.19. Spherical Aberration.   It has already been emphasized that the relations we have derived apply only to cases where the aperture is small and paraxial rays are used. Relation (3.11), for example, gives the focal length of a thin lens only for a small portion near the axis. If rays, parallel to the axis but incident at a region distant h cm from the axis, are considered, the focal length for this region differs from that given by (3.11) by an amount which is greater the greater the value of h.   In other words, a wide beam of parallel rays cannot be brought to a single sharp focal point by a spherical lens of wide aperture. This variation in the focal length of a lens when we pass from the central portion to the periphery is called *spherical aberration*.   It is possible to correct a lens for this defect by grinding suitable aspherical surfaces, but since spherical surfaces are the only kind which can be worked commercially in quantity, single lenses invariably have this defect.   It follows that it is impossible to obtain an ideally sharp image of a point object using a single lens of wide aperture.   Spherical aberration can be eliminated, of course, by reducing the aperture to a small region around the center of the lens.   With a lens of wide aperture it may be reduced to a minimum by a suitable choice of the curvatures of the faces of a lens.   The point is illustrated by the following examples in which the numbers are taken from a table in *The Principles of Optics* by Hardy and Perrin.*   In each example the aberration, which is measured by the difference between the focal length of the axial region and that of a small region 1 cm from the axis, is for a lens of focal length 10 cm.

(a) For a plano-convex lens, with plane face next the object and radius of curvature of the other face 5.2 mm, the aberration is 4.4 mm.   When the lens is reversed, so that the curved face is next the object, the aberration is 1.1 mm.

When using a single plano-convex lens the advantage of turning the curved face towards the object is obvious.

(b) When the shape of the lens is double-convex, with each face having a radius of curvature of 10 cm, the aberration is 1.5 mm.

By suitably choosing combinations of lenses, spherical aberration may also be lessened.   When discussing eyepieces in section 5.5, reference will again be made to this point.

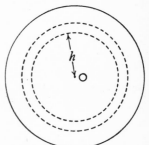

3.20. Other Aberrations.   A brief reference only will be made to other aberrations which may be present when an ordinary uncorrected lens is used.

(a) **Coma.**   This has to do with the formation of an image of a point source *off the axis*, and, like spherical aberration, becomes more marked the wider

Fig. 3.29.   The dotted circles represent an annular area of radius h on the surface of a lens.

the aperture of the lens.   It can be explained by reference to Fig. 3.29 in which O represents the center of a lens viewed face on and the dotted circles outline a narrow annular region of radius h, which has the same significance as in the last section.   In an uncorrected lens the image of a point source *off the axis*, due to all rays which pass through this annular region, is a circle whose diameter is greater, the greater the value of h.   When rays passing through the whole face of the lens are considered, it follows that

* McGraw-Hill Book Company, Inc., 1932.

the image consists of a series of overlapping circles whose radii get less and less the smaller h. For the small area around O the center of the lens, the circle reduces to a point. Since the image due to the whole lens has a comet-like appearance, the name *coma* has been given to this type of aberration.

(b) **Astigmatism.** Like coma, this aberration is concerned with the formation of an image of a point source off the axis, although it is usually restricted to the case when the source is at some distance from the axis. Consider Fig. 3.30, which, in diagram (a), represents the face of a lens whose axis passes through the center O. If, in diagram (b), Q is a point well off the axis and above the

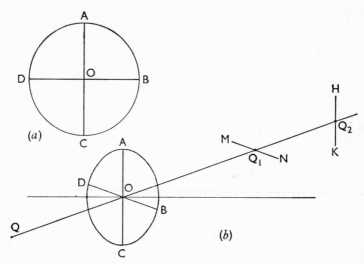

Fig. 3.30. When Q is a point source well off the axis of a lens, all rays in the plane QAC give rise to a point image at Q_1, rays in the plane QBD to the point image at Q_2. On spreading out from Q_1 the rays pass through the line HQ_2K, while the rays making for Q_2 pass through the line MQ_1N. In between Q_1 and Q_2 is the circle of least confusion.

plane of the paper, then, if coma is absent, all rays from Q in the plane QAC give rise to a point image at Q_1, on the central ray QOQ_1, but rays from Q in the plane QBD form a point image at Q_2 also on the central ray. The convergent beam making for Q_2 after emergence from the lens, as it passes Q_1, gives rise to a line image MN parallel to DB. Similarly the beam making for Q_1 spreads out again, giving rise to another line image HK, parallel to AC. It can be shown that rays from planes between QAC and QDB also pass through these lines after passage through the lens. The result is that nowhere can a sharp point or *stigmatic* image of Q be obtained; hence the name *astigmatism** for this type of aberration. In between Q_1 and Q_2 there is a region called the *circle of least con-*

---

* The student should not confuse this type of astigmatism with the defect of the human eye which goes by the same name.

fusion. This is the place where the most satisfactory image can be obtained by the use of a lens uncorrected for astigmatism.

(*c*) **Curvature of Field.** When an *extended object* in a plane perpendicular to the axis is used, it can be shown that, with astigmatism present, two ellipsoidal images result, the two touching at a point on the axis, but separated more and more as rays of greater and greater obliquity are considered. The correction for astigmatism brings these two images together, but the resulting image is curved, not flat. This fourth type of aberration called *curvature of field* is evidently closely connected with astigmatism. In photography a lens which has been corrected for astigmatism to give a flat field is called an *anastigmat.*

(*d*) **Distortion.** In a system so corrected that an extended object in a plane gives rise to a corresponding plane anastigmatic image, there may be still another aberration whose importance is greater, the greater the distance of points on the object from the axis. This aberration is due to the variation in magnification with the distance from the axis, and is called *distortion.* When it is present, a square object gives rise to a figure with sides curved, sometimes outward, sometimes inward.

(*e*) **Chromatic Aberrations.** The preceding five aberrations are present when monochromatic light is used and the change in them arising from a change in wavelength is fortunately slight. There is, however, an important type of aberration called *chromatism* arising from changing wavelength, which is usually subdivided into *longitudinal chromatism* and *lateral chromatism.* This will be discussed in Chapter VI.

The correction or lessening of aberrations is a work primarily for the expert in technical optics, and details need not concern us in this book. The methods involve laborious calculations, the use of suitably placed stops, a suitable choice of curvatures of lens faces, and combinations of lenses, both in contact and separated. Perfect elimination of a single aberration is rarely possible, but extremely satisfactory combinations are obtained for the particular product which is needed. When we are discussing the objective of a telescope or a microscope, the student should not forget that it is a combination of lenses, functioning as a single one, designed to be as free from aberrations as possible.

3.21. We conclude this chapter with a summary of the important general relations, together with one or two examples of their use in solving problems.

(*a*) $\dfrac{1}{q} + \dfrac{1}{p} = \dfrac{1}{f}$, applicable to all (spherical) mirrors.   (3.06)

(*b*) $\dfrac{1}{q} - \dfrac{1}{p} = \dfrac{1}{f}$, applicable to all thin (spherical) lenses.   (3.12)

(*c*) $\dfrac{1}{f} = (n - 1)\left(\dfrac{1}{r_1} - \dfrac{1}{r_2}\right)$ applicable to all thin (spherical) lenses.   (3.11)

All relations are subject to the sign convention.

PROBLEM 1. *An object is placed 10 cm in front of a concave mirror whose radius of curvature is 30 cm. Find the position and nature of the image.*

Here we are given $p = -10$ cm and $f = r/2 = -15$ cm. Therefore, substituting in the formula for spherical mirrors,

$$\frac{1}{q} + \frac{1}{p} = \frac{1}{f},$$

we obtain $q = +30$ cm.

The image, therefore, is virtual and is situated 30 cm from the mirror and behind it.

PROBLEM 2. *The radii of curvature of the faces of a biconvex lens are 20 cm and 30 cm. Its focal length is 24 cm. What is the index of refraction of the glass?*

Here we are given $f = +24$ cm; $r_1 = +20$ cm; $r_2 = -30$ cm. Hence, substituting in the general formula,

$$\frac{1}{f} = (n - 1)\left(\frac{1}{r_1} - \frac{1}{r_2}\right),$$

$$\frac{1}{24} = (n - 1)\left(\frac{1}{20} - \frac{1}{-30}\right)$$

from which

$$n = 1.5.$$

PROBLEM 3. *A convex glass lens has a focal length of 40 cm in air. What is the focal length when immersed in water? Index for air-glass = 1.54; for air-water = 1.33.*

For glass lens in air, we are given $n = 1.54, f = +40$; therefore, substituting in the general formula, we have

$$\frac{1}{40} = (1.54 - 1)\left(\frac{1}{r_1} - \frac{1}{r_2}\right). \tag{a}$$

For the same glass lens in water, we are given $n = 1.54/1.33$, and therefore can write

$$\frac{1}{f} = \left(\frac{1.54}{1.33} - 1\right)\left(\frac{1}{r_1} - \frac{1}{r_2}\right). \tag{b}$$

Combining equations (a) and (b), we find the required $f = +137$ cm.

PROBLEM 4. *An object is placed 100 cm from a thin diverging lens of focal length 20 cm. Find where the image is.*

In this problem we must use the general formula

$$\frac{1}{q} - \frac{1}{p} = \frac{1}{f}.$$

We are given $p = -100$, $f = -20$, and hence by substitution readily find $q = -16.7$ cm. We have, therefore, a virtual image 16.7 cm from the lens on the negative side.

PROBLEMS

1. An observer looks vertically downward at a stone on the bottom of a pond 3 ft deep. What is the apparent depth of the stone? (Index of refraction of water = 1.33.)

2. A small lamp is suspended in a room 4 ft below the center of a circular mirror of diameter 2 ft, fastened to the ceiling above it. Find the diameter of the patch of reflected light on the floor if the room is 12 ft high.

3. A small, bright object P is placed 1 ft vertically above a large vessel containing a thickness of 2 ft of a transparent liquid. The bottom of the vessel is a highly silvered plane surface. When an eye is placed, in the same horizontal plane as P, 4 ft away from it, the image of P, as a result of refraction at the surface of the liquid and reflection from the silvered surface, appears to be along a line which makes an angle of 45° with the vertical. Find the index of refraction of the liquid.

4. If the index of refraction of water is 1.33 and that of sulphuric ether is 1.36, find the critical angle when light is incident on the surface separating sulphuric ether from water.

5. A layer of ether (index = 1.36) rests on water (index = 1.33). Prove that rays of any obliquity incident on the surface of the ether enter the water.

6. A layer of sulphuric ether (index = 1.36), 5 cm deep, rests on water (index = 1.33), 10 cm deep. If one looks vertically downward, what is the apparent distance of the bottom of the vessel below the surface?

7. A source emitting waves travels through a medium with a velocity of v, which is greater than the velocity V with which the wave disturbance travels in the medium. (a) Apply Huygens' Principle to show that a conical wave surface is produced. (b) Give an illustration of the above (in two dimensions) in the case of water waves on the surface of a lake. (c) Find an expression for the angle between the two "bow" waves from a boat in terms of v and V.

8. A beam of parallel rays of light is incident perpendicularly on the surface of water in a vessel in which an air-cell is immersed. The air-cell consists of a layer of air between two flat pieces of glass with plane and parallel sides. (a) If the cell is rotated so that rays strike the air cell obliquely, prove that no light is transmitted through it when the angle of incidence exceeds a certain value. (b) Find the value of this angle. (c) Make a careful diagram to illustrate your explanation. (d) Explain why a knowledge of the index of refraction of glass is not necessary. (Index of refraction of water = 1.33.)

9. Parallel rays of light are incident perpendicularly on the face AB of a prism whose angle BAC is 90°. Prove that no light is transmitted through the face BC when the angle ABC exceeds a certain value. Find the value of this angle. (Index of prism = 1.624.)

10. Parallel rays of light are incident perpendicularly on the face AB of a prism whose angle BAC is 90° and angle ABC is 60°. Find the angle at which light emerges from the face AC. (Index of prism = 1.624.)

11. If the angle ABC is 45°, when using a prism otherwise similar to the one described in problem 10, prove that the incident light emerges from the prism in a direction turned through a right angle.

12. Prove that, when parallel rays are incident in air obliquely on any number of transparent slabs, with plane parallel sides, made of different materials, the emergent rays are parallel to the original direction.

13. A narrow beam of light is incident at an angle of 60° on one face of a slab of glass, 3 cm thick, with plane and parallel sides. Prove that the emergent beam is parallel to the incident but shifted sideways. Find the amount of shift.

14. A point source of light is placed in air in front of a convex surface whose radius of curvature is equal to 20 cm. If this surface separates air from glass (index = 1.640), find, by the method of change of curvature of wave-front, where the source should be placed so that parallel rays traverse the glass.

15. A small object is placed 50 cm from a concave refracting surface of radius of curvature 20 cm, separating air from glass whose index of refraction is 1.62. Find, by the method of change of curvature of wave-front, where the image is.

16. Plane waves traveling in air fall on a convex surface, with radius of curvature 20 cm, separating air from glass. Find, by the method of change of curvature of wave-front, at what point the waves are brought to a focus. (Index for glass = 1.640.)

17. A water tank is closed at one end by a very thin glass window, curved outward, with radius of curvature equal to 20 cm, and at the other end by a very thin window of plane glass. The distance from window to window is 164.6 cm. A small, bright source is placed on a horizontal axis passing through the centers of each window, at a distance of 100 cm outside the curved window. Find, *by the method of change of curvature of wave-front*, the position of the image of the source. (Index of refraction of water = 1.33.)

18. Parallel rays of light after traversing a tank of water are incident on a double convex glass lens through which the light emerges into air. Find, by the method of change of curvature of wave-front, where the image is formed. Radii of curvature of lens faces are 36 cm (next water) and 24 cm; index, air-glass = 1.62; air-water = 1.33.

19. A window consisting of a very thin piece of glass, curved outward, with radius of curvature 20 cm, closes one end of a horizontal tank filled with water whose index of refraction = 1.333. Plane waves (traveling in a horizontal direction) fall on the window. Find, by the method of change of curvature of wave-front, to what point in the water they are focused.

20. A glass double convex lens, each of whose faces has a radius of curvature 30 cm, is surrounded by air on one side, by water on the other. If plane waves are incident on the air side, find (by the method of change of curvature of wave-front) to what point the waves are focused. (Index, air-glass = 1.56; air-water = 1.33.)

21. A glass double convex lens, each of whose faces has a radius of curvature of 20 cm, is surrounded on one side by air, on the other by water. A small source of light is placed on the axis of the lens on the air side at such a distance that parallel rays traverse the water. *Using the method of change of curvature of wave-front*, find the position of the small object. (Index, air-glass = 1.60; air-water = 1.33.)

22. (a) A thin double convex glass lens has faces whose radii of curvature are 36 cm and 24 cm, respectively. Find, *by the method of change of curvature of wave-front*, where a point object should be placed (on the side of the lens next the 36-cm face), so that the wave-front just emerging from the lens coincides with the 24-cm face. (Index for air-glass = 1.56.)

(b) Check your solution by finding: (i) the value of the focal length of the lens; (ii) the position of the image (using p, q, and f).

23. A long tank is separated into two compartments by a thin, double concave air lens, bounded by very thin glass walls each of which has a radius of curvature of 24 cm. One compartment is filled with water, index 1.33, the other with a transparent liquid of index 1.67. If a parallel beam of light traversing the water strikes the lens, find by the method of change of curvature of wave-front, where it is focused.

24. Find the focal length of the following thin lenses, for each of which the index of refraction is 1.524.

(a) Double convex, each face of radius of curvature 20 cm.

(b) Plano-convex, radius of curvature of curved face = 20 cm.

(c) Plano-concave, radius of curvature of curved face = 20 cm.

(d) A lens meniscus, thicker at the center than at the edges, with radius of curvature of one face = 30 cm, of the other = 36 cm.

(e) A lens meniscus, thinner at the center than at the edges, with radii of curvature as in part (d).

25. The curved surface of a plano-convex lens has a radius of curvature of 20 cm. Find its focal length when immersed in water. (Index, for air-water = 1.333; for air-glass = 1.624.)

26. Prove graphically that the position of the image of a distant object formed by a thin converging lens does not alter when the lens is rotated, through a small angle, about an axis through its center.

27. A glass lens has a focal length of 150 cm in water and is converging. Find the focal length of an air lens of the same shape and dimensions, in water. Is it converging or diverging? (Index, air-glass = 1.624; air-water = 1.333.)

28. (a) Light from a small object in air falls on a convex surface separating air from glass (index = 1.524). If, when the object is 40 cm from the surface, the image is formed at a point in the glass 40 cm from the surface, find the linear magnification. (*Assume paraxial rays and apply the sine condition.*) (b) Find the radius of curvature of the surface.

29. Find the linear magnification in problem 15. (Apply the sine condition.)

30. A small object is placed 36 cm from a thin converging lens of focal length 24 cm. By the use of the sine condition find the linear magnification. (In this case the sine condition leads at once to $m = q/p$. See section 4.10.)

31. A double convex lens each of whose faces has a radius of curvature of 24 cm closes one end of a long tank filled with water. Apply the sine condition to find the linear magnification when a point source is placed outside the tank at a point on the axis 36 cm from the lens. (Index, air-glass = 1.624; air-water = 1.333.) (N.B. First find the position of the image, using method of change of curvature of wave-front.)

IV

Further Study of Lenses

4.1. In Chapter III we have seen how, by a consideration of waves and Huygens' Principle, it is possible to show the formation of images by mirrors and lenses. While the method is applicable to waves in general, in this book we are primarily interested in light waves. Now, in light, especially in problems relating to the use of such combinations of lenses as are found in telescopes, microscopes, and other optical instruments, it is frequently more convenient to deal with rays. In Figs. 3.23, 3.24, 3.25, 3.26, and 3.27, bundles of rays have

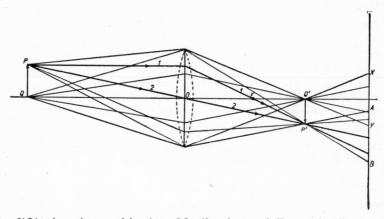

Fig. 4.1. *P'Q'* is the real image of the object *PQ*. If unobstructed all rays making for image points such as *P'* and *Q'* spread out in divergent beams.

been shown in accordance with the definition of a ray given on p. 23. The student is advised to examine these diagrams again carefully so that, in dealing with the formation of images by lenses, he will think rather of whole bundles of rays than of the principal rays by means of which such images may be located geometrically. For example, in Fig. 4.1, *P'* the image of the point source *P* has been located by finding the point of intersection of: (1) ray 1, which, incident parallel to the axis, emerges through the principal focus *F*; (2) ray 2, which goes through the center of the lens unchanged in direction. It is important to realize, however, that a whole cone of rays leaves the source *P*, completely filling the aperture of the lens, and that after emergence, a corresponding cone goes to the image P'. Similarly for Q and for every other point on the object, there will be other complete cones falling on the lens, and eventually making for corresponding point images.

If a screen be placed at $P'Q'$ a sharp image will be seen, which will be *brighter* the wider the aperture, since a wider lens collects a larger bundle of rays. (Because of spherical aberration, the image may not be so *sharp*.) If there is no screen, the rays continue to spread out from each point on the image, such as Q' and P'. Such images will be seen by an eye placed anywhere in the region AB, for P', in the region XY for Q', and so on for other points. A clear understanding of where an eye must be placed in order to see an image is so important that a numerical example will be given.

4.2. *A point source is placed at a point on the axis 4.5 cm from a convex lens of focal length 5 cm and aperture 2 cm. Find through what distance an eye (considered as a point) may be moved in a direction at right angles to the axis, at a distance 2 cm from the lens, and in all positions see the image.*

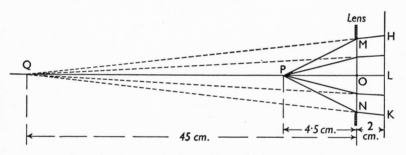

Fig. 4.2. Diagrams for the problem solved in section 4.2.

The *position* of the image may at once be calculated from the relation $\frac{1}{q} - \frac{1}{p} = \frac{1}{f}$, for we are given $p = -4.5$, $f = +5$, and by substitution find $q = -45$ cm.

In Fig. 4.2, therefore, $PO = 4.5$, $QO = 45$, $MN = 2$, and the incident cone of rays leaves the lens as if coming from Q. An eye moved along the line HLK evidently can see the image Q only when between the points H and K.

Moreover, since triangles QOM and QHL are similar,

$$\frac{HL}{QL} = \frac{OM}{QO}$$

or

$$\frac{HL}{47} = \frac{1}{45}$$

from which

$$HL = \frac{47}{45} = 1.04$$

and $HK = 2.08$ cm.

NOTE.—Since the lenses we are dealing with are thin, it is desirable in diagrams drawn approximately to scale, such as Fig. 4.2, to represent the lens by a straight line.

4.3. Distant Point Source and Parallel Rays.   Suppose we are looking through a lens at a distant object, for example, a tree 50 ft high, 100 yd away. If we represent the tree by the line PQ, Fig. 4.3, and make any attempt at

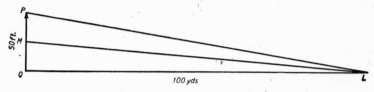

Fig. 4.3.   In a diagram drawn to scale, when a finite object *PQ* is at some distance from a lens *L,* the lens is represented by a point.

drawing a diagram to scale, it is evident that a lens of an inch or two aperture will be represented by an extremely small dot at L.   Moreover, all the rays coming from a point on the object such as P, and incident on the lens, will be represented by the line PL, all rays from another point M by the line ML whose direction differs from PL.

Suppose, however, we represent the *lens* by the line AB, Fig. 4.4, and again attempt to make a diagram to scale.   It will now be evident that it is impossible

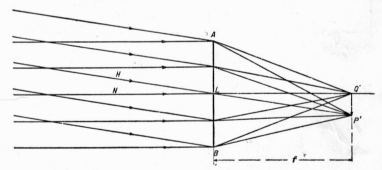

Fig. 4.4.   *P'Q'* is the image of a distant object formed by a converging lens.   Note that when the lens is represented by a line *AB* of finite magnitude all incident rays from each point on the object are parallel.

to show the distant object, and that we must represent all rays coming from the point P by a bundle of rays which for all practical purposes are parallel; those from Q by another parallel bundle whose direction is different from the one from P.   The first bundle will give rise to the point image P', the second to the point Q', and so for every point on the object there will be a corresponding point on the image located in the *focal plane of the lens.*

It will be seen, too, that HLN is the angle subtended at the lens by the object, as well as (since $Q'LP' = HLN$) that subtended by the image. If, then, the angular size of an object is known, the *linear* size of the image may be readily calculated, since

$$\tan Q'LP' = \frac{P'Q'}{LQ'}$$

or

$$\tan HLN = \frac{P'Q'}{f},$$

or $P'Q'$, the linear size of the image, equals f multiplied by the tangent of the angle subtended at lens by object.

In actual practice we have as a rule only to do with angles so small that we may use either the tangent, the sine, or the angle expressed in radian measure.

4.4. Combination of Thin Lenses. Problems dealing with the passage of light through two or more coaxial lenses may readily be solved either graphically or by calculation, if we take one lens at a time. A concrete example will best illustrate the method. (An alternative method using principal planes is given in section 4.9.)

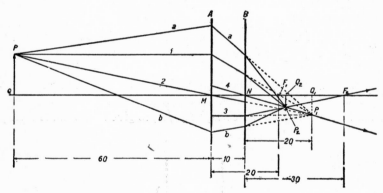

Fig. 4.5. Diagram for the problem solved in section 4.4.

Two converging lenses, with focal lengths 20 cm and 30 cm are placed coaxially 10 cm apart. Find the position of the image of an object placed 60 cm from the first lens (a) by calculation, (b) graphically.

(a) If we take the first lens, A, Fig. 4.5, we have, using the relation $\frac{1}{q} - \frac{1}{p} = \frac{1}{f}$, and substituting for $p = -60, f = +20$,

$$\frac{1}{q} - \frac{1}{-60} = \frac{1}{+20},$$

from which $q = +30$ cm.

This means that each cone of light emerging from lens A is incident on lens B

in such a way that the rays would meet at a point 20 cm beyond B, had this lens been absent.

Therefore, dealing with lens B, since for it $p = +20, f = +30$, we have

$$\frac{1}{q} - \frac{1}{+20} = \frac{1}{+30},$$

from which $q = +12$ cm.

(b) In solving the problem graphically we first of all represent to scale the positions of the object P, the two lenses and the two principal foci, F_1 and F_2. We then locate the image P_1Q_1 due to lens A, by drawing the principal rays 1 and 2 in the usual way, dotting that portion of the rays beyond B. By next drawing the complete cone of rays from P, we know the path of every ray in this cone in the region between the lenses, since each must fall on lens B in a direction making for the point P_1.

To find the final image all that is now necessary is to take those two rays between the lenses whose paths can be drawn on *emergence* from lens B. Thus ray 3 incident on B parallel to the axis (and making for P_1) emerges through F_2, while ray 4 incident on the center of B (and also making for P_1) goes through this lens with direction unchanged. P_2, the point of intersection of these two rays, then gives the position of the final image of P.

Similarly for every other point on the object we might trace corresponding bundles, obtaining finally the complete image P_2Q_2. If such a diagram is carefully made to scale, it will be found by actual measurement that the distance NQ_2 is close to 12 cm.

It will readily be seen that both methods may be applied to the case of any number of lenses placed coaxially. The image due to one becomes the object for the next. Care must be exercised, however, to give all distances their proper signs.

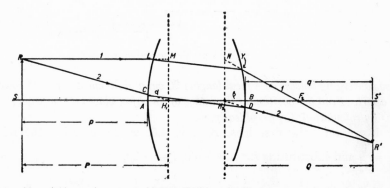

Fig. 4.6. H_1 and H_2 are the principal points; MH_1 and NH_2 the principal planes of a thick lens. In locating images by a graphical method, principal rays may be used as for thin lenses if the incident light falls on an imaginary thin lens coincident with the first principal plane, the lens being shifted to coincide with the second principal plane for the emergent light.

4.5. Thick Lens. Sometimes the thickness of a lens cannot be neglected. It is important, therefore, to consider the problem of a thick lens, particularly because in doing so we learn something about principal planes. Our attention is limited to the case of a thick lens bounded on both sides by the same (less dense) medium—a glass lens in air, for example.

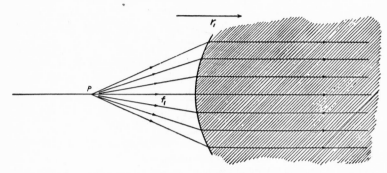

Fig. 4.7. A point source *P* placed at such a distance from a spherical surface separating two media that parallel rays traverse the second medium.

Our problem then is, given a source such as *RS*, Fig. 4.6, placed p cm from the first surface of a lens of thickness $AB = t$, with faces of known curvatures, to find where the image is situated. In solving this problem we shall apply the same general method as has been used for the combination of two thin lenses, treating the image formed by the first *surface* as the object for the second. Use

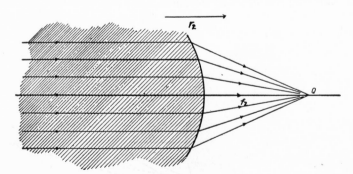

Fig. 4.8. Parallel rays traversing the first of two media separated by a spherical surface form a point image *Q* in the second medium.

will be made of the following relations which the student should prove for him-self by the method of change of curvature of wave-front, but none of which he should attempt to memorize.

(1) If a point source P, Fig. 4.7, is placed in air at such a distance f_1 from a convex surface separating air from a denser medium of index n that parallel rays

traverse this medium, then

$$\frac{1}{f_1} = -\frac{n-1}{r_1},\tag{4.01}$$

where r_1 = radius of curvature of the surface.

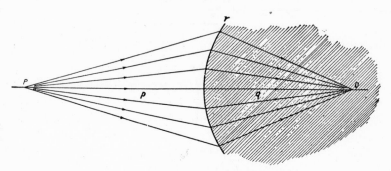

Fig. 4.9. A point source P in the first of two media separated by a spherical surface gives rise to a point image Q in the second.

(2) Similarly, if parallel rays (as in Fig. 4.8), traversing a more dense medium, are incident on a spherical surface, from which they emerge converging to a point Q in air, distant f_2 from the surface, then

$$\frac{1}{f_2} = -\frac{n-1}{r_2},\tag{4.02}$$

where r_2 = radius of curvature of the surface.

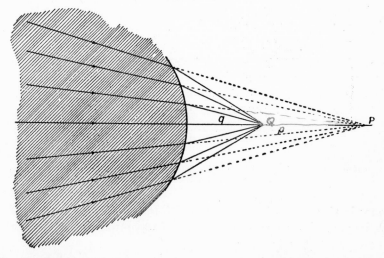

Fig. 4.10. Rays incident on a spherical surface separating two media and making for a virtual object P give rise to a point image in the second medium at Q.

(3) If a point source P is placed as in (1) but at a distance not equal to f_1 so that an image Q is formed at a finite distance from the surface, as in Fig. 4.9, then

$$\frac{n}{q} - \frac{1}{p} = \frac{n-1}{r_1} = -\frac{1}{f_1}. \tag{4.03}$$

(4) Again, if rays which are not parallel strike a refracting surface as in Fig. 4.10, where they are making for a *virtual object* P (or when coming from a real object) and a point image is formed in air, as at Q, then

$$\frac{1}{q} - \frac{n}{p} = -\frac{n-1}{r_2},$$

or

$$\frac{1}{q} - \frac{n}{p} = \frac{1}{f_2}. \tag{4.04}$$

(See section 3.14 for proof.)

Consider now the case of the thick lens represented in Fig. 4.6. Dealing with refraction *at the first surface*, and using relation (4.03), we have

$$\frac{n}{q'} - \frac{1}{p} = \frac{n-1}{r_1} = -\frac{1}{f_1}, \tag{4.05}$$

where q' = the distance of the image from this surface.

Since the image formed by the first surface becomes the object for the second surface, we have, for that surface,

$$p = q' - t \text{ (due regard being paid to sign of } q'),$$

and, therefore, applying relation (4.04),

$$\frac{1}{q} - \frac{n}{q' - t} = -\frac{n-1}{r_2} = \frac{1}{f_2}, \tag{4.06}$$

where q is the distance of the final image *from the second surface*.

By combining relations (4.05) and (4.06), eliminating q', we obtain by simple but somewhat laborious algebra

$$\frac{1}{q - \beta} - \frac{1}{p - \alpha} = \frac{1}{F}, \tag{4.07}$$

where for simplicity we have written

$$\alpha = -\frac{f_1 t}{n(f_2 - f_1) - t}, \tag{4.08}$$

$$\beta = -\frac{f_2 t}{n(f_2 - f_1) - t}, \tag{4.09}$$

$$F = -\frac{n f_1 f_2}{n(f_2 - f_1) - t}. \tag{4.10}$$

Since α, β, and F are quantities depending only on the constants r_1, r_2, n, and t, their values in any given problem can readily be found. Hence relation

(4.07) provides us with the desired means of locating the image formed by a thick lens. Its use is illustrated by the following example.

4.6. *An object is placed 60 cm from a thick double convex lens, with faces of radii of curvature 20 cm and 30 cm, with thickness = 2 cm, and index = 1.5. Find the position of the image.*

Here we have

$$f_1 = -\frac{r_1}{n-1} = -\frac{+20}{1.5-1} = -40 \text{ cm},$$

$$f_2 = -\frac{r_2}{n-1} = -\frac{-30}{1.5-1} = +60 \text{ cm},$$

$$F = -\frac{1.5 \times -40 \times +60}{1.5(+60+40)-2} = +24.3 \text{ cm},$$

$$\alpha = -\frac{-40 \times 2}{1.5(+60+40)-2} = +0.54 \text{ cm},$$

$$\beta = -\frac{+60 \times 2}{1.5(+60+40)-2} = -0.81 \text{ cm}.$$

Therefore, since $p = -60$,

$$\frac{1}{q-(-0.81)} - \frac{1}{-60-(+0.54)} = +\frac{1}{24.32},$$

from which $q = +39.85$ cm.

4.7. Suppose, now, we let

$$Q = q - \beta,$$

$$P = p - \alpha,$$

relation (4.07) then becomes

$$\frac{1}{Q} - \frac{1}{P} = \frac{1}{F}. \tag{4.11}$$

Since the *form* of this relation is identical with that used for a thin lens, we conclude that with a knowledge of α, β, and F the problem of a thick lens is reduced to that of a thin one. Putting it in another way, this means that if we measure the object distance not from the first surface (when it is p) but from a point on the axis distant α from this surface (when it is P), and the image distance, not from the second surface (when it is q), but from a point distant β from this surface (when it is Q), *then the thin lens relation holds.* Such points are called *principal points*, and planes through them perpendicular to the axis *principal planes.*

It follows, moreover, that the graphical method of locating images for thin lenses must hold also for thick lenses, provided we fulfill this condition which makes the same mathematical relation applicable; that is, provided we measure object distances from the first principal plane, image distances from the second, and use F as the focal length. This means that, if we imagine light incident on a thin lens coincident with the first principal plane, and emergent from the lens when coincident with the second principal plane, the usual principal rays may be used. The method will be clear from a re-examination of Fig. 4.6.

In this diagram RS is an object, the position of whose image as formed by a thick lens we wish to find. Having calculated α, β, and F, we locate on the axis the principal points by measuring from the first surface $AH_1 = \alpha$ (assumed positive in this example), and from the second surface $H_2B = \beta$ (negative in this case). The point F_2, the principal focus, is then located by measuring $H_2F_2 = F$, while the principal planes are drawn through H_1 and H_2.

It then follows from the preceding paragraph that a ray 1 leaving the point R parallel to the axis and incident on the first principal plane at M will leave the second principal plane at the point N, where $H_1M = H_2N$, and finally emerge in a direction passing through F_2.

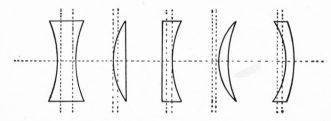

Fig. 4.11. The dotted lines show the position of principal planes for lenses of different shapes.

Similarly a ray 2 leaving P in a direction that passes through the point H_1 will leave the lens in a parallel direction which passes through H_2. The point of intersection of these two rays will then give the required position of R', the image of P.

The student should realize that the actual path of these rays *inside* the lens is not along the lines LM, CH, nor NY, H_2D, but rather along the lines LY and CD.

The position of the principal points depends on the shape of the lens. By taking concrete examples it is left to the student to show that for lenses of the standard shapes illustrated in Fig. 4.11, the principal planes have the positions indicated by the dotted lines. No attempt has been made to draw these diagrams to scale. They indicate, for each lens shape, the approximate position of the planes.

4.8. Nodal Points.   In the general case of a thick lens bounded by two *different* media *nodal points* are defined as points on the axis such that a ray traversing the first medium in a direction passing through one point, emerges in the second medium in a parallel direction, which passes through the second point.

Obviously, by this definition, H_1 and H_2 in the above diagram (where the medium is the same on both sides of the lens) are nodal as well as principal points. In the general case, however, there are four distinct points, principal points being defined in the following way.

Let NF_2, Fig. 4.12, be the emergent path of a ray LP incident on a thick lens parallel to the axis, and let M be the point of intersection of these two directions. Then, by taking MH_2 perpendicular to the axis, the position of H_2, the principal point related to the second surface, is defined. Similarly by taking a ray parallel to the axis in the opposite direction, we define the other principal point H_1. When the bounding media are different, as already noted, these points are not nodal points. This case, however, it is not our purpose to consider further. We have simply sought to show how, when we have to do with a

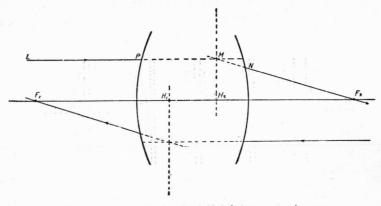

Fig. 4.12. Graphical method of defining principal points.

thick lens made of a material such as glass and surrounded by air, the ideas are essentially similar to those necessary for the study of a thin lens.

4.9. Equivalent Focal Length of Two Thin Lenses Not in Contact. An alternate method to that given in section 4.4 may be used to solve problems relating to a combination of two thin lenses separated by a finite distance. The method consists in replacing the two lenses by principal planes, and then, with the aid of an equivalent focal length, applying equation (4.11) and Fig. 4.6 in almost exactly the same way as has been used in the treatment of a thick lens.

Consider an object p cm away from a thin lens of focal length f_1 beyond which, at a distance of t cm, there is a second lens of focal length f_2. Then, if q' is the distance of the image formed by the first lens from it, and q is the distance of the final image from the second lens, we can write (remembering that the image due to the first lens is the object for the second)

$$\frac{1}{q'} - \frac{1}{p} = \frac{1}{f_1},$$

and
$$\frac{1}{q} - \frac{1}{q' - t} = \frac{1}{f_2}.$$

Eliminating q' from these relations, we can obtain by straightforward but laborious algebra

$$\frac{1}{q - \beta} - \frac{1}{p - \alpha} = \frac{1}{F},$$

or
$$\frac{1}{Q} - \frac{1}{P} = \frac{1}{F},$$

where
$$F = +\frac{f_1 f_2}{f_1 + f_2 - t}, \tag{4.12}$$

$$\alpha = +\frac{f_1 t}{f_1 + f_2 - t}, \tag{4.13}$$

and
$$\beta = -\frac{f_2 t}{f_1 + f_2 - t}. \tag{4.14}$$

All these relations, it must never be forgotten, are to be used in accordance with the sign convention adopted in this book.

It follows from the foregoing work, that, provided (1) object distances P are measured from the first principal plane, and image distances Q from the second, and (2) the equivalent focal length F is known, problems relating to a combination of two thin lenses may be solved by the use of the simple lens relation $\frac{1}{Q} - \frac{1}{P} = \frac{1}{F}$.

The method is illustrated by the following solution of the problem already worked in section 4.4.

In this problem we are given $f_1 = +20$, $f_2 = +30$, $t = 10$, and $p = -60$. Substituting these values in relations (4.12), (4.13), and (4.14), we obtain

$$F = +\frac{20 \times 30}{20 + 30 - 10} = +15,$$

$$\alpha = +\frac{10 \times 20}{20 + 30 - 10} = +5,$$

$$\beta = -\frac{10 \times 30}{20 + 30 - 10} = -7.5.$$

Using these values, the positions of the principal planes, through H_1 and H_2, and the focal points at F_1 and F_2 have been marked in Fig. 4.13.

We can now write $P = p - \alpha = -60 - 5 = -65$. Hence, applying the relation

$$\frac{1}{Q} - \frac{1}{P} = \frac{1}{F},$$

we obtain
$$Q = 19.5,$$

and therefore, $q - \beta = 19.5,$

or $q - (-7.5) = 19.5,$

or $q = +12.$

That is, the final image is 12 cm beyond the second lens as previously found by the other method.

It will be noticed that in Fig. 4.13 the second principal plane is nearer the first lens than the first principal plane. This not infrequently happens, but need cause no confusion in the mind of the student, because always the object distance P is measured from the first principal plane no matter where it is situated.

The student should examine, in Fig. 4.13, the graphical method of locating an image by the use of principal rays and principal planes.

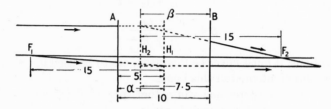

Fig. 4.13.   Diagram used for solving the double lens problem in section 4.4 by the use of principal planes.

Examples of the use of principal planes in the treatment of eyepieces are given in section 5.5. The student should realize that even such a complicated lens system as the objective in a good microscope (see Fig. 5.14) may be replaced by two equivalent principal planes.

4.10. Linear Magnification.   From his work in elementary physics, the student will recall that the linear magnification

$$m = \frac{\text{image length}}{\text{object length}} = \frac{q}{p}.$$

For a combination of two lenses, we may obtain the linear magnification by either of the methods which have been used in the solution of the problem in section 4.4. Thus, if we use the method of section 4.4, we write

$$m \text{ for the first lens} = \frac{30}{60},$$

and $m \text{ for the second lens} = \frac{12}{20},$

from which m for the combination $= \dfrac{30}{60} \cdot \dfrac{12}{20} = 0.3.$

Making use of the equivalent lens method, we write at once

$$m \text{ for the combination} = \frac{Q}{P} = \frac{19.5}{65} = 0.3.$$

PROBLEMS

1. Find at what distance an object should be placed from a thin converging lens of focal length 12 cm to give a linear magnification of: (a) 1; (b) 0.5; (c) 6.

2. A projecting lens forms an image, 2 ft 9 in. square, of a lantern slide 3 in. square. If the distance between the slide and the screen is 12 ft, find the focal length of the lens.

3. A point object is placed (a) 60 cm, (b) 8 cm from a converging lens of aperture 4 cm and focal length 12 cm. Find the greatest distance through which an eye, placed 40 cm from the lens, can be moved (in a direction normal to the axis) and in all positions see the image. Treat the eye as a point.

4. An object is placed 5 cm from a thin lens of focal length 6 cm and aperture 2 cm. Find the largest size the object can have so that it may be seen by an eye placed at a point on the axis 3 cm from the lens. (Treat the eye as a point.)

5. An object, placed at the focal distance from a converging lens of focal length 12 cm, is viewed through the lens by an eye placed at a point on the axis 6 cm from the lens. If the aperture of the lens is 2 cm, find the largest size of the object which can be seen by the eye (treated as a point) in this position.

6. When an object is placed in front of a simple magnifier of focal length 6 cm and aperture 1 cm, an image (virtual) is formed 30 cm from the magnifier. If the eye (treated as a point) views the image when placed at a point on the axis 2 cm from the magnifier, find the largest object which can be viewed without moving the eye.

7. A small object is placed at a point on the axis 18.0 cm from a converging lens of focal length 30 cm beyond which, at a distance of 30 cm, is a diverging lens of focal length 5.70 cm. Find by calculation where the final image is.

8. A beam of parallel rays falls on a divergent lens, of focal length 12 cm, beyond which, at a distance of 24 cm, a convergent lens of 18 cm focal length is placed. Find the position of the final image.

9. If the first lens in problem 8 is converging, of the same focal length, find the position of the final image.

10. Two convex lenses of focal lengths 12 cm and 20 cm are 8 cm apart. Calculate the position and the length of the image of an object 1 cm long, placed 36 cm in front of the first lens.

11. A small object is placed at a point on the axis 36 cm from a converging lens (of focal length 18 cm), 12 cm beyond which is a second coaxial diverging lens of focal length 12 cm. (a) Find where the image is. (b) If the aperture of the converging lens is 4 cm, that of the diverging lens at least as great, find through what distance an eye may be moved along a line (perpendicular to and intersecting the axis at a point 48 cm from the center of the diverging lens) and in all positions see the image.

12. An object is placed 60 cm from a converging lens (of focal length 30 cm), 40 cm beyond which is a diverging lens of focal length 10 cm. (a) Find (1) graphically, (2) by calculation, the position of the final image. (b) If the aperture of the converging lens is 2 cm and a point source is placed 60 cm from it, find the smallest aperture of the diverging lens (placed as above) such that all the light leaving the converging lens is transmitted by the diverging lens.

13. Light from a very distant object is incident on a combination of two coaxial converging lenses: one of focal length 100 cm, the other of focal length 40 cm, both placed 20 cm apart. The distant object subtends an angle of 4° at the first lens. Find: (a) graphically and by calculation the position of the final image; (b) the linear length of the final image.

14. A converging lens of focal length 60 cm and a diverging lens of focal length 20 cm, placed coaxially 50 cm apart, form a real image of a *distant* object on a screen placed beyond the diverging lens. The distant object subtends an angle of 5° at the converging lens. Find the linear size of the image.

15. (a) A small object is placed at a point on the axis 40 cm from a converging lens of focal length 20 cm. A diverging lens of focal length 24 cm is then placed beyond the first lens at such a distance that parallel rays emerge. Find the distance apart of the lenses. (b) If the aperture of the converging lens is 4 cm, find the width of the beam of parallel rays.

16. When a beam of parallel rays falls on a combination of two coaxial lenses, a diverging one of focal length 12 cm and beyond it a converging one of focal length 30 cm, parallel rays emerge from the second lens. Find the distance apart of the two lenses.

17. Solve problems 10, 11(a), and 12(a) by using principal planes and equivalent focal lengths.

18. Given, for a thick converging lens of focal length 20 cm, that $\alpha = +2.6$ cm, and $\beta = 0$; find the position of the image of an object 37.4 cm from the first face of the lens.

19. Prove that the distance apart of the principal points of a plano-convex lens $= t$. $\dfrac{(n - 1)}{n}$, where $t =$ thickness of the lens.

20. You are given a thick double convex lens, whose faces have radii of curvature of 24 cm and 36 cm; thickness of lens $= 2$ cm; index $= 1.524$. (a) Locate the principal points. (b) If an object is placed 40 cm from the nearer face of the lens, find, by calculation, the position of the image. (c) Solve part (b) graphically by making a diagram to scale. (d) Treating the lens as thin, and measuring distances from its center, calculate the position of the images. Note the error involved.

21. A thick lens, which has for constants $\alpha = +1.2$ cm and $\beta = -0.8$ cm, forms an image of a *distant* object 19.2 cm from the second surface of the lens. Find the position of the image of an object placed 38.8 cm from the first face.

V

Vision Through an Instrument.
The Telescope and the Microscope

In the experimental study of the nature of light there are few instruments used more frequently in one way or another than the telescope. It is essential, therefore, that the student of optics be thoroughly familiar with the basic principles involved in the construction and use of this instrument. In this chapter these will be discussed in detail.

Since the general object of looking through a telescope is to enable us to see better than with the unaided eye, it is first of all necessary to understand something about ordinary vision. From the viewpoint of optics the eye is an optical instrument, the essential part of which is the crystalline lens L,

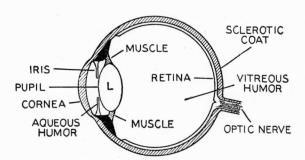

Fig. 5.1. Cross-sectional diagram of the eye.

Fig. 5.1, which (with the cornea and aqueous humor) forms a real image of an object on the retina. The aperture of this lens is fixed by the pupil, the transparent central portion of the opaque iris. This aperture is variable, contracting with intense light, dilating with a feeble beam. The image formed on the retina is inverted, just like any other real image formed by a converging lens. As the light which goes to the bottom of the image comes from the top, and as the position of an object "seen" by an individual is in the direction along which the light actually comes, the interpretation is that of an upright image.

71

5.1. Accommodation. As everyone knows, it is possible to see distinctly objects over a considerable range of distance. If the reader of these lines suddenly shifts his eyes from the print to an object across the room, he has probably no difficulty in seeing such an object almost as distinctly as the letters on the page of the book. On the other hand, it is not an uncommon experience when the reader's mind wanders from the page, to find that the print has become blurred and indistinct. In other words, although the retina is at a fixed distance from the eye lens, it is possible to obtain sharp images of objects at different distances from the eye, and it is equally possible to have the image of an object at a fixed distance either sharply focused (clearly seen) or indistinct. That this is so in the case of the eye is because of its power of *accommodation*. Muscles are attached to the crystalline lens by means of which the curvature of its faces may be altered, thus altering the focal length.

The question naturally arises: Is there any limit to the range over which a normal eye can see objects distinctly? Everyday experience gives the answer, because it is a matter of common observation that, if an object be brought closer and closer to the eye, eventually a position is reached within which clear vision is no longer possible. There is, therefore, a limit to the power of accommodation. A normal eye can see objects distinctly *without overstrain* when they are as near as 25 or 30 cm. Within this limit most people still can see objects clearly to some extent, but in that case the eye is probably overstrained. If persisted in, vision at a distance as close as 20 cm will lead to eyestrain and headache.

As a small object is brought nearer and nearer the eye from a distance, the image on the retina becomes larger and larger, and *detail* is seen better and better. For purposes of standardization and comparison with vision through an instrument, it is desirable to agree on some standard distance as the normal for unaided vision. Since 25 cm is about the nearest distance for which clear vision is normally possible *without overstrain*, this distance is chosen as the standard. It is well to realize again that, while for most people clear vision within this distance is quite possible, it is only so at the risk of eyestrain. The student should note also that the eye muscles are most relaxed when a *distant* object (or image) is being viewed, that is, when the incident rays from any point on the object (or image) are approximately parallel. For continued vision through an instrument, therefore, it is much easier on the eye if adjustment has been made so that the image is at infinity. (See section 5.7.)

5.2. Magnifying Power. In dealing with the advantages of vision through an instrument, we are concerned with *the number of times the eye can see better through the instrument than when the object is viewed directly*. In general terms, this number gives us a measure of what is called the *magnifying power* or *magnification* of the instrument, a quantity more accurately defined later in this section. The student must be careful to distinguish clearly between *linear* *magnification*, discussed in section 4.10, and magnifying power.   If the moon is viewed through a telescope the actual linear diameter of the image may be many times smaller than that of the moon, while the magnifying power, if vision were aided at all, would have to be greater than unity.   The difference should be clear from the following discussion.

If a small object PQ, Fig. 5.2, placed nearer a converging lens than its focal length, is viewed through such a lens, a magnified virtual image $P'Q'$ is observed. This is the principle of the magnifying glass, or magnifier, or Ramsden eyepiece. To find the magnifying power (M.P.) for this simple aid to vision, our definition must be made more exact.

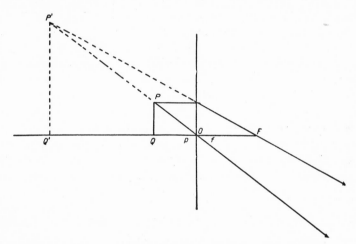

Fig. 5.2. $P'Q'$ is the magnified image of the object PQ.

It was pointed out in section 5.1 that the nearer the object to the eye, the larger the image on the retina and the better detail can be seen (always assuming we are outside 25 cm).   If, then, when viewing an object through an instrument, the size of the image *on the retina* is increased, vision will be improved and detail better seen.   Now a glance at (*a*) and (*b*), Fig. 5.3, where $P_1Q_1 = P_2Q_2$, will show that the greater the angle subtended at the eye by an object, the greater the size of the image on the retina.   We may, therefore, take as a measure of the distinctness of unaided vision, the angle subtended by a distant object at the eye, or, in the case of a small object which may readily be brought near the eye, by the angle subtended when it is at a distance of 25 cm.   Hence we have the following general definition for the magnifying power of a magnifying glass or magnifier:

$$\text{M.P.} = \frac{\text{angle subtended at eye by image}}{\text{angle subtended at eye by object when placed at 25 cm}}.$$

By this definition we have, again using Fig. 5.2, and (*a*), Fig. 5.3,

$$\text{M.P.} = \frac{\angle P' \, OQ' \ (\text{Fig. 5.2})}{\angle P_1OQ_1 \ (\text{Fig. 5.3}a)},$$

if PQ the object length in Fig. 5.2 equals P_1Q_1 and P_2Q_2 of Fig. 5.3.

In actual practice the angles with which we have to deal are essentially small (think, for example, of the angle subtended by a letter of print 1 mm wide at an eye 250 mm away). We may express those angles, therefore, most simply

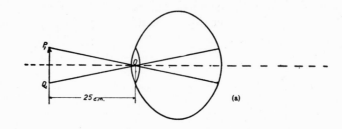

(a)

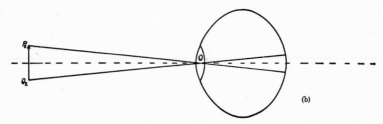

(b)

Fig. 5.3. The bigger the angle an object subtends at the eye, the larger the image on the retina.

and with sufficient accuracy in radian measure. Thus

$$\angle P_1OQ_1 \ (\text{Fig. 5.3}a) = \frac{P_1Q_1}{25}$$

and
$$\angle P'OQ' \ (\text{Fig. 5.2}) = \angle POQ,$$

$$= \frac{PQ}{p}.$$

$$\therefore \quad \text{M.P.} = \frac{\dfrac{PQ}{p}}{\dfrac{P_1Q_1}{25}},$$

$$= \frac{25}{p}, \tag{5.01}$$

since P_1Q_1 and PQ each represent the object viewed,

In actual practice a range of values of p is possible, but always subject to the restriction that the final image is clearly seen without eye strain. It may be at infinity or as near as 25 cm. To emphasize this point, the student is advised to take a convex lens of short focal length, say 5 cm, and try the following simple experiment. View a small object through the lens, adjusting until a sharp image is *first* seen (1) by moving the object from a position too close to the lens outward, (2) by moving from a distant position toward the lens. If the two distances are noted and the focal length of the lens measured, the usual calculation from the relation $\frac{1}{q} - \frac{1}{p} = \frac{1}{f}$ will give the corresponding image distances. The result will show not only the wide range but also that the nearest distance is often considerably less than 25 cm. As in each case the images are equally clear, overstrain and possible headache may be avoided when examining objects through a magnifying glass or an eyepiece, by focusing with the object (or image) far away rather than too near. (In the case of a telescope this means adjusting by moving the eyepiece initially from a position too far out.) There is, therefore, a range of values for the M.P. of a magnifier, depending on the position of the image. Consider the two extreme cases.

When the image is at infinity. For this to be the case, p must equal f and at once we may write

$$\text{M.P.} = \frac{25}{f}. \tag{5.02}$$

When the image is at 25 cm. In this case, since the image is virtual, $q = -25^*$ and we may write

$$\frac{1}{-25} - \frac{1}{p} = \frac{1}{f},$$

or

$$\frac{1}{p} = -\left(\frac{1}{25} + \frac{1}{f}\right).$$

Hence,

$$\text{M.P.} = \frac{25}{p}$$

$$= -25\left(\frac{1}{25} + \frac{1}{f}\right)$$

$$= -\left(1 + \frac{25}{f}\right). \tag{5.03}$$

Since M.P. is a pure number, the minus sign may be dropped.

Generally, therefore, the magnifying power of a magnifying glass or a simple microscope or a simple eyepiece lies between the two limits given in relations

---

* It is assumed that the eye is placed *immediately* behind the center of the lens and that the error is slight in taking the distance from the image to the eye as equal to q. The student should realize that M.P. is not a quantity whose value need be known to high accuracy.

(5.02) and (5.03). If f is small, it will be seen that the two differ very little. For example, when $f = 1$ cm, the M.P. ranges from 25 to 26.

The student should have no difficulty in proving that, *when the image is at 25 cm*, M.P. and linear magnification have the same numerical value. He will also understand, when it is stated that the M.P. of a microscope is so many *diameters*, that the assumption is made that the final image is at 25 cm. It is again emphasized that: (1) this is rarely the case when a magnifier or telescope or microscope is focused at random; and (2) for most comfortable vision, it is desirable to focus so that the final image is at infinity.

5.3. The Simple Telescope. The telescope, an instrument used to observe a *distant* object, consists essentially of (a) the *objective*, a converging lens which forms a real image of the distant object in its focal plane and (b) an *eyepiece*, which, in the simplest case, is a single converging lens through which this real

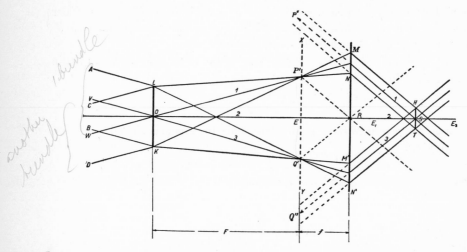

Fig. 5.4. Diagram showing the paths of two bundles of rays from two points on a distant object through a simple telescope. *LOK* is the objective, *MRN'* the single eye lens, and *HT* the eye ring.

image is viewed. The eye lens, then, is used as a magnifying glass forming a virtual image at any distance between 25 cm and infinity. Since, as already noted, the eye muscles are subject to the least strain when parallel rays fall on the eye, in the work that follows we shall assume that the instrument has been adjusted so that this is the case, that is, for most comfortable vision.

Fig. 5.4 shows the optical paths of two bundles through such an instrument: (1) AVB, parallel rays, from a point on one side of a distant object; and (2) CWD, another parallel bundle from a point on the other side of the object. Corresponding real point images are then formed by the objective at Q' and P', so that, if a screen (or photographic plate) is placed in the plane $P'Q'$, a sharp image of the distant object is seen (or photographed). Actually the rays spread out from P' and Q', eventually, on emergence from the eye lens, giving rise to the bundles $MNHT$ and $M'N'HT$. These emergent bundles will consist of parallel rays, if $ER = f$, the focal length of the eye lens. When these emergent bundles fall on the eye, point images are formed on the retina and the eye sees the final virtual image at $P''Q''$ (at infinity).

Magnifying Power. Since a large distant object obviously cannot be brought to the position of most distinct vision, the definition of M.P. applicable to a telescope is slightly different from that given for the magnifier. According to the new definition,

$$\text{M.P.} = \frac{\text{angular size of image}}{\text{angular size of object}},$$

$$= \frac{\angle P'RQ'}{\angle VOW},$$

since $P'R$ is parallel to rays apparently coming from a point on one side of the image, and $Q'R$ parallel to those apparently coming from a point on the other side. We have, then,

$$\angle P'RQ' = \frac{P'Q'}{f},$$

again remembering that this angle is much smaller than shown in the figure. Also

$$\angle VOW = \angle P'OQ',$$

$$= \frac{P'Q'}{F},$$

where $F = OE$, the focal length of the objective.

$$\therefore \quad \text{M.P.} = \frac{F}{f}. \tag{5.04}$$

5.4. The Eye Ring. Eye Point. It will be observed that the emergent parallel bundles from the two point sources represented in Fig. 5.4 pass through the area HT. This area is called the *exit pupil* or the *eye ring;* and S, the point where the area HT intersects the axis of the telescope, is called the *eye point.* A little consideration will show that through this area pass not only these two bundles but also those coming originally from every other point on the object which can be seen through the instrument. The exit pupil, therefore, defines the place at which an eye must be placed in order to see the biggest range of object. If placed immediately behind R, the center of the eye lens, for example, or at some point E_2, beyond S, the outer bundles shown in the figure would not fall on the eye at all. In such positions the corresponding outer points would then not be seen.

Diameter of Eye Ring. For visual observation there is no gain in brightness once the pupil of the eye is filled with light. Thus if HT is greater than the diameter of the pupil, the outermost rays of each individual bundle cannot enter the eye, and, as far as vision is concerned, are useless. It is important, therefore, to know the diameter of the eye ring. That it becomes greater, the greater the aperture of the objective, should be evident by a glance at the diagram. To find its exact magnitude, we proceed as follows:

$$HT = M'N' = MN$$

$$= \theta \times f,$$

where $\theta = \angle M'Q'N'$ or $\angle MP'N$, and $f = ER$ = focal length of eye lens. This relation holds only provided θ is small and provided the bundles passing through the telescope are inclined at a small angle to its axis. In actual practice the error is not great in assuming that these conditions are fulfilled, as the student can readily verify for himself by taking suitable approximate dimensions for a concrete case.

But $$\angle MP'N = \angle LP'K,$$

and $$\angle M'Q'N' = \angle LQ'K,$$

$$\therefore \quad \theta = \frac{a}{F},$$

where $a = LK$ = aperture of the objective,

and $F = OE$, the focal length of the objective.

We have, therefore,

$$HT = \frac{a}{F} \cdot f,$$

or, diameter of eye ring, $$= \frac{a}{\text{M.P.}} \qquad (5.05)$$

We see, then, that HT, the diameter of the eye ring, varies directly as the aperture of the objective and inversely as the M.P. of the telescope.

Now it will be seen when we study diffraction that it is desirable to have objectives with big apertures (to enable distant objects very close together to be seen). The consequent increase in the diameter of the eye ring may be offset by increasing the M.P. of the telescope, that is, by having an objective of long focal length as well as an eyepiece of small focal length. The use of objectives with wide apertures is a great advantage, because the bigger the aperture, the greater the light collected by the instrument and the brighter the image. For visual work, this is only true provided all the light can enter the eye, but, as we have just seen, this condition can be fulfilled by using high magnifying power.

Position of Eye Point. An examination of Fig. 5.4 will show that rays 1, 2, and 3, all passing through O, the center of the objective, after emergence from the eye lens, intersect at S, the eye point. This point, therefore, must coincide with the position of the image of the center of the objective formed by the eye lens. Since OR, the object distance $= F + f$, and since the focal length f is known, the corresponding image distance may readily be found from the usual lens relation. Calculation will show that S lies at a distance from the eye lens a little greater than its focal length.

Field of View. In the first paragraph of this section it has been pointed out that the maximum *field of view* is obtained when the eye is placed at the eye point. When the eye is in this position, the actual extent of the field of view depends on the diameter of the eye lens. In Fig. 5.4, for example, unless the aperture of this lens is NRM', the outermost bundles from an object of the angular width shown in that figure could not be transmitted through the eye lens. Obviously the smaller the aperture of this lens, the less the angular width of the largest object which can be seen.

Because of defects in simple lenses, a question to which further reference is made in the next section, it is frequently not wise to use the full aperture of the eye lens, and the field of view is still further restricted by a *stop*, or diaphragm. In the simple telescope, as illustrated in Fig. 5.4 or Fig. 5.6, this should be placed in the plane $P'Q'$ where the real image is formed by the objective. This diaphragm conveniently carries the crosshair lines. (See section 5.6.)

5.5. The Eyepiece. When a single lens is used as the eye lens, there are several objections to placing the eye at the eye point, where, as we have just seen, maximum field of view is obtained. We note three.

(1) It is desirable to have the eye immediately behind the eye lens, at E_1, Fig. 5.4, for example, rather than at S, so that it may be shielded from light not coming through the telescope.

(2) When the eye is at the eye point, it sees the outermost portions of the image by means of little bundles of rays which have passed through the edges of the eye lens, the central portion by means of rays through the centre of the lens. Now the student will recall the phenomenon of spherical aberration, the fact that, for apertures of any considerable width, the focal length of the central portion of a single lens differs from that of the outer portions. It follows that vision through such a lens, with the eye at the eye point, will give rise to an image, not all portions of which are at the same distance from the eye. In such a case, therefore, a good clear image over the whole field of view is not possible. As we have noted previously, this defect may be remedied by using a stop to reduce the aperture, but the remedy involves cutting down the field of view.

(3) In the next chapter it will be shown that the focal length of a single lens varies with the color (wavelength), a defect called *chromatic aberration*. With a single eye lens, therefore, particularly one of wide aperture, the image may show a certain amount of color.

Because of these objections, in a good practical telescope the foregoing simple telescope is somewhat modified. In the first place, the objective, instead of being a single lens, is an *achromatic combination* consisting of a converging and a diverging lens, in close contact, each made of a different kind of glass. As such a combination functions exactly in the manner of the objective shown in Fig. 5.4, no further reference need here be made. (See, however, section 11.3.)

In the second place, the eye lens is replaced by a combination of two lenses, called an *eyepiece*. There are several kinds of eyepieces, but in this section we shall confine our discussion to the *Ramsden*, the one in common use in telescopes attached to such instruments as the spectrometer (see section 6.2). When cross-hairs are necessary, this is the usual type used.

The Ramsden eyepiece consists of a combination of two converging lenses, of equal focal length, separated by a distance equal to two-thirds their common focal length. The lens nearest the eye we shall call the eye lens, that nearest the object, the field lens. While this eyepiece functions in exactly the same way as the single eye lens, it is an improvement on it because the defects enumerated above are much less marked. To begin with, the eye ring is now much nearer

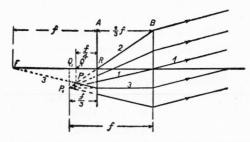

Fig. 5.5. Graphical method of locating the position of a point object placed at such a distance from a Ramsden eyepiece that parallel rays emerge.

the eye lens. In locating its position we shall again assume that the instrument is adjusted, as in the previous case, so that parallel bundles of rays leave the telescope. We must first of all, therefore, find where the eyepiece should be placed with reference to the image $P'Q'$ formed by the objective, so that parallel bundles of rays emerge.

This is essentially a problem of the type worked in section 4.4 and may be solved by either of the two methods there given.

(*a*) *By calculation.* It is left as an exercise for the student to prove that if p = distance of an object from lens A, Fig. 5.5, where A and B represent the two lenses of a Ramsden eyepiece from which parallel rays emerge

$$p = -\frac{f}{4}.$$

The real image $P'Q'$, therefore, should be placed at this distance from the field lens of the eyepiece.

(*b*) It is more instructive, however, to solve the problem *graphically*. Suppose, again, that a bundle of parallel rays leaves the lens B, Fig. 5.5. We may locate the exact position of P_1 by taking on the central ray 1 the point which is distant f cm from the lens B. Once P_1 is located the direction of the complete bundle incident on B may then be drawn as shown in the figure. Now lens A is present and the position of P_1 enables us, as yet, to draw the actual rays only in between the lenses. Since, however, we know that the principal ray 2 emerges from A through its centre unchanged in direction, and that the principal ray 3 emerging from A parallel to the axis (and apparently from P_1) must have been incident on A in a direction passing through F (a point f cm from R), P the point of intersection of these two rays gives us the original point from which the parallel rays must have come. If such a diagram is made to scale, the student will find by actual measurement that the distance $QR = f/4$.

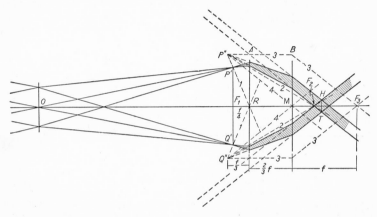

Fig. 5.6. Ray diagram for telescope when a single eye lens is replaced by a Ramsden eyepiece.

When, therefore, we replace the simple eye lens of Fig. 5.4 by a Ramsden eyepiece, the image $P'Q'$, formed by the objective, must be at a distance $f/4$ from the field lens. The diagram for such a case is given in Fig. 5.6, in which the focal length of the objective has been taken three times f. In tracing the outermost bundles through the eyepiece, one lens has been taken at a time and the usual principal rays used. Thus, taking lens A, P'' has been located as for any converging lens, by using rays 1 and 2, 1 through R the center of A, 2 incident parallel to the axis, emerging in a direction passing through F_2, where $RF_2 = f$. When P'' has been found, it is then possible to draw the actual path of the shaded bundle in between the lenses, since all such rays must emerge from A as if coming from P''. Finally, the direction of the bundle emerging from B is found by making use of the principal rays 3 and 4. Ray 4 incident on the center of B as if coming from P'' goes through unchanged in direction, while ray 3 incident on B, parallel to the axis, but again as if from P'', emerges in a direction passing through F_3, where $MF_3 = f$.

If the diagram is made carefully, 3 and 4 on emergence will be parallel, thus showing that the final image is at infinity, as well as giving the direction of the actual emergent bundle of parallel rays (shaded in the figure). In Fig. 5.6, all rays which do not actually exist have been indicated by dotted lines.

In a similar manner, the path of a bundle of rays from a point on the other side of the object may be drawn, and hence the position of the eye ring HT located. It will be seen by comparing Fig. 5.4 with Fig. 5.6, that, in the case of a telescope equipped with a Ramsden eyepiece, the eye ring is considerably closer to the instrument than when a single eye lens is used. This may be proved by direct calculation, since the eye point coincides with the image of O, the center of the objective, formed by the eyepiece. It is left as an exercise for the student to make the necessary calculation. The first objection to the simple arrangement noted at the beginning of this section has, therefore, to a considerable extent been overcome by the use of an eyepiece.

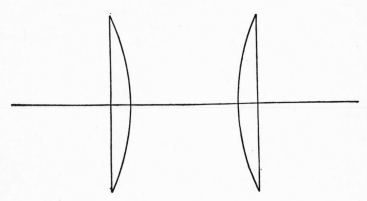

Fig. 5.7. Spherical aberration is lessened by using a combination of two plano-convex lenses placed as in the figure.

Defects due to aberrations are decreased with a combination of two plano-convex lenses, placed as in Fig. 5.7. Details of corrections need not concern us, but there is one point worth noting. Although to obtain the best correction for lateral chromatism d (see section 6.7) the distance apart of a pair of lenses should be one-half the sum of their focal lengths and so in this case equal f, in the Ramsden eyepiece d is only $\frac{2}{3}f$. With $d = f$, crosshairs and the real image $P'Q'$ in Fig. 5.6 would be against the field lens A, and dust particles on this lens would be visible.

Magnifying Power. The M.P. of a telescope equipped with a Ramsden eyepiece is increased somewhat, as will be evident from the following proof. Since the outermost parallel bundles emerging from the telescope are parallel to $P''M$ and $Q''M$ respectively, the angle $P''MQ''$ is the angle subtended at the eye by the image. Therefore,

$$\text{M.P.} = \frac{\angle P''MQ''}{\angle P'OQ'}$$

$$= \frac{\dfrac{P''Q''}{f}}{\dfrac{P'Q'}{F}},$$

since $P''Q''$ is formed at a distance f from lens B.

$$\therefore \quad \text{M.P.} = \frac{P''Q''}{P'Q'} \cdot \frac{F}{f}.$$

But

$$\frac{P''Q''}{P'Q'} = \frac{\dfrac{f}{3}}{\dfrac{f}{4}} = \frac{4}{3}$$

and hence,

$$\text{M.P.} = \frac{4}{3} \cdot \frac{F}{f}.$$

COROLLARY: If a Ramsden eyepiece is used as a magnifier, it follows that it is equivalent in M.P. to a single lens of focal length $\frac{3}{4}f$.

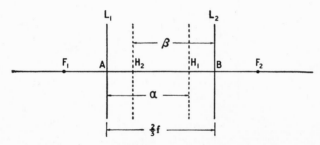

Fig. 5.8. The dotted lines represent the principal planes of a Ramsden eyepiece.

Alternative Treatment. Problems relating to the Ramsden eyepiece may be solved readily by the use of principal planes and the equivalent focal length. Using the relations (4.12), (4.13), (4.14), given in section 4.9, we obtain at once

$$F = +\frac{f_1 f_2}{f_1 + f_2 - t} = \frac{f^2}{2f - \frac{2}{3}f} = +\frac{3f}{4},$$

$$\alpha = +\frac{f_1 t}{f_1 + f_2 - t} = +\frac{f}{2},$$

and

$$\beta = -\frac{f_2 t}{f_1 + f_2 - t} = -\frac{f}{2}.$$

With the aid of these values, in Fig. 5.8 the positions of the principal points H_1 and H_2 and the focal points F_1 and F_2 have been marked.

A glance at this diagram shows that the distance of the first focal point from the field lens of the eyepiece is given by

$$F_1A = F_1H_1 - \alpha = \frac{3f}{4} - \frac{f}{2} = \frac{f}{4},$$

the result obtained previously by the method illustrated by Fig. 5.5. Note, also, that BF_2, the distance of the eye lens to the second focal point, is also $f/4$.

Since the equivalent focal length of the eyepiece is $\frac{3}{4}f$, it is not difficult to prove that

$$\text{M.P. of telescope} = \frac{F}{\frac{3}{4}f} = \frac{4F}{3f}.$$

It is interesting to note that, if the eye is placed at F_2, the second focal point of the Ramsden eyepiece—and in actual practice it would not be far from this point—its magnifying power is $\dfrac{25}{\text{equivalent focal length}}$ *regardless of where the image is.*

To prove this, consider a small object, such as PQ, Fig. 5.9, viewed through a Ramsden eyepiece used as a magnifier. A ray PN, parallel to the axis and

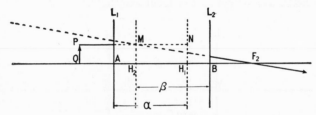

Fig. 5.9.   Diagram for proof that, if the eye is at F_2, the second focal point of a Ramsden eyepiece, its magnifying power is independent of the position of the image.

striking the first principal plane at N, emerges from the combination in the direction MF_2, M being the point on the second principal plane corresponding to N on the first principal plane, and F_2 the second focal point. If P is the top of the object, then this ray through F_2 leaves the eyepiece as if coming from the top of the image. Hence, if the eye is at F_2, the angle MF_2H_2 is the angle subtended at the eye by the image.

$$\therefore \quad \text{M.P. of the eyepiece} = \frac{\text{angular size of image}}{\text{angular size of object at 25 cm}}$$

$$= \frac{MF_2H_2}{\dfrac{PQ}{25}}.$$

But $$MH_2 = NH_1 = PQ,$$

$$\therefore \quad \angle MF_2H_2 = \frac{MH_2}{H_2F_2} = \frac{PQ}{\frac{3}{4}f}.$$

Hence $$\text{M.P.} = \frac{\dfrac{PQ}{\frac{3}{4}f}}{\dfrac{PQ}{25}} = \frac{25}{\frac{3}{4}f}.$$

This proof, it will be noted, applies whether the image is at infinity or not, provided, of course, that it is not so near that the eye has to over-accommodate in order to see it.

5.6. Huygens' Eyepiece. This is another type frequently used, especially in instruments where crosshair lines are not necessary. It consists of two converging lenses separated by a distance equal to one-half the sum of the focal lengths, a condition which ensures that the focal length of the combination is achromatic. The focal length f_1 of the field lens is always greater than f_2, the

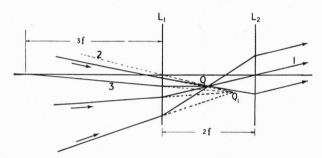

Fig. 5.10.   Ray paths through a Huygens' eyepiece when parallel rays emerge.

focal length of the eye lens, but the ratio f_1/f_2 is not always the same. The diagrams in Figs. 5.10 and 5.11 are made for a ratio of 3 to 1, the highest value used.

With the aid of either of these figures, the student should have no difficulty in proving that, when parallel rays emerge from a Huygens' eyepiece, rays incident on the field lens must make for a virtual point (Q_1 in Fig. 5.10, F_1 in Fig. 5.11) which is distant $3f/2$ from this lens.

Fig. 5.10 shows the graphical solution when use is made of the same method as is illustrated in Fig. 5.5 for a Ramsden eyepiece.

Fig. 5.11 illustrates the solution when principal planes and the equivalent focal length are used. The student can easily verify that $\alpha = AH_1 = 3f$; $\beta = H_2B = -f$; and the equivalent focal length $= F_1H_1 = H_2F_2 = \dfrac{3f}{2}$. Taking the beam of parallel rays represented by 1, 2, and 3, we see that, since rays 1 and 2 leave the second principal plane at M and M_1, they must have been (virtually) incident on the first principal plane at N and N_1. Since F_1 is the first focal point, F_1N and F_1N_1 are the virtual paths of these incident rays, and hence C and D must be the actual points of incidence on the field lens. PC and RD (whose directions produced run through F_1) are, therefore, the actual paths of the incident rays which on emergence give rise to rays 1 and 2.

Two things will be evident from either Fig. 5.10 or Fig. 5.11. (1) A Huygens' eyepiece cannot be used as a magnifier of a real object. (2) If this eyepiece is used in a telescope, it must be so placed with respect to the objective that the image formed by the objective would, in the absence of the eyepiece, be at Q_1 in Fig. 5.10, or F_1 in 5.11.

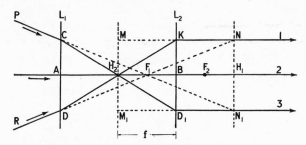

Fig. 5.11. Use of principal planes to trace ray paths through a Huygens' eyepiece when parallel rays emerge.

5.7. Crosshair Lines or Crosshair. It is frequently necessary to set a telescope in an exact position with reference to the real image formed by the objective. When this is the case, crosshair lines are used, filaments of a spider's web being useful for this purpose. When the telescope with a Ramsden's eyepiece is properly adjusted, the crosshair lines should coincide with the real image $P'Q'$ (Fig. 5.4 or Fig. 5.6). They are attached, therefore, to a diaphragm placed in the barrel of the telescope a short distance from the field lens of the eyepiece. In adjusting the instrument, first of all the eyepiece is moved with reference to the crosshair (preferably from a position too far out) until a sharp image of it is obtained. Then, by means of the main focusing screw of the telescope, the system, crosshair plus eyepiece, is moved with reference to the objective until a clear image of the distant object is obtained. (This operation, too, should be done starting with the eyepiece too far out. See section 5.2.) When proper adjustment has been made, there should be no parallax between the image of the crosshair and that of the distant object.

If a telescope is equipped with a Huygens' eyepiece and it is necessary to use a crosshair, it would have to be placed between the field and the eye lenses in a position coinciding with the real image at Q, Fig. 5.10, or H_2, Fig. 5.11.

5.8. The Microscope. The magnifying powers of magnifiers are of the order of 10 or 20. When much higher powers are wanted, use is made of the microscope. With the aid of Fig. 5.12, the student will recall the elementary principles of this instrument. The objective L_1, a combination of lenses functioning as a

single converging lens, forms at P_1Q_1 an enlarged real image of the small object
PQ. A magnified virtual image of this real image is then viewed through an
eyepiece or magnifier L_2, just as in the telescope. When the magnification is
moderate, the Huygens' eyepiece is frequently the type used. To save the eye,
adjustment is preferably made with the final image at infinity.

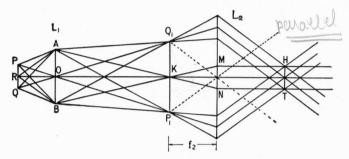

Fig. 5.12. Ray paths through a microscope from points P and Q on a small object. L_1 is a simple
objective, L_2 a single eye lens, HT the eye ring.

If m is the *initial magnification*, that is, the linear magnification of the
image P_1Q_1,

$$\text{M.P. of microscope} = m \cdot \frac{25}{f_2}, \qquad (5.06)$$

where f_2 is the equivalent focal length of the eyepiece. Since the value of the
second factor ranges approximately from 5 to 20, f_2 does not exceed a few centimeters.

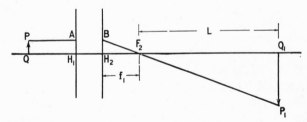

Fig. 5.13. An objective of many component lenses may be replaced by the principal planes AH_1
and BH_2.

If the combination of lenses comprising the objective is replaced by equivalent principal planes, as in Fig. 5.13, the value of m, which we have previously
taken as image distance/object distance, may be written L/f_1.* In this expression L, as shown in Fig. 5.13, is the distance of the image P_1Q_1 from F_2, the
second focal point of the objective, and $f_1 = H_2F_2$, the focal length of the ob-

$$*m = \frac{P_1Q_1}{PQ} = \frac{P_1Q_1}{AH_1} = \frac{P_1Q_1}{BH_2} = \frac{F_2Q_1}{H_2F_2} = \frac{L}{f_1}.$$

jective.* Since it is a common practice among manufacturers to design the
length of microscope tubes so that $L = 18$ cm, we may write

$$\text{M.P.} = m \cdot \frac{25}{f_2}$$

$$= \frac{L}{f_1} \cdot \frac{25}{f_2}$$

$$= \frac{18 \times 25}{f_1 f_2} = \frac{450}{f_1 f_2}. \tag{5.07}$$

When the value of m is marked on an objective and the power $(25/f_2)$ on the
eyepiece, the M.P. of the microscope is at once found by multiplying these two
values together.

The objective is an achromatic combination of a number of lenses, sometimes
as many as ten, so designed that correction is made for chromatism, spherical

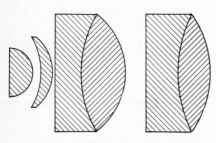

Fig. 5.14.   The component lenses of a high-power objective.

aberration, and other defects. Fig.
5.14, for example, shows the component
parts of a high-power objective of focal
length 1.8 mm. A firm like Bausch and
Lomb, of Rochester, N. Y., lists objectives whose focal lengths range from less
than 2 mm to as high a value as 50 mm,
with the initial magnification ranging
from 2 to almost 100. A good microscope is invariably provided with several objectives of varying powers and
two or more eyepieces.

There are several important types of objectives in common use. One frequently used is the *achromat*, a system of glass lenses made achromatic for two
wavelengths. "The images formed are excellent in every respect, except that
some color is present which becomes disturbing when high-power eyepieces and
oblique illumination are resorted to." (Bausch and Lomb.) In higher grade
achromats, chromatic correction is improved by replacing some of the component
glass lenses by fluorite.

The *apochromat* is a system made achromatic for three wavelengths and in
general is more perfectly corrected so that "much higher power eyepieces with
subsequent higher total magnification than is recommended for achromatic
objectives can be used to good advantage." (Bausch and Lomb.) This type
has also a higher numerical aperture (N.A.), for the same initial magnification,
than the achromat, an advantage which will appear later.

When an *oil-immersion* objective is used, an oil, whose index of refraction is

---

* If the medium is not the same on each side of the objective the focal length on the object
side is different from that on the image side, and f_1 is then the value of the latter.

the same as that of the lowest lens of the objective, is the medium between the object and the objective. The advantage of this type is explained in section 11.4.

5.9. Numerical Aperture. The magnifying power of a microscope may be expressed in terms of a very important quantity called the *numerical aperture* (N.A.). Although N.A. is important chiefly in connection with resolving power (section 11.4), it may conveniently be introduced at this stage by showing its relation to magnifying power. To do so, (1) we make use of the sine condition $n_1 y_1 \sin \alpha_1 = n_2 y_2 \sin \alpha_2$ (see, again, section 3.15); and (2) without in any way altering the correctness of the work given previously, we redefine M.P. as follows:

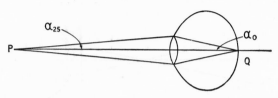

Fig. 5.15. α_{25} is the object slope angle; α_0, the corresponding image slope angle when a small object is viewed by the eye at 25 cm.

$$\text{M.P.} = \frac{\text{linear size of image of a small object formed on retina by microscope}}{\substack{\text{linear size of image on retina when the small object is viewed} \\ \text{directly at a distance of 25 cm from the eye}}}.$$

Let y_0 = linear size of image on the retina when a small object of linear size y is viewed at 25 cm from the eye;

y'_0 = linear size of image on the retina when the same object is viewed through a microscope;

α_{25} = the object slope angle of a ray from the axial point P, Fig. 5.15, of the small object 25 cm from the eye, to the periphery of the pupil of the eye;

α_0 = the image slope angle of the corresponding ray from the periphery to the axial image Q, Fig. 5.15;

α = the slope angle of a ray to the periphery of the objective, from the axial point R, Fig. 5.16, when the small object is viewed through the microscope; and

α'_0 = the image slope angle of the corresponding ray to the image Q, Fig. 5.16, on the retina.

Applying the sine condition to Fig. 5.15, we can write

$$ny \sin \alpha_{25} = n_0 y_0 \sin \alpha_0,$$

where n_0 is the index of the medium within the eye. Since the object, when viewed directly, is invariably in air, $n = 1$, and hence

$$y \sin \alpha_{25} = n_0 y_0 \sin \alpha_0. \qquad (a)$$

Similarly the sine condition applied to Fig. 5.16 gives us

$$ny \sin \alpha = n_0 y'_0 \sin \alpha'_0. \qquad (b)$$

Combining (a) and (b), and recalling the definition of M.P. given at the beginning of this section, we have

$$\text{M.P.} = \frac{y'_0}{y_0} = \frac{ny \sin \alpha}{y \sin \alpha_{25}} \cdot \frac{\sin \alpha_0}{\sin \alpha'_0}$$

$$= \frac{n \sin \alpha \sin \alpha_0}{\sin \alpha_{25} \sin \alpha'_0}. \qquad (c)$$

The quantity $n \sin \alpha$, that is, the product of the index of refraction of the object medium (generally air but not always) multiplied by the slope angle of the outer-

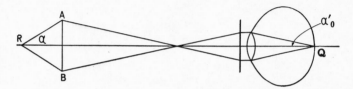

Fig. 5.16.   Diagram used in explaining numerical aperture and normal magnifying power.

most ray from an axial point on the object, is called the *numerical aperture* (N.A.) of the objective of a microscope.   Its value ranges from less than 0.1 to as high as 1.4.

5.10. Normal Magnifying Power.   If the optical system is such that the pupil of the eye is completely filled with light by the beam emerging from the eyepiece, the magnifying power is said to be *normal*.   For all practical purposes,* this means that $\alpha_0 = \alpha'_0$, from which it follows that

$$\text{normal M.P.} = \frac{\text{N.A.}}{\sin \alpha_{25}}. \qquad (d)$$

But α_{25} is the slope angle of a ray from an axial point 25 cm from the eye to the periphery of the pupil.   If, therefore, we take 2.5 mm as a reasonable value for the diameter of the pupil when the eye is examining a small object in average illumination, then

$$\alpha_{25} = \frac{1.25}{250} = \frac{1}{200}, \text{ from which we have}$$

$$\text{normal M.P.} = 200 \text{ N.A.}$$

This expression, it should be clearly understood, does not give the actual M.P. of a microscope.   It is a useful approximation when the beam emerging from the eyepiece is wide enough to fill the pupil of the eye.   The actual diameter of this beam depends on the size of the exit pupil of the microscope.

* The aperture of the pupil varies with the intensity of the light.

5.11. Radius of Exit Pupil. By referring to the discussion of the telescope in section 5.4, the student should have no difficulty in seeing (1) that HT, in Fig. 5.12, represents the exit pupil of the microscope; and (2) that HT is the image of AB, the aperture of the objective, formed by the eye lens L_2. As in the telescope, so in the microscope, the eye should be placed at the exit pupil to see the greatest range of object. Microscopes are designed so that the exit pupil is at a convenient distance, 10 mm or so from the upper surface of the eyepiece.

Frequently magnifying powers much greater than normal are used. When this is the case, the diameter of the exit pupil is less than that of the pupil of the eye, as the following proof shows.

If r = radius of exit pupil, then, in Fig. 5.12,

$$2r = HT = MN$$

$$= 2f_2 \tan \phi,$$

where f_2 is the focal length of the eye lens, and $\phi = \angle AKO$.

Since $\angle ARO = \alpha$ is the object slope angle for the objective, and ϕ is the corresponding image slope angle, then by the sine condition

$$ny \sin \alpha = n_1 y_1 \sin \phi,$$

where y_1 is the linear length of the image formed by the objective of a small axial object of corresponding length y.

It follows that m, the initial magnification, is given by

$$m = \frac{y_1}{y} = \frac{n \sin \alpha}{n_1 \sin \phi} = \frac{\text{N.A.}}{\sin \phi}, \text{ since } n_1 = 1.$$

Since OK is many times greater than AO, the angle ϕ is small; hence, with little error $\sin \phi = \tan \phi$, and

$$m = \frac{\text{N.A.}}{\tan \phi}.$$

But M.P., the magnifying power $= m \dfrac{25}{f_2}$

$$= \frac{\text{N.A.}}{\tan \phi} \cdot \frac{25}{f_2}$$

$$= \frac{25 \text{ N.A.}}{r},$$

or $\qquad r$, the radius of the eye ring $= \dfrac{25 \text{ N.A.}}{\text{M.P.}}$ cm.

Let us examine three cases.

(a) $\qquad\qquad$ M.P. = normal

$$= 200 \text{ N.A.}$$

Then
$$r = \frac{25 \text{ N.A.}}{200 \text{ N.A.}} \text{ cm}$$

$$= 1.25 \text{ mm},$$

which is the radius of the pupil of the eye used above, as of course it should be.

(b)   M.P. > normal.

Suppose, for example, a M.P. of 500 and a N.A. of 1 is used. Then

$$r = \frac{25 \text{ N.A.}}{500} \text{ cm}$$

$$= \frac{250}{500} \text{ or } 0.5 \text{ mm},$$

a value which is considerably less than the radius of the pupil. The higher magnifying power has been gained, therefore, at the expense of light. This, however, is not a serious matter, because it is generally possible to compensate for the loss of light due to reduced diameter of the beam entering the eye by increasing the illumination.

The advantage of M.P. higher than normal is discussed when the question of the resolving power of a microscope is considered in section 11.4.

(c)   M.P. < normal.

In this case the radius of the exit pupil exceeds that of the eye pupil, and the whole beam of light is not utilized. This means that, although the actual brightness of the image observed by the eye is the same as for normal magnifying power, the numerical aperture which is actually used is reduced, and consequently, as we shall see later, the resolving power is lessened.

PROBLEMS

1. A very distant object subtends an angle of 4° at the objective of a telescope adjusted so that the final image viewed through the telescope is at infinity. The eyepiece consists of a single lens and the angular width of the image is 20°. If the objective and the eyepiece are 36 cm apart, find the focal length of each.

2. A converging lens of focal length 6 cm is used as a simple magnifier. Over what range of distances can an object be viewed and in all cases the image be seen clearly without undue eyestrain?

3. Explain under what condition the linear magnification is numerically equal to the magnifying power of a converging lens.

4. A simple telescope, consisting of an objective of focal length 60 cm and a single eye lens of focal length 5 cm, is focused on a distant object in such a way that parallel rays emerge from the eye lens. If the object subtends an angle of 2° at the objective, find the angular width of the image.

5. If the telescope in problem 4 is adjusted so that the final image is 25 cm from the eye lens, find: (a) the distance between the lenses; (b) the linear width of the image.

6. In a simple telescope, you are given $F = 24$ cm; $f = 4$ cm; aperture of objective $= 2$ cm; aperture of eye lens $= 1$ cm. Find: (a) where the eye (treated as a point) must be placed to see the greatest extent of a distant object; (b) the diameter of the eye ring; (c) when the eye (treated as a point) is at the eye point, the angular size of the largest object which can be seen. Solve part (c), (i) using magnifying power, (ii) without making any use of magnifying power.

7. If the aperture of the eye pupil $= 2.8$ mm, and $F = 30$ cm, $f = 6$ cm, find the aperture of the objective of a simple telescope so that the pupil is just completely filled with rays of light. What would be the effect of (a) reducing, (b) enlarging the aperture of the telescope?

8. When focused on a star, the distance of the eye lens of a simple telescope from the objective is 82 cm. The focal length of the eye lens is 2.0 cm. To see a certain tree (with the telescope focused so that the final image is at the same distance as when focused on the star), the eye lens must be drawn out 1.0 cm. Find the distance of the tree from the telescope.

9. (a) A small object is viewed through a magnifying glass of focal length 4 cm at distances of (i) 4 cm; (ii) 3.5 cm. In each case find the magnifying power and the linear magnifications. (b) Would it be wise to use the magnifying glass with an object at 3 cm? Discuss.

10. When a small object is viewed through a simple magnifier of focal length 4 cm, the resulting (virtual) image is 36 cm from the **magnifier**. Find the magnifying power and the linear magnification.

11. A distant object is observed through a telescope consisting of an objective lens of focal length 30 cm and a single eyepiece lens of focal length 5 cm. The telescope is adjusted so that the final image observed by the eye is 40 cm from the eye lens. (a) Find the distance apart of the two lenses. (b) Make a careful diagram tracing a bundle of rays from a point at one side of the distant object through the telescope. (c) Calculate the magnifying power for this arrangement. (Work fundamentally.)

12. A beam of parallel rays, parallel to the axis, falls on the objective of a telescope equipped with a Ramsden eyepiece and adjusted so that the final image is at infinity. If the focal length of the objective $= 30.00$ cm and the common focal length of each of the lenses of the eyepiece $= 6.0$ cm, find the diameter of the beam of light emerging from the telescope. (Diameter of objective $= 3.0$ cm.)

13. A Ramsden eyepiece, each of whose lenses has a focal length of 6 cm, is used as a magnifying glass to view details of a small object placed 1.5 cm from the lens next the object. Find the magnifying power. Work fundamentally.

14. A small object is viewed through a combination of two converging lenses, each of focal length 6 cm, placed 2 cm apart. If the final image is located 34 cm from the lens next the eye, find the *magnifying power* of the combination.

15. In a Ramsden eyepiece prove that rays will emerge "parallel" if a point source is placed at a distance $f/4$ (where f is the focal length of each lens) from the field lens.

16. Solve problem 15 by making a diagram to scale. (Trace an inclined parallel beam backward through the combination.)

17. What advantages has a Ramsden eyepiece over a single eye lens?

18. The objective of a telescope equipped with a Ramsden eyepiece has a focal length of 36 cm and an aperture of 6 cm, and each lens of the eyepiece has a focal length of 5 cm.

If it is adjusted so that parallel rays emerge, find: (a) the diameter; (b) the position, of the eye ring.

19. Prove that the magnifying power of a telescope equipped with a Huygens' eyepiece is $2F/3f$, where F is the focal length of the objective, and $3f, f$, are the focal lengths of the component lenses of the eyepiece.

20. A small object is viewed through a simple magnifier of focal length 4 cm at a distance of 3.6 cm from the magnifier. If the angular size of the image viewed is 2°, find the linear size of the object.

21. When a small object 2.18 mm long is viewed through a simple magnifier of focal length 6 cm the angular size of the image is 2.5°. Find: (a) the magnifying power; (b) the position of the object; (c) the linear magnification.

22. A distant object is viewed through a telescope whose objective has a focal length of 36 cm, and (single) eye lens a focal length of 6 cm, the centers of the two lenses being separated 41.0 cm. Find, from fundamental considerations, the *magnifying power* of the telescope *for this arrangement*. Illustrate by a good diagram.

23. Under what condition is it correct to state that the magnifying power of a telescope is equal to

$$\frac{\text{diameter of objective}}{\text{diameter of exit pupil}}?$$

24. A small object is placed 1.05 cm from the first principal plane of the objective of a microscope, the objective having a focal length of 1.0 cm. If the magnifying power of the eyepiece is 8, find the magnifying power of the microscope.

25. A microscope has an objective with N.A. 0.4, an initial magnification of 30, and with an eyepiece which magnifies 5 times. Find: (a) the M.P. of the microscope; (b) the normal M.P., if the aperture of the pupil of the eye is taken as 3 mm.

26. (a) An objective with N.A. 0.80 gives an initial magnification of 30. If this objective is used with an eye lens of focal length 6 cm, find the radius of the exit pupil. Assume the final image is at infinity.

(b) Find the normal M.P. for this microscope, if the diameter of the pupil of the eye is taken as 2.6 mm.

27. A microscope has an objective of N.A. 0.50 and an ocular magnifying 4 times. If the initial magnification of the objective is 16, find the diameter of the exit pupil. Hence, show that the full N.A. of the objective is not utilized.

28. A small object is placed (a) 1.5 cm, (b) 1.0 cm, in front of a Ramsden eyepiece, each of whose lenses has a focal length of 6 cm. In each case, find, using principal planes and equivalent focal length, the position of the final image. Check your solution by taking one lens at a time.

29. You are given a Huygens' eyepiece, with converging lenses of focal lengths 6 cm and 2 cm, placed 4 cm apart. Prove, using principal planes and equivalent focal length, that, if parallel rays are to emerge, the beam incident on the first lens must be convergent making for a virtual object situated midway between the two lenses. Check your solution by dealing with one lens at a time.

VI

Dispersion

6.1 Refraction through a Prism. Suppose plane waves are incident on a portion of a refracting medium in the form of a prism, the medium being more dense than the surroundings. Because of the slower velocity of the wave disturbance in the prism, it is readily seen by applying Huygens' Principle that an incident wave-front, such as MM', Fig. 6.1, gives rise, at the time the outer edge has reached A, to the wave-front AH, while, by the time the other edge has passed through the face AC, the emergent wave-front L is formed. Plane waves, therefore, incident on the prism in the direction KN emerge in the direction OS, being *deviated* through the angle NOS.

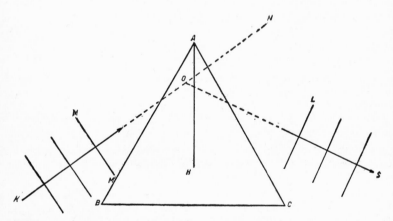

Fig. 6.1.   An incident plane wave-front MM' is deviated in its passage through a prism.

In the case of light, it is more usual to discuss such questions as the amount of deviation by dealing with rays. Suppose, then, that ray EM is one of a parallel bundle of rays incident at an angle i_1 on the face HB, Fig. 6.2, of a prism of index n and refracting angle A, and emergent from the second face HC at an angle i_2. For the moment we are confining our attention to rays of what is called *monochromatic* light—in other words, light corresponding to a single wavelength. A good practical illustration (to a first approximation) is found in the yellow light emitted from a flame colored with common salt. If, then, D represents the angle of deviation, we have

$$D = \angle SOR$$
$$= \angle OMN + \angle ONM$$
$$= i_1 - r_1 + i_2 - r_2, \tag{6.01}$$

where $K'MK$ and $K''NK$ are normals to the surfaces HB and HC and

$i_1 = \angle K'ME$, the angle of incidence,
$r_1 = \angle NMK$, the corresponding angle of refraction,
$i_2 = \angle K''NR$, the angle of emergence,
$r_2 = \angle MNK$, the corresponding angle of refraction.

Since $r_1 + r_2 + \angle MKN = \pi,$
and $A + \angle MKN = \pi,$
                        $\therefore\ \ r_1 + r_2 = A,$
and we have, $D = i_1 + i_2 - A. \tag{6.02}$

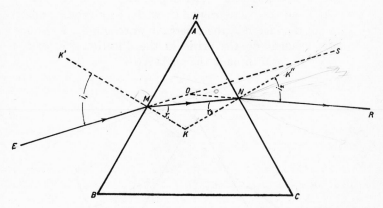

Fig. 6.2.   Diagram used in deriving an expression for the angle of deviation.

Angle of Minimum Deviation.   The magnitude of D obviously depends on the angle at which the parallel bundle of rays is incident on the prism.   If, now, when the emergent light is focused on a screen or is observed in a telescope, the *prism* is rotated, it will be found by actual trial that there is one position of the prism and only one, for which the deviation is a minimum.   When this is the case, the angles i_1 and i_2 are equal.   This may be proved experimentally, or mathematically, or by the following *reductio ad absurdum* method.

Suppose that, when the prism is in the position of least deviation, i_1 is not equal to i_2.   Then, imagine the beam of light reversed in direction, that is, incident parallel to RN, emergent parallel to ME.   The deviation is not altered, being still equal to $\angle SOR$, and is, therefore, still a minimum.   On our hypothesis, therefore, we have minimum deviation for *two* angles of incidence i_1 and i_2.

But by experiment this cannot be the case.   Therefore, the hypothesis cannot

PLATE II. SPECTRA

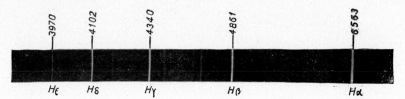

Fig. 1.   Vacuum tube spectrum of hydrogen.   (Glass Prism Spectrograph)

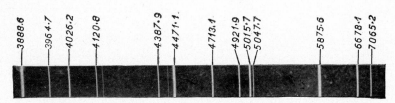

Fig. 2.   Vacuum tube spectrum of helium.   (Glass Prism Spectrograph)

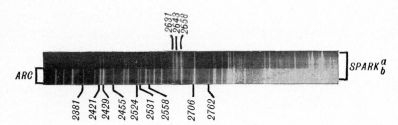

Fig. 3.   A portion of the ultraviolet spectrum of tin, spark overlapping arc.

Fig. 4.   Ultraviolet spectrum of mercury (Quartz Spectrograph)

PLATE III. SPECTRA

Fig. 1. Three spectra of magnesium, with different degrees of excitation (electronic bombardment). (Foote, Meggers and Mohler)

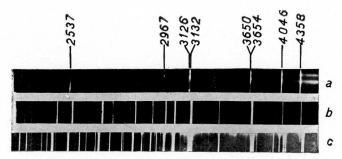

Fig. 2. Three spectra of mercury with different degrees of excitation.

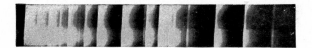

Fig. 3. A typical unresolved band spectrum.

Fig. 4. To show individual lines of a single band. (Pearse)

be true; that is, in the position of minimum deviation

$$i_1 = i_2.$$

In much experimental work the prism is set in this position. When this is the case, frequent use is made of an important relation which we shall now derive.

Since
$$i_1 = i_2 = i,$$

and
$$r_1 = r_2 = \frac{A}{2},$$

$$\therefore \quad D = 2i - A,$$

or
$$i = \frac{D + A}{2}.$$

But
$$n = \frac{\sin i}{\sin r},$$

$$\therefore \quad n = \frac{\sin \dfrac{D + A}{2}}{\sin \dfrac{A}{2}}. \tag{6.03}$$

N. B.

Small-Angled Prisms. If an angle is sufficiently small, we may write $\sin A = A$, in which case relations (6.02) and (6.03) reduce to

$$D = (n - 1)A. \tag{6.04}$$

Relation (6.03) is applicable accurately only to cases of minimum deviation, while relation (6.04) is restricted to prisms of small angles, with deviation not necessarily a minimum.

6.2. The Spectrometer. Relation (6.03) provides us with one of the standard methods of measuring the index of refraction of a material, for monochromatic light, when in the form of a prism. The method consists in measuring the angles A and D by means of a spectrometer. While it is not the purpose of this book to discuss details of experimental procedure, certain principles cannot be considered without a clear understanding of the fundamental ideas involved in the construction and use of this instrument.

The essential parts of a spectrometer are (*a*) a collimator C, Fig. 6.3, consisting of a slit S whose width and whose distance from the converging lens L may be adjusted; (*b*) a telescope T, provided with crosshair lines, and capable of rotation about a central vertical axis passing through (*c*), a table M, on which a prism or other objects may be placed. The position of the telescope may be described by means of the circular scale whose center is the axis of rotation. When the instrument is adjusted for ordinary use the telescope is focused for parallel rays, while the slit S is placed so that parallel rays emerge from the collimator lens.

Fig. 6.3 shows the passage of a parallel beam of rays, originally emerging from a very narrow slit S, through a prism placed in the position of least deviation. It will be seen that a real image of the slit is formed at F in the focal plane of the objective of the telescope. By observing this image through the eyepiece,

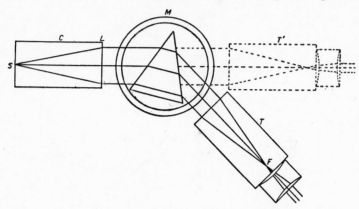

Fig. 6.3. Ray paths when a prism is set on the table M of a spectrometer in position of minimum deviation. C is the collimator; T, the telescope.

the crosshair may be set on it and the position of the telescope carefully read off the scale. If the prism is then removed, and the telescope shifted to position T' where the direct beam is received, a second scale reading can be taken. The difference between the two readings is, of course, equal to D.

To find the angle A, the prism is set on the table of the spectrometer with its refracting angle pointing into the beam of parallel rays leaving the collimator, as in Fig. 6.4. Since a beam of parallel rays is reflected from each of the polished surfaces AB and AC, an image is observed in the telescope when it is placed in position I and again in position II. The scale reading is read when the crosshair is set on each of these images. It is left as an exercise in elementary geometry for the student to prove that the difference between the scale readings equals twice the angle A.

Table I.   Refractive Index of Various Glasses for D Light

Glass	Trade Number	Density	Index
Ordinary Crown..................	0.203	2.54	1.5174
Borosilicate Crown...............	0.144	2.47	1.510
Very Heavy Crown..............	0.2994	3.60	1.613
Extra Light Flint................	0.726	2.87	1.540
Ordinary Flint...................	0.118	3.58	1.613
Very Heavy Flint................	0.198	4.99	1.778
Extra Heavy Flint..............	S.386	6.01	1.917

With the values of A and D (minimum) known, the width of refraction n is obtained, using relation 6.03. Values of indices for a few materials, for yellow (D) light, are given in Table I.

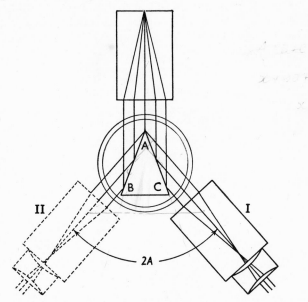

Fig. 6.4.   Arrangement of spectrometer for measurement of the refracting angle of a prism.

Should the slit S be made wider, the student should realize that from each point in the plane of the slit a separate bundle will spread out, each giving rise to its own parallel beam emerging from the collimator lens. It follows, therefore (as is represented in Fig. 6.5), that for each point in the slit, such as S_1 and S_2,

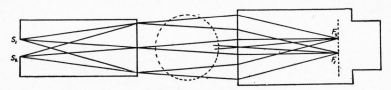

Fig. 6.5.   Points S_1 and S_2 on the slit of a spectrometer give rise to corresponding point images at F_1 and F_2.

there are corresponding point images in the focal plane of the objective, such as F_1 and F_2. In other words, the wider the slit used, the wider is the image observed in the telescope. (Try problem 11 at end of chapter.)

6.3. Dispersion. Suppose, now, instead of using as our source of light a flame colored with common salt and thus giving us a yellow slit image, we change to a flame colored by another salt, lithium chloride, for example. We then observe a *red* image of the slit and one, moreover, in a position not the same as the yellow. On measuring the angle of minimum deviation for this light, we find a value less than that obtained for yellow light. As a result of such observations, we reach the important conclusion that the velocity of red light *in the prism* is more than the velocity of yellow.

If once more we change our source of light, this time to a mercury arc lamp, we now see two yellow slit images: a very bright green, a bright violet, and possibly a few others, all, of course, in different positions. We conclude that the mercury arc emits several different kinds of light, each of which travels in the prism with its own velocity. Moreover, by actual measurement of the value of n for each slit image, we can readily find the corresponding velocity. This collection of slit images for any given source of light constitutes its spectrum. In Plate II and Plate III, facing pp. 96 and 97, respectively, the student will find actual photographs of various spectra.

White Light.   If the slit is illuminated with sunlight (see, however, section 17.5) or by an incandescent lamp, one sees the familiar "rainbow" spectrum with colors ranging continuously from red to violet. This classic experiment, in a slightly different manner, was first performed by Sir Isaac Newton, who drew the important conclusion that "light is not similar or homogeneal but consists of difform rays, some of which are more refrangible than others. . . ." It is perhaps not out of place to state that in the ante-chapel of Trinity College Chapel, Cambridge, England, a life-size statue of Newton represents him holding a prism in his hand.

What now, we ask, physically distinguishes one color from another, or even a slit image in one color from another of the same color but in a slightly different position? If we consider light as a wave phenomenon, the answer is not difficult. Since it is an experimental fact that *in free space* light of all colors travels at the same rate, it follows that differences in color must be due to differences in frequency and in wavelength, one of which is inversely proportional to the other (at constant velocity). We describe a kind of light, therefore, by stating either the frequency giving rise to it, or the resulting wavelength in some standard medium. Light of a particular quality then corresponds to a note in sound. The latter is usually described by giving its frequency but might be described by giving its wavelength in air. In light it is usual to describe the quality in terms of wavelength in air at 15° C and 760 mm pressure, although sometimes frequency is used.

For example, the two yellow slit images in the case of mercury correspond to air wavelengths 0.00005790 cm and 0.00005770 cm; the bright green to 0.00005461 cm; a violet to 0.00004358 cm. Methods of obtaining such values will later be discussed in detail. At this stage it may be pointed out that certain important wavelengths, of which we shall make some use in this chapter, have been designated by letters. A few of these, as well as the luminous substance giving rise to them, are tabulated for reference in Table II.

Table II. Designation of Certain Wavelengths

Designation	Color	Source	Wavelength (A)
A'	red	potassium	7682
A	red	oxygen	7594
C	red	hydrogen	6563
D_1	yellow	sodium	5896
D_2	yellow	sodium	5890
d	yellow	helium	5876
e	green	mercury	5461
F	blue	hydrogen	4861
g	violet	mercury	4358
G	violet	calcium	4308
h	violet	mercury	4047
H	ultraviolet	calcium	3968

The Angstrom. Because of the shortness of light waves the unit of length generally used is the angstrom or 10^{-8} cm. The wavelength of the mercury green line, for example, is usually given as 5461 angstroms, or 5461 A, or sometimes just 5461. The name angstrom is in honor of Ångström (Sweden, 1814–1874), a man who made a chart of the solar spectrum which for a number of years was used as a standard in the measurement of wavelengths. The unit of wavelength adopted by international agreement is called the *international angstrom* (I.A.). For ordinary purposes, there is no objection to defining this in the way we have just done, that is, as 10^{-8} cm, but more accurately it is defined in terms of the wavelength of a red spectral line, emitted by cadmium, in dry air, at 15° C, 760 mm pressure, with $g = 980.67$. This wavelength has been measured with high accuracy, and the value of 6438.4696 I.A. adopted as a standard by the International Astronomical Union. (See, however, section 9.12.)

The student must not fail to realize that, because of the change in velocity when we pass from one medium to another, the wavelength of any given kind of light will also change. In water, for example, the wavelength of the green mercury line is only approximately three-quarters of 5461 A. Even in air wavelengths are not exactly the same as in free space, although for some purposes the difference is so slight that we may neglect it. This change in wavelength with changing medium, for a given quality of light, must not be confused with the dispersion of a medium. *The dispersion of a medium refers to the change in velocity in that medium when we change the kind of light, or, as we may now more accurately state it, when we change the wavelength.* Because of this change in velocity, we have the difference in deviation already noted. Indeed, sometimes

dispersion is thought of as the change in deviation resulting from changing wavelength. If a prism is set in a fixed position, the deviation measured for a series
of wavelengths, and a graph made by plotting deviation against dispersion, we
obtain what may loosely be called a dispersion curve for that prism.   More
accurately, however, a dispersion curve for any substance is obtained by plotting
the index of refraction against the wavelength.   Fig. 6.6 is a graph obtained by
making use of data for the crown glass given in Table III.

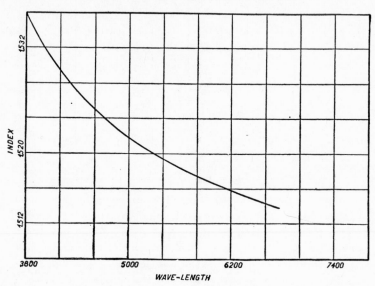

Fig. 6.6.   A typical dispersion curve for a transparent medium like glass.

As an exact measure of the dispersion of a medium, we use the value of
$dn/d\lambda$, which, it will be seen, is just a measure of the slope of the graph at any
given point.   The student should also note that the dispersion is greater in the
region of the shorter wavelengths at the violet end of the spectrum than at the
red end.   (Examine again Fig. 6.6.)

Table III.   Refractive Indices for Certain Materials
(from Kaye and Laby tables)

Wavelength (A)	Light Jena Crown Glass (15° C)	Dense Jena Flint Glass (15° C)	Rock Salt (18° C)	Water (20° C)
6708	1.5140	1.6434	1.5400	1.3308
6563	1.5145	1.6444	1.5407	1.3311
5893	1.5170	1.6499	1.5443	1.3330
5461	1.5191	1.6546	1.5475	1.3345
4861	1.5230	1.6637	1.5534	1.3371
4047	1.5318	1.6852	1.5665	1.3428

Dispersion Formulae.   The graph of Fig. 6.6 illustrates a case of *normal* dispersion as distinguished from anomalous dispersion, a question which will be considered in a later chapter.   This graph may be represented mathematically by simple empirical relations, two of which will be noted.   According to the first, due to Cauchy, we write

$$n = A + \frac{B}{\lambda^2},^*$$ (6.05)

where A and B are constants for any given medium.   For example, for a certain kind of glass, $A = 1.616$, $B = 0.100 \times 10^{-9}$, and we therefore, to a fair degree of accuracy, may, at once calculate the value of n for any wavelength.

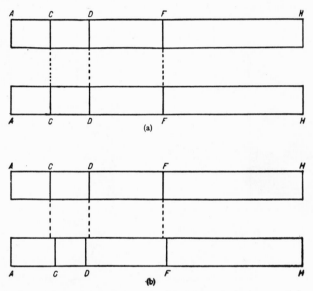

Fig. 6.7.   The pair of corresponding spectral lines in (b) illustrate irrational dispersion.   Compare with the upper pair.

By simple differentiation, we have from relation (6.05)

$$\frac{dn}{d\lambda} = -\frac{2B}{\lambda^3}.$$ (6.06)

In the case of the glass whose constants have been given, for G light, $dn/d\lambda = -2500$.   (What is the significance of the minus sign?)

A second dispersion formula, which is useful if not applied to too great a range of wavelengths, is the following due to Hartmann:

* More accurately $n = A + \frac{B}{\lambda^2} + \frac{C}{\lambda^4} + \cdots$ but for many purposes relation (6.05) is sufficiently accurate.

$$n = n_0 + \frac{c}{\lambda - \lambda_0}. \qquad (6.07)$$

To take another concrete example, for a certain glass,

$$n_0 = 1.58882; \quad \lambda_0 = 2.2906 \times 10^{-5}; \quad c = 0.10113 \times 10^{-5}.$$

6.4. Irrational Dispersion. Suppose prisms of two different substances are chosen with refracting angles such that the angular separation between spectral lines A and H is exactly the same for each. It might then be expected that the angular separation between A and some intermediate wavelength such as F would also be the same in the spectrum produced by each prism—as represented in Fig. 6.7(a). As a matter of fact this is not the case, the actual state of affairs being somewhat as represented in Fig. 6.7(b). It will be noted that intermediate spectral lines do not occupy exactly corresponding positions; that is, one spectrum is not an exact duplicate of the other. This feature of prismatic spectra is what is known as *irrational dispersion*. While the magnitude of the effect is not great, it is important, and the student should note carefully the numerical example given in Table IV. Here the numbers give the angular separations in minutes between A light and each of four other wavelengths, for two different kinds of glass prisms so chosen that the angular width between A and H lines is the same for each.

Table IV.   Angular Width between A Line and each of C, D, F, and H, for Two Prisms

	A	C	D	F	H
Crown glass........	0	1.8	3.6	7.2	13.8
Flint glass.........	0	1.9	3.45	7.3	13.8

6.5. Spectrometer, Spectroscope, Spectrograph. From the brief description of the essential features of a spectrometer, it should not be difficult to see that, in addition to its use for the measurement of refractive indices, it is also of use in observing a spectrum, that is, the various wavelengths emitted by a source

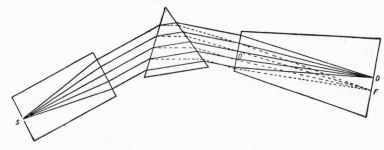

Fig. 6.8.   Ray paths in a prism spectrograph for two wavelengths D and F.

of light.   An instrument specially designed for such visual observation is called a *spectroscope*.

It is frequently desirable to have a permanent record of the spectrum of a source, in which case a *spectrograph* is used.   In a prism spectrograph essentially all that is done is to remove the eyepiece of the telescope and to place a photographic plate in the focal plane of the objective lens.   Fig. 6.8 shows the arrangement of such an instrument, while the following problem should make clear some of the fundamental ideas better than detailed description.

A 60° flint glass prism, having an index = 1.6222 for D light, and = 1.6320 for F light, is set in the position of minimum deviation for D light.   (a) When the incident light consists of a beam of parallel rays, find the angular separation between the emergent D and F beams.   (b) If the emergent light is focused on a screen (or camera plate) by an achromatic lens of focal length 60 cm, find the linear distance (or length of spectrum) between the D and the F images.

Part (*a*).

Since the deviation is a minimum for *D* light, therefore, for this light,

$$r_1 = r_2 = 30°,$$

$$\therefore \quad \frac{\sin i_1}{\sin 30°} = 1.6222,$$

from which $\qquad\qquad i_1 = 54° \ 12'.$

$\therefore$ for *D* light $\qquad\qquad i_2 = 54° \ 12'.$

To find i_2 for *F* light, it must be remembered that for this wavelength, the prism is not in the position of least deviation (although very approximately so). We must, therefore, deal with refraction at each surface separately.

At the first surface, since i_1 is the same for all wavelengths,

$$i_1 = 54° \ 12'$$

$$\therefore \quad \frac{\sin 54° \ 12'}{\sin r_1} = 1.6320,$$

from which $\qquad\qquad r_1 = 29° \ 48'.$

But $\qquad\qquad\qquad r_1 + r_2 = 60°,$

$$\therefore \qquad\qquad r_2 = 30° \ 12'.$$

Finally, since $\qquad \dfrac{\sin i_2}{\sin 30° \ 12'} = 1.6320,$

$$\therefore \qquad\qquad i_2 = 55° \ 11'.$$

Therefore, the required angular separation between the *F* and *D* images

$$= 55° \ 11' - 54° \ 12' = 59',$$

Part (*b*).

Referring to Fig. 6.8, we see at once that if D represent the D image of the slit, F the F image,

$$\angle FOD = 59'.$$

Since this is a small angle, we can put $OF = OD = 60$ cm, and write

$$FD = 60 \tan 59'$$
or
$$= 60 \sin 59'$$
or
$$= 60 \cdot (\text{angle } FOD \text{ in radians})$$
$$= 1.03 \text{ cm}.$$

6.6. Dispersion of an Instrument. Sometimes the word dispersion has reference to the separation of any two wavelengths produced by an instrument, and in that case is measured by the magnitude of $d\theta/d\lambda$. For example, if $\theta_1 = $ deviation of wavelength λ_1, and $\theta_2 = $ deviation of wavelength λ_2, then the quantity $(\theta_2 - \theta_1)/(\lambda_2 - \lambda_1)$ is a measure of the average dispersion in the region λ_1 to λ_2, provided the wavelengths are fairly close together. In the limit, when λ_2 differs from λ_1 by a small amount, this expression becomes $d\theta/d\lambda$. Its actual magnitude, which may be expressed in such units as radians per centimeter, degrees per centimeter, radians per angstrom, obviously depends on (*a*) the refracting angle of the prism and (*b*) the material of which the prism is made, that is, the dispersion of the medium. As the solution of the foregoing problem shows, the linear separation between any two images also depends on the focal length of the camera lens.

Sometimes the dispersion of an instrument is also expressed in terms of the number of angstroms corresponding to a distance of 1 mm on the photographic plate. In the preceding problem, for example, we can state that in the region between the F and D lines, the average dispersion is

$$\frac{5893 - 4861}{10.3}, \text{ or } 100 \text{ A per mm.}$$

6.7. Achromatism. From the general fact of dispersion, as well as from the standard lens relation $\frac{1}{f} = (n - 1)\left(\frac{1}{r_1} - \frac{1}{r_2}\right)$, it follows that the focal length of a lens varies with the wavelength. For example, if we are dealing with a double convex crown glass with each face of 20 cm radius, and with indices as given in Table III, the student can readily verify that the focal length for wavelength 6708 A is 19.46 cm, while for wavelength 4047 A it is 18.80 cm. This variation of the focal length because of dispersion is called *chromatic aberration*. Its existence may be nicely shown by the arrangement of Fig. 6.9, where light from a small white source S falls on a lens of tolerably wide aperture and is received on a ground glass screen, first in position A, then in position B. In the former case the outer edge of the spot on the ground glass is reddish; in the latter, blue or violet.

The term *axial chromatism* is used when the *position* of an image along the axis varies with the wavelength; *lateral chromatism,* when the *dimensions* of the image vary. When using a thick lens or a combination of lenses, it is possible to correct so that the axial position of the image is the same for all wavelengths, and yet to have lateral achromatism. In a thin lens this difficulty does not arise, and in our treatment of the means of making an *achromatic* lens we shall restrict ourselves to thin lenses. Consider first the problem of making an achromatic pair of prisms.

If two prisms, each of the same refracting angle, one of crown glass, the other of flint, are used to project the spectrum of a source of white light on a screen, two things are observed. (*a*) As might be expected, because of the higher re-

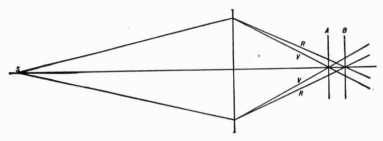

Fig. 6.9. Chromatic aberration. *A* is focal plane for violet light; *B* for red.

fractive index, the average deviation is greater in the case of the flint than of the crown glass. (*b*) The total length of spectrum is considerably greater for the flint than for the crown glass prism. To make the matter concrete, consider two 10° prisms with indices as given in Table III. Then, using the simple relation $D = (n - 1)A$, we have, for crown glass,

$$D, \text{ for } \lambda 6708 = (1.5140 - 1)10° = 5.14°,$$
$$D, \text{ for } \lambda 4047 = (1.5318 - 1)10° = 5.318°.$$

Therefore, the angular width between these two wavelengths = 0.178°. Similarly, for flint glass,

$$D, \text{ for } \lambda 6708 = (1.6434 - 1)10° = 6.434°,$$
$$D, \text{ for } \lambda 4047 = (1.6852 - 1)10° = 6.852°.$$

and angular width between the same two wavelengths = 0.418°.

We see, then, that the length of the spectrum due to the flint glass prism is over twice as great as that due to the crown, although the deviation of any one color is only slightly greater in the case of the flint. Flint glass, therefore, is said to have a greater dispersive power than crown glass. By comparing different transparent substances in this way, marked differences are found in dispersive powers.

Because of this fact, it is possible to choose a combination of two different kinds of prisms so that one counteracts the dispersion of the other, while a resultant deviation remains. We then have an *achromatic combination* of two prisms, giving deviation without dispersion. Again, a concrete numerical example will make the point clearer.

PROBLEM. *Using the constants given in Table III, find the angle of a flint glass prism which gives the same length of spectrum between C and F wavelengths as a 10° crown glass prism.*

Since $D_C = (n_C - 1)A$, where the subscript indicates the wavelength, we have, for crown glass, $D_F - D_C = (n_F - n_C)A$

$$= (1.5230 - 1.5145)10°$$
$$= 0.085°.$$

Also for flint glass, $D_F - D_C = (1.6637 - 1.6444)A$

$$= 0.0193°A.$$
$$\therefore \quad 0.0193°A = 0.085$$

or
$$A = 4.40°.$$

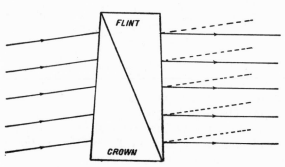

Fig. 6.10. An achromatic pair of prisms, giving deviation without dispersion.

If, then, these two prisms are placed together as in Fig. 6.10, it follows that one prism will counteract the dispersion of the other, while, because of the much smaller refracting angle of the higher dispersive flint prism, there will be a resultant deviation in the same direction as that due to the crown.

To find the resultant deviation, we have at once,

net deviation of C light $= (1.5145 - 1)10 - (1.6444 - 1)4.40 = 2.31°$
net deviation of F light $= (1.5230 - 1)10 - (1.6637 - 1)4.40 = 2.31°$
net deviation of D light $= (1.5170 - 1)10 - (1.6499 - 1)4.40 = 2.31°$

In making achromatic combinations for visual purposes usually C and F wavelengths are used. To a first approximation, it does not matter what two wavelengths are used, but because of irrational dispersion, slight differences in the refracting angles may be found for different pairs of wavelengths. Irrational dispersion is also responsible for the fact that a combination of two prisms may not be *perfectly* achromatic for every wavelength in the spectrum. The achromatism may be made more perfect by using three different prisms and three wavelengths.

6.8. Achromatic Lens. The same principle is applied to lenses. Thus, if a converging crown lens is combined with a diverging flint of higher dispersive power, dispersion of the first lens can be counteracted by the second and a resultant converging lens obtained with focal length the same for all colors.

In dealing with this question quantitatively it is well to note the following:
(a) When two thin lenses are in contact, if

f_1 = focal length of the first, for any wavelength,
f_2 = focal length of the second, for the same wavelength,

then F the resultant focal length is given by

$$\frac{1}{F} = \frac{1}{f_1} + \frac{1}{f_2}. \tag{6.08}$$

(b) The condition for achromatism, using C and F wavelengths, gives at once

$$F_C = F_F. \tag{6.09}$$

Bearing these relations in mind, as well as the standard lens relation

$$\frac{1}{f} = (n-1)\left(\frac{1}{r_1} - \frac{1}{r_2}\right),$$

any ordinary achromatic lens problem may readily be solved. One example will be given.

PROBLEM. *A converging crown glass lens and a diverging flint form a converging achromatic lens of focal length 50 cm. Using the indices given in Table III, find the focal length of each lens for C, D, and F light.*

We are given

$$F_C = F_F = +50,$$

$$\therefore \quad +\frac{1}{50} = \frac{1}{f_1} + \frac{1}{f_2} \text{ for any wavelength.}$$

Therefore, using C light,

$$+\frac{1}{50} = (1.5145 - 1)\left(\frac{1}{r_1} - \frac{1}{r_2}\right) + (1.6444 - 1)\left(\frac{1}{r_3} - \frac{1}{r_4}\right),$$

and using F light

$$+\frac{1}{50} = (1.5230 - 1)\left(\frac{1}{r_1} - \frac{1}{r_2}\right) + (1.6637 - 1)\left(\frac{1}{r_3} - \frac{1}{r_4}\right),$$

where r_1, r_2 are radii of curvature of faces of crown lens and r_3, r_4 are radii of curvature of faces of flint lens.

Putting $\qquad \left(\dfrac{1}{r_1} - \dfrac{1}{r_2}\right) = x,$ and $\left(\dfrac{1}{r_3} - \dfrac{1}{r_4}\right) = y,$

we have the two equations

$$+\frac{1}{50} = 0.5145x + 0.6444y,$$

$$+\frac{1}{50} = 0.5230x + 0.6637y,$$

from which $\qquad x = +0.08773, \quad y = -0.03863.$

Finally, for the crown glass lens, we have

$$\frac{1}{f_C} = 0.5145 \times 0.08773, \quad \text{or} \quad f_C = +22.16 \text{ cm},$$

$$\frac{1}{f_D} = 0.5170 \times 0.08773, \quad \text{or} \quad f_D = +22.05 \text{ cm},$$

$$\frac{1}{f_F} = 0.5230 \times 0.08773, \quad \text{or} \quad f_F = +21.79 \text{ cm},$$

while, for the flint lens,

$$\frac{1}{f_C} = 0.6444 \times (-0.03863) \quad \text{or} \quad f_C = -40.2 \text{ cm},$$

$$\frac{1}{f_D} = 0.6499 \times (-0.03863) \quad \text{or} \quad f_D = -39.8 \text{ cm},$$

$$\frac{1}{f_F} = 0.6637 \times (-0.03863) \quad \text{or} \quad f_F = -39.0 \text{ cm}.$$

6.9. Measure of Dispersive Power. Achromatic lens problems are sometimes solved by making use of a numerical measure of dispersive power. What such a measure is obviously must be a matter of definition. Since, in the case of a prism, the actual length of a spectrum depends on the material of which it is made, and moreover increases as the refracting angle is increased (or as the mean deviation is increased), it is agreed to measure the dispersive power, usually represented by ω, by the angular width between C and F wavelengths, per unit angle of mean deviation. In symbols,

$$\omega = \frac{D_F - D_C}{D_D}, \tag{6.10}$$

the mean deviation being taken as that of D light, intermediate between C and F.

By using the relation giving the deviation for small-angled prisms, this may be written

$$\omega = \frac{(n_F - 1)A - (n_C - 1)A}{(n_D - 1)A}$$

$$= \frac{n_F - n_C}{n_D - 1}. \tag{6.11}$$

It will be seen that this expression, involving only indices, is a function of the medium alone, and, therefore, is a suitable general measure of dispersive power.

6.10. General Condition for an Achromatic Combination of Two Lenses. Making use of notation which now should need no explanation, we have, for C light, and two lenses in contact,

$$\frac{1}{F_C} = (n_{1C} - 1)\left(\frac{1}{r_1} - \frac{1}{r_2}\right) + (n_{2C} - 1)\left(\frac{1}{r_3} - \frac{1}{r_4}\right).$$

Also for F light:

$$\frac{1}{F_F} = (n_{1F} - 1)\left(\frac{1}{r_1} - \frac{1}{r_2}\right) + (n_{2F} - 1)\left(\frac{1}{r_3} - \frac{1}{r_4}\right).$$

Since $F_C = F_F$,

$$(n_{1F} - n_{1C})\left(\frac{1}{r_1} - \frac{1}{r_2}\right) + (n_{2F} - n_{2C})\left(\frac{1}{r_3} - \frac{1}{r_4}\right) = 0.$$

$$\therefore \quad \frac{(n_{1F} - n_{1C})}{(n_{1D} - 1)}(n_{1D} - 1)\left(\frac{1}{r_1} - \frac{1}{r_2}\right) + \frac{(n_{2F} - n_{2C})}{(n_{2D} - 1)}(n_{2D} - 1)\left(\frac{1}{r_3} - \frac{1}{r_4}\right) = 0.$$

$$\therefore \quad \frac{\omega_1}{f_1} + \frac{\omega_2}{f_2} = 0, \tag{6.12}$$

where f_1 and f_2 represent the mean focal lengths, that is, for wavelength D, of the lenses.

Problems dealing with achromatic lenses are frequently solved using this general condition, but, in the writer's opinion, it is preferable to use the more fundamental method illustrated in the solution of the above problem.

6.11. Direct Vision Spectroscope. It is sometimes convenient to have a spectroscope which gives a spectrum with but little deviation—indeed, for one wavelength, with no deviation at all. This can be done by a proper choice of two or more (generally more) prisms. The problem is a very simple one, for, taking the case of two prisms as an example, all that is necessary is to choose the refracting angles so that the resultant deviation is zero for some wavelength about the middle of the spectrum. Red light is then deviated a little to one side of the direction of the incident light, violet to the other. A numerical example will be found in problem 14 at the end of this chapter.

PROBLEMS

Note: Unless otherwise stated, use the following indices in the solution of the problems in this exercise.

	A	C	D	F	H
Crown glass	1.5035	1.5062	1.5086	1.5144	1.5194
Flint glass	1.6102	1.6154	1.6202	1.6324	1.6436

1. A 40° crown glass prism is set in the position of minimum deviation for F light. Find: (a) the angle of incidence of the light striking the first face of the prism; (b) the deviation; (c) with the position of the prism unchanged, the deviation for A light.

2. Find the deviation when parallel rays of D light are incident on a 60° flint glass prism at an angle of 45°. (Note that the prism is *not* in the position of least deviation.)

3. Plot the indices given at the beginning of this set of problems, for flint glass, against the wavelengths of A, C, D, F, H light. From the slope of the graph, find the value of the dispersion $(dn/d\lambda)$ of the glass at 6000 A.

4. Check your answer in problem 3 by using 2 points on the graph to find the value of the constant B in Cauchy's dispersion formula and then evaluating $dn/d\lambda$, using relation 6.06.

5. The slit of a spectrometer adjusted in the usual manner is illuminated by a source emitting light of two wavelengths λ_1 and λ_2. The light emerging from the collimator falls on a prism set in the position of minimum deviation for λ_1 and the light leaving the prism is observed in a telescope. The deviation for λ_2 is 2° more than for λ_1.

(a) Make a *careful* diagram, showing the paths through the whole instrument of the bundles of rays which give rise to the two images observed. Assume that final images are at infinity.

(b) If the focal length of the objective of the telescope is 20 cm and the focal length of the eye lens 4 cm, find: (i) the angular separation of the final images; (ii) the linear separation in the focal plane of the objective.

6. Make a complete diagram of the optical system of a spectrograph. Trace the path of bundles of rays corresponding to two different wavelengths, and use your diagram to show how you could calculate the linear length of the spectrum included between these two wavelengths.

7. The narrow slit in the collimator of a spectrograph having a single 60° flint glass prism is illuminated with a mixture of C and H light, and the prism is set in the position of least deviation for C light. Find the distance between the C and H images on the camera plate of the spectrograph, if the focal length of its focusing lens is 50 cm.

8. A spectrometer is adjusted with a very narrow slit so that parallel rays leave the collimating lens and are incident at a small angle on the face of a 10° glass prism. The refracted light is observed in the focal plane of an objective lens of focal length 60 cm.

(a) If the light contains only two wavelengths, find the linear separation of the two images observed in the focal plane of the objective lens, given that the difference in the indices of refraction of the prism for these wavelengths is 0.003.

(b) If these two images are viewed through an eye lens of focal length 4 cm, placed so that the final images are at infinity, find the angular separation of the final images.

9. A beam of parallel rays, composed of C and F light, is incident (at a small angle) on one face of a small-angled flint prism. When the emergent light is focused on a screen by a lens of focal length 500 mm, the distance apart of the C and the F images is 0.725 mm. Find the angle of the prism.

10. A parallel beam containing light of two wavelengths λ_1 and λ_2 falls on a 45° prism placed in the position of minimum deviation for λ_1. When the emergent light is focused on a screen by a lens of focal length 60 cm, the linear distance between the two images is 2.62 cm. Find the total deviation for λ_2. $(\lambda_2 < \lambda_1)$ (Index for $\lambda_1 = 1.608$; for λ_2, not given.)

11. A spectrograph is provided with two narrow slits 1 mm apart. If the focal length of the collimating lens is 20 cm, that of the camera lens 30 cm, find the distance apart of the two images in the focal plane of the camera lens.

12. Given a flint glass prism of angle 5°, find approximately the angle of a crown glass prism which in combination with a flint gives deviation without dispersion. Find also the deviation. Use C and F light.

13. (a) What is the angle of a prism of heavy flint glass that will achromatize an 8° crown glass prism for the C and F lines?

(b) Achromatize the same combination for A and H lines. Account for the difference in the result, if any.

14. A beam of parallel rays of white light falls on a combination of two prisms, one of flint glass of angle 6°, the other of crown glass. The combination is so chosen that light of wavelength 5461 A is undeviated. (a) By plotting the indices at the beginning of this set of problems against wavelength, find the index of each prism for 5461. (Read off values directly from the graphs, or, alternately, find the values of the constants A and B in Cauchy's dispersion formula.) (b) Find the angle of the crown glass prism. (c) Find the angular width of the spectrum produced by the combination, between C and F wavelengths.

15. A small-angled crown glass prism forms an achromatic combination (C and F light) with a flint glass prism, the resultant deviation being 3°. Find the refracting angles of the two prisms.

16. A converging and a diverging lens, of different materials, form an achromatic combination. If the combination is to be converging, which lens must have the greater dispersive power? Explain.

17. A converging crown lens, whose focal length for C light is 20 cm, and a diverging flint lens form an achromatic combination of focal length 60 cm. (a) Find the focal length for C light of the diverging lens. (b) If the crown lens is double convex, with each of its surfaces having a radius of curvature equal to 20 cm, find the index of refraction of this lens for C light.

18. An achromatic lens consists of a converging crown lens and a diverging flint. The crown lens has a focal length of 20.0 cm for C light and of 19.6 cm for F light; and the flint lens has a focal length of 40.0 for C light. Find the focal length of the flint lens for F light.

19. A converging crown and a diverging flint lens in contact form an achromatic combination of focal length $+$ 60 cm. Find the focal length of each lens for C and for F light.

20. A converging crown and a diverging flint lens in contact form an achromatic combination. If the focal length of the crown lens for C light is 24.00 cm, find the focal length of the combination.

21. A converging crown lens and a diverging flint lens, having a common surface of radius of curvature 30 cm, form an achromatic converging combination (C and F light) of focal length 60 cm. Find the radius of curvature of each of the other faces of the two lenses.

22. It is desired to make an achromatic lens (for C and F light), of focal length 80 cm, by means of a convex crown glass lens combined with a plano-concave flint, the two surfaces in contact having the same radius of curvature. Calculate the necessary radii of curvature of the surfaces of the crown glass lens, if the combination is converging. (Use given indices.)

23. When a double convex crown glass converging lens, each of whose faces has the same curvature, is placed in contact with a diverging flint lens whose focal length for D light is 60 cm, the focal length of the combination for D light is 30 cm. If the index of the crown lens for D light is 1.5086, find the radius of curvature of each of its faces.

24. Find the dispersive powers of the crown and the flint glass whose indices are given at the beginning of this set of problems. Use C, D, and F light.

25. A lens has a focal length of 19.44 cm for C light, of 19.35 cm for D light, and of 19.12 cm for F light. Find the dispersive power of the material of which it is composed.

26. A flint glass lens, made of material whose indices are given at the beginning of this set of problems, has a focal length of 20.00 cm for D light. Find its focal length for C and for F light.

27. Parallel rays of white light fall on a double convex converging lens, of aperture 2 cm, whose index for A light is 1.6102 and for F light 1.6324. If a screen is placed normal to the emergent light at a distance from the lens equal to its focal length for F light, find the radius of the patch of light received on the screen. Take radius of curvature of each face of the lens to be 20 cm, and neglect spherical aberration.

28. In the case of a small-angled prism, prove that the rate at which the deviation varies with the wavelength is equal to the angle of the prism multiplied by the rate at which the index of refraction of the prism varies with the wavelength.

29. Prove that, whether the deviation is a minimum or not, provided all angles involved are small,

deviation $= (n - 1)\, A$, where A is the angle of the prism.

30. A spectrometer whose collimator lens (adjusted in the standard way) has a focal length of 20 cm is equipped with two very narrow slits illuminated with monochromatic light, whose centers are 1.746 mm apart. A 60° prism whose index of refraction for this kind of light is 1.6316 is set in the position of least deviation *for one of the two beams*, and the emergent light is photographed in the focal plane of a lens of focal length 60 cm. Find the linear separation of the two images.

VII

Study of Wave Motion

7.1. We shall begin our study of wave motion by considering what may be learned from ordinary water waves with which every student is familiar. An observer sitting beside the shore of a lake and watching waves on its surface cannot fail to be struck with two things: (1) a floating object, such as a block of wood, executes a to and fro motion without altering appreciably its distance from the shore; (2) at any given instant, crests (places at each one of which the surface is displaced above its normal position a maximum amount) and troughs (places were the displacement is a maximum below the normal level) are repeated at regular intervals. If the observer wished to express these facts in more mathematical language, he might proceed, first of all, by taking an imaginary line along which the waves are traveling. He could then define the position of a particle at any instant by giving (1) its distance x from some point of reference on his imaginary line (such as a stake in the water); and (2) the amount y the particle is displaced from its normal position. With changing time, y would alternate between a maximum plus value (at a crest) and a maximum minus value (at a trough). Our observer would then be able to restate his observations as follows:

(1) When x is constant, y is a periodic function of the time, or
$$y = \text{periodic } f\,(t), \; x \text{ constant, and}$$
(2) when t is constant, y is a periodic function of x, or
$$y = \text{periodic } f\,(x), \; t \text{ constant.}$$

These two statements, which presently we shall combine into one, give the fundamental characteristics of a train of waves. They tell us that the same to and fro motion is handed on from particle to particle in the medium along which the disturbance is traveling.

At any instant, two particles whose times of vibration differ by an integral multiple of the periodic time are said to be in the same phase. Two consecutive particles in the same phase are separated by a *wavelength*.

7-2. The Cause of a Train of Waves. Particles cannot be set vibrating in this manner without a cause. We must somewhere have a vibrating source. If, for example, we wish to send waves along a cord under tension, we first of all pluck aside a portion at one end. On releasing the cord the *restoring force* due to the component of the tension at right angles to the cord quickly brings the displaced portion back to its normal position. Because of its momentum, however, it does not remain there but overshoots the mark until a displacement is caused in the opposite direction. Once more the restoring force brings the displaced portion back, and so a to and fro motion is set up. A vibrating source has then resulted from the initial displacement. Generally speaking, this will be the case whenever a particle of finite mass, when displaced from its normal position, brings into play a sufficiently large restoring force.

The student will recall other examples. When a stone is thrown into a pond, a certain amount of water is displaced from its normal position, the restoring force of gravity is brought into play, and we have a vibrating source from which ordinary water waves spread out. If the displacement is very slight, the restoring force is largely the result of surface tension and we have the tiny waves called ripples. To have sound waves in air, by some means (*e.g.* a vibrating tuning fork) the air particles must be displaced from their normal position, thus bringing into play the restoring force of the elasticity of the air.

In this connection one further point should be noted. The restoring force which comes into play on displacement of a portion of a medium is the result of some sort of elastic connection between contiguous particles of the medium. For that reason a single particle cannot be displaced without some displacement of its immediate neighbor. It follows, therefore, since the displacement of any particle calls into play restoring forces, that the motion of a vibrating source is going to be passed on from particle to particle, thus constituting a wave motion.

7.3. A simple quantitative example may not here be out of place.

A source particle executing a periodic motion defined by $y = 6 \sin \pi t$ sends out waves which travel through a homogeneous medium at the rate of 6 cm per second. Find the displacement of a second particle 80 cm from the source one minute after the source began to vibrate. (Assume the medium of one dimension like a stretched cord.)

Solution: Since the wave disturbance travels at the rate of 6 cm per sec, the second particle will not begin to vibrate until 80/6 or 13.3 sec after the source.

Therefore, since $y = 6 \sin \pi t$ defines the motion of the source, and since in simple wave motion each particle executes the same to and fro motion,

$$y = 6 \sin \pi \left(t - \frac{80}{6} \right)$$

defines the motion of the second particle.

Hence, when $t = 60$ sec, the displacement of the second will be given by

$$y = 6 \sin \pi \left(60 - \frac{80}{6} \right)$$

$$= 5.2 \text{ cm.}$$

This solution neglects a change of amplitude with increasing distance from the source, a question considered in section 7.18.

7.4. The Fundamental Wave Equation. The student is asked to refer to the explanation of wave-fronts given in section 3.1, and, in particular, to Fig. 3.1. A consideration of the diagrams in that figure should make it clear that, during the time of one vibration, the wave disturbance travels a distance equal to one wavelength; during two complete vibrations, two wavelengths, and so on. In general, if

$$\lambda = \text{wavelength},$$
$$V = \text{velocity of wave disturbance},$$
$$T = \text{periodic time},$$

it follows that $\qquad \lambda = VT.$ $\hfill (7.01)$

This important relation is sometimes expressed in another form by substituting for T in terms of ν, the *frequency*, that is, the number of vibrations per second. Since $\nu = 1/T$, relation (1) becomes

$$V = \nu\lambda. \hfill (7.02)$$

7.5. The Form of a Train of Waves. A curve passing through all the particles at any given instant represents the *wave form*, which, therefore, in the case of a source executing the simple periodic motion we have assumed, is approxi-

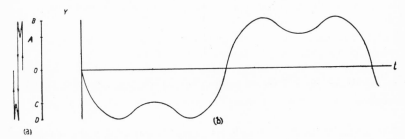

Fig. 7.1.   Wave form of a disturbance caused by a source executing the periodic motion shown on extreme left.

mately represented in Fig. 3.1, diagrams (d) and (e). If we had assumed a different kind of motion for the source, the wave form would have been different. For example, if a complete vibration of the end particle had consisted of a motion from O to A to B, B back to A, A to B through O to D, D to C, C back to D, D through O, somewhat as shown in Fig. 7.1(a), the student can verify for himself that the wave form would be as illustrated in Fig. 7.1(b). In general, the wave form depends on the nature of the vibration of a single particle, complex wave forms corresponding to complex periodic motions of individual particles. It will be seen presently, however, that the most complicated vibrations can be built up by combining a number of simple to and fro motions of the type we have first considered. It is highly important, therefore, to study in detail this special periodic motion, which is called Simple Harmonic (S.H.M.).

7.6. Simple Harmonic Motion. First of all, let us define, with reference to Fig. 7.2, exactly what is meant by S.H.M. When a particle P moves around a circle with uniform velocity, the to and fro motion of the projection of P on any diameter is called a Simple Harmonic Motion. Thus, as P moves around the circle, the point M executes a S.H.M. along the line YOY', the point N along the line XOX', and so for any diameter.* It is important for the student to guard against confusing the motion of the particle P in what is called the *circle*

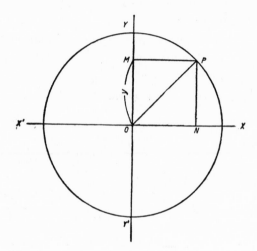

Fig. 7.2. Diagram used for deriving the equation of a S.H.M. when, at $t = 0$, the phase angle is zero.

of reference, with the S.H.M. which is a *linear* motion. A good example of the latter is found in the vibratory motion of a mass at the end of a spring.

Consider now the S.H.M. of the point M along the diameter YOY'. It moves about a mean position O, having a maximum displacement, equal to OY or OY', called the *amplitude* of the motion. Suppose, after t sec, it has moved from its normal position at O until its displacement $y = OM$. The corresponding particle in the circle of reference in the same time has moved from X to P, the radius having swept out the angle POX.

---

* S.H.M. may also be defined as the motion of a particle in a straight line when it moves with reference to a centre of attraction subject to the law that the acceleration is proportional to the displacement, and of opposite sign. It is left as an exercise in mechanics, for the student to prove that the two definitions mean essentially the same thing.

Then, we have,

$$y = OP \sin OPM$$
$$= a \sin POX$$
$$= a \sin \omega t, \qquad (7.03)$$

where ω = angular velocity of the particle in the circle of reference, in radians per second. Frequently the displacement is expressed in terms of T the periodic time. Since the radius sweeps out a complete revolution or 2π radians in T sec, we have at once

$$\omega = \frac{2\pi}{T},$$

and relation (7.03) becomes

$$y = a \sin \frac{2\pi t}{T}. \qquad (7.04)$$

Equation (7.04) is the definition of a S.H.M. in mathematical language. By means of it we can calculate the displacement, at any time t, of a particle executing a S.H.M. of amplitude a and period T, provided the particle is in its normal position at the beginning of the time considered. Note again that this relation has reference to a linear motion.

7.7. Graphical Representation of a S.H.M. It is frequently convenient to plot a graph of equation (7.04), that is, a curve from which we can read off the displacement at any instant. This can be done in two ways.

(1) By giving t successive values, calculating corresponding values of y, and plotting y against t. In Table V this has been done for $T = 12$, $a = 10$.

Table V.

t	$\dfrac{2\pi t}{12}$	$10 \sin \dfrac{2\pi t}{12}$
0	0°	0
1	30°	5
2	60°	8.6
3	90°	10
4	120°	8.6
5	150°	5
6	180°	0
7	210°	−5
8	240°	−8.6
9	270°	−10
10	300°	−8.6
11	330°	−5
12	360°	0
13	390°	5

The resulting curve is plotted in Fig. 7.3. It will readily be seen that, instead of using particular values of T and of a, we might give t values such as $T/12$, $2T/12$, $3T/12$, etc. In the graph, accordingly, we have represented the time and the displacement in this more general way, as well as using the particular values of Table V.

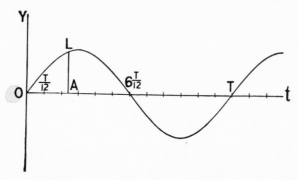

Fig. 7.3. Graph representing the S.H.M. of a single particle, displacement plotted against time.

(2) Since the particle in the circle of reference moves with uniform velocity, equal arcs on this circle represent equal time intervals. If we subdivide the circle of reference into 12 equal parts, for example, as in Fig. 7.4, we can find by dropping perpendiculars on the diameter YOY', the positions of the particle

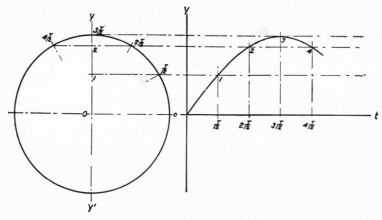

Fig. 7.4. Diagram for explaining one method of plotting the graph representing a S.H.M.

executing a S.H.M. along this line, after successive equal time intervals. Thus, if the S.H.M. particle is at O at the beginning of the time, after $T/12$ sec, it is at 1, after $2T/12$ at 2, and so on. Hence, by taking as our time axis an extension of the perpendicular through O, and marking on it any equal distances to represent these equal time intervals, we can locate points on the curve we desire by extending the perpendiculars through the corresponding positions of the S.H.M. particle after the manner illustrated in Fig. 7.4. The complete curve, of course, will be exactly the same as that obtained by the other method.

The student must be careful not to confuse this curve with that representing a wave form at any instant, as in (d) and (e), Fig. 3.1. Fig. 7.3 is simply a graph illustrating the to and fro motion of a single particle. From it we may read off the displacement at any instant. For example, when the time is equal to that represented by OA, the displacement is represented by AL.

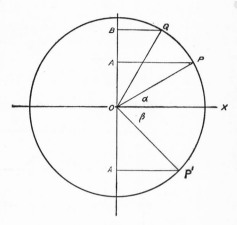

Fig. 7.5. Diagram used to derive the equation of a S.H.M. when, at t = 0, the phase angle is not zero.

7.8. More General Equation of a S.H.M. Equation (7.04) is true for a particle which is in its normal position when $t = 0$. This, however, is not necessarily the case, for we may measure the time from any starting point. Suppose, for example, that, when $t = 0$, the S.H.M. particle is at A (Fig. 7.5), after t sec at B, the corresponding positions of the particle in the circle of reference being P and Q. Then, proceeding as before, we have, at the time t,

$$y = OB = a \sin BQO$$

$$= a \sin QOX$$

$$= a \sin (POQ + POX)$$

$$= a \sin (\omega t + \alpha), \text{ where } \alpha = \angle POX$$

$$= a \sin \left(\frac{2\pi t}{T} + \alpha\right). \tag{7.05a}$$

Similarly, if when $t = 0$, the S.H.M. particle was at A', we can deduce,

$$y = a \sin \left(\frac{2\pi t}{T} - \beta\right), \text{ where } \beta = \angle XOP'. \tag{7.05b}$$

Equations (7.05a and b), therefore, represent a little more generally than equation (7.04), a S.H.M.

EXAMPLE. *Plot a graph representing* $y = 10 \sin \left(\frac{2\pi t}{12} - \frac{\pi}{3}\right)$.

By applying either of the methods outlined, the student can verify the solution which is given in Fig. 7.6.

7.9. Phase Angle. From relation (7.04) and (7.05) it is at once evident that the position of a particle at any instant can be found from a knowledge of the angle,

$$\frac{2\pi t}{T} \quad \text{or} \quad \left(\frac{2\pi t}{T} + \alpha\right) \quad \text{or} \quad \left(\frac{2\pi t}{T} - \beta\right).$$

For that reason this angle is called the *Phase Angle*. The value of phase angle when $t = o$, is sometimes called the *Epoch*.

The following example may be of assistance to the student.

A particle executing a S.H.M. given by the relation $y = 4 \sin\left(\dfrac{2\pi t}{6} + \alpha\right)$ *is displaced* +1 *units when* $t = o$. *Find:* (1) *the phase angle when* $t = o$; (2) *the differ-*

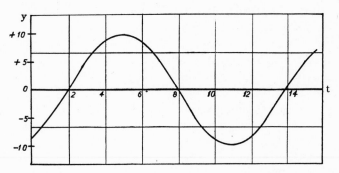

Fig. 7.6. Graph representing the S.H.M. $y = 10 \sin\left(\dfrac{2\pi t}{12} - \dfrac{\pi}{3}\right)$.

ence in phase between any two positions of the particle 2 sec apart; (3) *the phase angle corresponding to a displacement of* +2; (4) *the time to reach a displacement of* +3 *from the initial position.*

Solution:

(1) When $t = o$, $y = 1$,

$$\therefore \quad 1 = 4 \sin\,(o + \alpha),$$

from which $\sin \alpha = 0.25$

and $\qquad\qquad \alpha = 14° 30' = .25 \text{ radian} = \dfrac{\pi}{12.4}.$

(2) Let t_1 and t_2 be any two times such that $t_2 - t_1 = 2$ sec.

Then since $\qquad\qquad y_1 = 4 \sin\left(\dfrac{2\pi t_1}{6} + \alpha\right)$

and $\qquad\qquad\qquad y_2 = 4 \sin\left(\dfrac{2\pi t_2}{6} + \alpha\right)$

the required phase difference

$$= \left(\frac{2\pi t_2}{6} + \alpha\right) - \left(\frac{2\pi t_1}{6} + \alpha\right)$$

$$= \frac{2\pi}{6}(t_2 - t_1)$$

$$= \frac{2\pi \cdot 2}{6} = 120°.$$

(3) When $y = 2$, we have

$$2 = 4 \sin\left(\frac{2\pi t}{6} + \alpha\right)$$

$$= 4 \sin \text{(phase angle)}$$

from which

$$\sin \text{(phase angle)} = \tfrac{1}{2}$$

or   phase angle $= 30°.$

(4) When $y = 3$, we have

$$3 = 4 \sin\left(\frac{2\pi t}{6} + \alpha\right)$$

$$\therefore \quad \tfrac{3}{4} = \sin\left(\frac{2\pi t}{6} + \frac{\pi}{12.4}\right)$$

$$\therefore \quad \frac{2\pi t}{6} + \frac{\pi}{12.4} = \sin^{-1}\tfrac{3}{4}$$

$$= 48° \, 40'$$

from which $t = 0.57$ sec.

In problems of this kind where periodic functions are involved, more than one numerical answer is possible. Thus, in part (1) of the preceding problem, where $\sin \alpha = 0.25$, α may not only have the value 14° 30' but also (180° − 14° 30'), as well as (14° 30' + 360°), (14° 30' + 720°), etc. Note this when solving problems at the end of this chapter.

7.10. Composition of S.H.M. There are many problems in light which can be solved by finding the resultant motion of a particle which is acted on simultaneously by two or more S.H.M. We shall, therefore, next discuss this general problem with special reference to two important cases: (1) when each of two or more S.H.M. if acting alone would cause *motion in the same straight line;* (2) when two S.H.M. act, the motion due to one being *in a line at right angles* to the motion due to the other.

Composition of S.H.M. in the Same Straight Line. Two methods may be used, each of which will be considered with reference to the following problem.

Find the resultant motion when a single particle is acted on simultaneously by three S.H.M. given by the relations,

$$y_1 = a \sin \frac{2\pi t}{T}; \quad y_2 = a \sin \frac{2\pi}{T}\left(t - \frac{T}{12}\right); \quad y_3 = a \sin \frac{2\pi}{T}\left(t - \frac{T}{6}\right).$$

Method I. Give t successive values; calculate for each the corresponding displacement due to each S.H.M.; find the resultant displacement by algebraic summation; and finally plot resultant values of the displacement against corresponding values of t. A few of such values are given in Table VI.

Table VI.

t	y_1	y_2	y_3	Resultant y
0	0	$-0.5\,a$	$-0.86\,a$	$-1.36\,a$
$1\,T/12$	$+0.5\,a$	0	$-0.5\,a$	0
$2\,T/12$	$+0.86\,a$	$+0.5\,a$	0	$+1.36\,a$
$3\,T/12$	$+1.0\,a$	$+0.86\,a$	$+0.5\,a$	$+2.36\,a$

By obtaining in this manner a large number of corresponding values of y and t, and plotting, a curve is obtained similar to the broken one in Fig. 7.7. This curve then represents the required resultant motion of the particle.

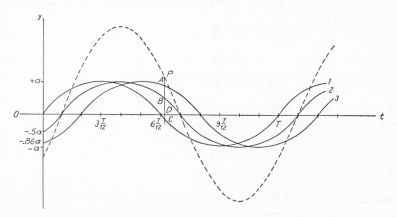

Fig. 7.7.   Graphs of 3 S.H.M. of the same period, in the same straight line, and of the resultant (dotted curve) when they are superimposed.

The method involves an important principle, called the *Principle of Superposition*, according to which the resultant displacement at any instant is equal to the algebraic sum of the individual displacements at that instant. This holds, provided the displacements are small, its justification being found in the fact that it leads to correct results.

Method II. The method just outlined involves a good deal of calculation, and for that reason the following more graphical method is recommended. In this, the graph of each S.H.M. is plotted separately to the same scale and with the same set of coordinates. Points on the resultant graph are then obtained by applying the principle of superposition. For example, at the time represented by OD (Fig. 7.7), the displacement due to the first S.H.M. is $DC(-)$, due to the second $DB(+)$, due to the third $DA(+)$, from which the resultant displacement at this instant $= DA + DB - DC = DP$. Similarly, other points are obtained in sufficient number to enable a smooth graph to be drawn. The curve obtained, of course, will be exactly the same as by Method I.

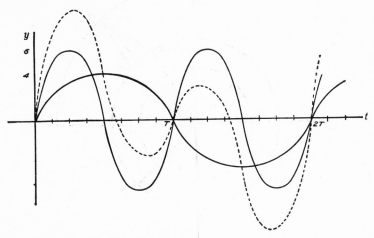

Fig. 7.8.   Graphs of 2 S.H.M. in the same straight line, with periods in the ratio 1 to 2, and of their resultant (dotted curve) when they are superimposed.

By inspection we see that the resultant motion (a) is periodic; (b) because of its shape, probably is simple harmonic (see next section); (c) by actual measurement has an amplitude $= 2.7a$.

Both these methods are perfectly general and may be applied whether the individual S.H.M. are of the same period, as in this problem, or of different periods, as in Fig. 7.8, where two S.H.M. are superimposed, with periods in the ratio of 1 to 2. The essential condition is that they all represent motion in the same straight line.

7.11. Resultant Amplitude for S.H.M. of the Same Period. This case is so important (because of its application to diffraction problems) that a simple graphical method of obtaining directly the resultant amplitude will be given. Let us, first of all, consider the combination of two such S.H.M. given by

$$y = a \sin \frac{2\pi t}{T}, \text{ and } y = b \sin\left(\frac{2\pi t}{T} + \alpha\right),$$

which the student should now see represent two S.H.M. of the same period, of unequal amplitude, differing in phase by α, and in the same straight line.

Suppose these two motions are executed along the line YOY_1, Fig. 7.9, and that, at *any* time t, the displacement due to the first alone is OA_1, to the second alone OA_2. P_1 and P_2 will then represent the corresponding positions of the particles in the circles of reference, the angle P_1OM being equal to $\dfrac{2\pi t}{T}$, the angle

$$P_2ON = \left(\frac{2\pi t}{T} + \alpha\right).$$

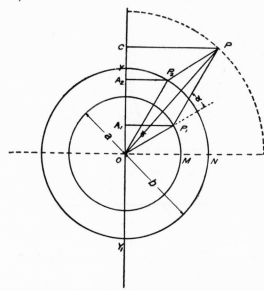

Fig. 7.9. Diagram used to prove that when 2 S.H.M. of the same period and in the same straight line are superimposed, the resultant is S.H.M.

Now complete the parallelogram, P_1OP_2P by drawing P_1P through P_1 parallel to the radius OP_2 and P_2P through P_2 parallel to the radius OP_1. Drop a perpendicular PC to the YOY_1 line.

Applying the principle of superposition, we have the resultant displacement at time $t = OA_2 + OA_1$

$$= OA_2 + A_2C,$$

since $OA_1 = A_2C$ (because OP_1 and P_2P are equal and parallel), or resultant displacement $= OC$.

But, if the point P revolves in a circle of radius OP with the same period as the two S.H.M., then OC represents the displacement of a S.H.M. of amplitude OP, the radius of this circle, at the time P is in the position shown in the figure. Since the foregoing construction is perfectly general, we conclude that the resultant of two S.H.M. *of the same period* is also a S.H.M. of amplitude given by OP and differing in phase from the one of amplitude OP_1 by the angle POP_1.

If, therefore, we wish only the resultant amplitude it can quickly be found, because it is represented by the side OP of the triangle OP_1P, the other two

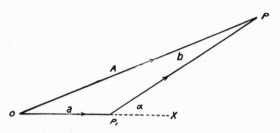

Fig. 7.10. OP is the resultant amplitude when 2 S.H.M. of the same period, with amplitudes a and b, differing in phase by α, are superimposed.

sides of which represent the two individual amplitudes.   In the problem we have been discussing, for example, all that is necessary is to make a diagram like Fig. 7.10, in which the angle $PP_1X = \alpha$.   We see, too, that since

$$OP^2 = OP_1^2 + PP_1^2 + 2OP_1 \cdot P_1P \cos \alpha,$$

the resultant amplitude A may be calculated from the relation

$$A^2 = a^2 + b^2 + 2ab \cos \alpha. \tag{7.06}$$

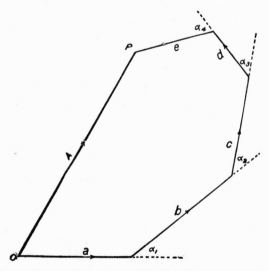

Fig. 7.11. OP is the resultant amplitude when 5 S.H.M. of the same period, with amplitudes a, b, c, d, and e, with phase differences as shown, are superimposed.

This method may readily be extended to any number of S.H.M. in the same straight line. For, having taken two of them, and having found the resultant OP in the manner just described, we may then combine this resultant with the third, and so on. Thus, OP in Fig. 7.11 represents the resultant of 5 S.H.M. of the same period, with individual amplitudes a, b, c, d, e, with phase difference between first and second $= \alpha_1$, between second and third $= \alpha_2$, etc.

An application to the problem discussed in section 7.10 by the general methods may perhaps help the student. Here we have 3 S.H.M. of the same period, each of amplitude a, with phase difference between the first and second $= \pi/6$, between the second and third $= \pi/6$. The resultant amplitude is therefore represented by OC of Fig. 7.12. By actual measurement or by trigonometrical calculation OC is found $= 2.7a$. The same result may be obtained by actual measurement from the resultant graph of Fig. 7.7.

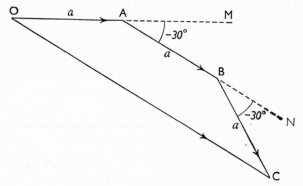

Fig. 7.12. Diagram used in explaining a second method of finding the equation of the resultant S.H.M. when the 3 S.H.M. plotted in Fig. 7.7 are superimposed.

7.12. Equation of Resultant S.H.M. Referring to Fig. 7.9, we see that, since the angle α, that is, P_1OP_2, represents the difference in phase between the two individual S.H.M., it follows that the angle P_1OP must represent the phase difference between the resultant S.H.M. and the one whose amplitude is OP_1. The equation of the resultant motion is represented, therefore, by

$$y = OP \sin\left(\frac{2\pi t}{T} + P_1OP\right),$$

or, referring to Fig. 7.10, by

$$y = A \sin\left(\frac{2\pi t}{T} + P_1OP\right).$$

Similarly the equation of the resultant of the three S.H.M. represented by Fig. 7.7 and Fig. 7.12 can be written down once Fig. 7.12 is constructed. It is given by

$$y = OC \sin\left(\frac{2\pi t}{T} - AOC\right)$$

$$= 2.7a \sin\left(\frac{2\pi t}{T} - 30°\right).^*$$

If it should be required to find the equation of the resultant from Fig. 7.7, not from Fig. 7.12, then we proceed as follows:

By actual measurement (from Fig. 7.7) the amplitude of the dotted curve (the resultant) is found $= 2.7a$. The equation is then of the form

$$y = 2.7a \sin\left(\frac{2\pi t}{T} + \theta\right)$$

where the value of θ has yet to be found. To find its magnitude, we must use some value of y and the corresponding value of t. For example, from the graph of Fig. 7.7, by actual measurement,

$$y = -1.35a, \text{ when } t = 0.$$

We have, therefore,

$$-1.35a = 2.7a \sin(0 + \theta),$$

from which $\theta = -30°.$

The final equation of the resultant becomes

$$y = 2.7a \sin\left(\frac{2\pi t}{T} - 30°\right).$$

Or, again, we can see from the graph that

$$y = 0, \text{ when } t = \frac{T}{12}.$$

Therefore, we have

$$0 = 2.7a \sin\left(\frac{2\pi}{T} \cdot \frac{T}{12} + \theta\right)$$

or $$\frac{\pi}{6} + \theta = 0$$

or $$\theta = -30°, \text{ as before.}$$

7.13. Composition of Two S.H.M. in Lines at Right Angles. This is another example of superposition which has a very important application in the study of light. Two general methods may be used, just as in the composition of S.H.M.

---

* The minus sign is used here, because in this problem the phase difference between the first and the second S.H.M. (as well as the second and the third) is $-30°$. That is, in Fig. 7.12, the angles MAB and NBC represent minus angles; hence the angle AOC is also a minus angle. *In combining S.H.M. where both + and − values occur, it is advisable to draw + angles above the direction chosen to represent* $y = a \sin\dfrac{2\pi t}{T}$ *and* − *angles below this direction.*

in the same straight line, discussed in section 7.10. These may best be explained by solving the following problem.

Find the resultant motion of a particle acted on by two S.H.M., in lines at right angles, subject to the relations

$$y = 6 \sin \frac{2\pi t}{T}, \quad x = 8 \sin \left(\frac{2\pi t}{2T} - \frac{\pi}{3}\right).$$

Method I. Give t a series of values, work out corresponding values of x and of y, and plot x against y. A few of such values are recorded in Table VII.

Proceeding in this way, the graph shown in the upper right-hand corner of Fig. 7.13 is obtained, points marked 0, 1, 2, 3, etc., corresponding to the equal time intervals given in the first column of Table VII. This graph shows the resultant path of the particle.

Table VII.

t	y	x
0	0	−6.9
1 T/12	3	−5.6
2 T/12	5.2	−4.0
3 T/12	6	−2.1
4 T/12	5.2	0

Method II. This is a more graphical method, although essentially the same as the first. It will best be understood by reference to Fig. 7.13. The y motion

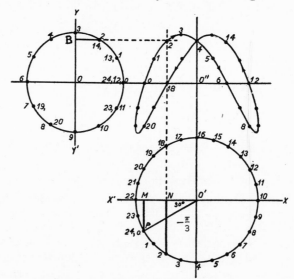

Fig. 7.13. Graphical method of finding the nature of the resultant motion when 2 S.H.M. along lines at right angles are superimposed.

is supposed to take place along the line YOY'; the x motion along $XO'X'$. By dividing the y circle of reference into, say, 12 equal parts, the y displacements at the end of the corresponding time intervals, each equal to $T/12$, may be obtained as already explained in section 7.7. The same may be done for the x motion, but, since in this case the period is $2T$, compared with T for the y motion, the circle of reference must be divided into 24 equal parts to obtain time intervals of magnitude $T/12$. At any of these time instants, therefore, the displacement for each motion may be found graphically. Thus, when $t = 0$, $y = 0$, and the displacement for y motion is 0; when $t = 0$, $x = 8 \sin(-\pi/3)$ or the phase angle $= -60°$, and the position of particle in the x circle of reference is at point P marked 0, while the actual x displacement $= O'M$.

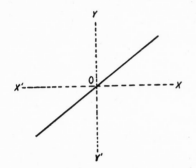

Fig. 7.14. Superposition of 2 S.H.M. of same period along lines at right angles with zero phase difference.

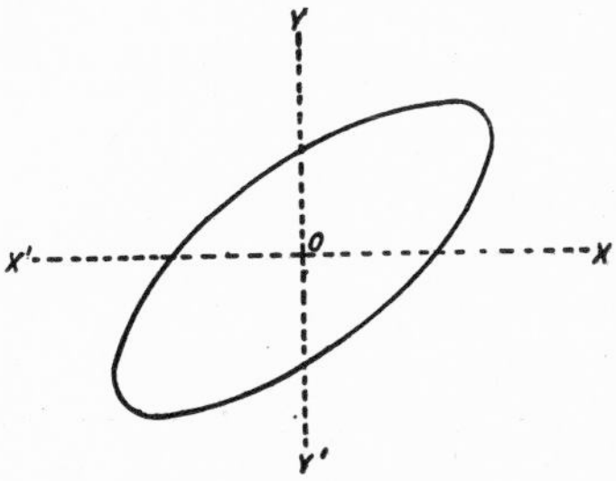

Fig. 7.15. Superposition of 2 S.H.M., as in 7.14, with phase difference 45°.

Again, when $t = 2(T/12)$, it will be seen at once that the y displacement $= OB$, the particle in y circle of reference being at 2, while the x displacement $= O'N$, the corresponding particle in x circle of reference being also at the point 2 on that circle.

Suppose, now, we take as our origin for plotting the resultant path, the point O'', that is, the point of intersection of the perpendiculars through the normal positions for the x and the y motions. Then, by extending the perpendiculars through any other corresponding positions of x and y, the point of intersection will give the *resultant* position due to the two motions, with reference to the origin O''. Thus, the perpendicular through N (x motion) intersects that through B (y motion) at the point 2, which, therefore, is the actual position of the particle at the time $2(T/12)$. In this way all other points on the resultant path were obtained, after which a smooth curve was drawn through them as shown in Fig. 7.13. This resultant path will obviously be repeated every $2T$ seconds; that is, generally speaking, in every time interval which is an exact multiple of each of the periodic times. Of such resultant paths actual examples are provided in the well-known Lissajous figures, obtained by receiving a spot of light on a screen after reflection from two small mirrors, one at the end of the prong of a vibrating tuning fork, the second at the end of a second fork vibrating in a line at right angles to the first.

The composition of two S.H.M. in lines at right angles is of very great im-

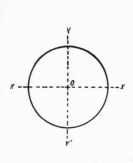

Fig. 7.16. Superposition of 2 S.H.M. of equal amplitude, as in Fig. 7.14, with phase difference 90°.

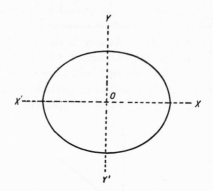

Fig. 7.17. Superposition of 2 S.H.M. of unequal amplitude, with phase difference 90°.

portance in the study of polarized light. It is well, therefore, for the student to work out for himself the resultant of two such S.H.M., of equal periods, amplitudes equal or unequal, with phase differences of varying amounts. In Figs. 7.14, 7.15, 7.16, 7.17, and 7.18, the solutions of a few cases have been given. In Fig. 7.14, amplitudes are unequal, phase difference = 0; in Fig. 7.15, amplitudes unequal, phase difference 45°; in Fig. 7.16, amplitudes equal, phase difference 90°; in Fig. 7.17, amplitudes unequal, phase difference 90°; in Fig. 7.18, amplitudes unequal, phase difference 180°.

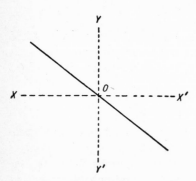

Fig. 7.18. Superposition of 2 S.H.M. as in Fig. 7.14, with phase difference 180°.

7.14. Fourier's Theorem. The work of section 7.10 shows graphically that the most complex periodic motions may be built up by combining a number of S.H.M. of varying periods and amplitudes. Conversely, we may resolve a complex periodic motion into a number of S.H.M. This is a result embodied in a mathematical theorem due to Fourier, which we may express in this way. Any function of t which is finite and continuous between values of $t = 0$ and $t = T$ may be expressed as a simple sum of sine and cosine terms. Symbolically,

$$f(t) = a_0 + a_1 \cos \frac{2\pi t}{T} + a_2 \cos \frac{4\pi t}{T} + a_3 \cos \frac{6\pi t}{T} + \cdots$$

$$+ b_1 \sin \frac{2\pi t}{T} + b_2 \sin \frac{4\pi t}{T} + b_3 \sin \frac{6\pi t}{T} + \cdots,$$

where the values of the coefficients a_0, a_1, a_2, $\cdots$ b_1, b_2, $\cdots$ can be calculated from the form of the function.

Since $y = b_n \sin \dfrac{2n\pi t}{T}$ and $y = a_n \cos \dfrac{2n\pi t}{T}$

$$= a_n \sin \left(\frac{2n\pi t}{T} - \frac{\pi}{2} \right)$$

represent S.H.M., our graphical method of adding a number of S.H.M. in the same straight line, is seen to be just a special example of Fourier's theorem.

7.15. Equation of a Plane Wave. In sections 7.6 to 7.14 we have been discussing the periodic motion of a single particle. We return now to our consideration of wave motion. If a S.H.M. gives rise to a train of waves in a medium, what relation describes the resulting wave motion?

To answer that question, consider first a line of particles along which waves are traveling at the rate of V cm per sec, and define the position of any particle P by its distance x from the source O. Suppose, further, that the source executes a S.H.M. given by the relation

$$y = a \sin \frac{2\pi t}{T}.$$

Then, since each particle executes the same motion, and since the particle at P does not begin to vibrate until x/V seconds after that at O, it follows that the motion of P is given by

$$y = a \sin \frac{2\pi}{T} \left(t - \frac{x}{V} \right) \tag{7.07a}$$

or since $\lambda = VT$,

by

$$y = a \sin 2\pi \left(\frac{t}{T} - \frac{x}{\lambda} \right). \tag{7.07b}$$

Equations (7.07a) and (7.07b) enable one to find the displacement of any particle at any time, (7.07a) in terms of a, T, and V; (7.07b) in terms of a, T, and λ. They are, therefore, two forms of the fundamental equation of a plane wave traveling along the x-axis. In either of them we have combined into a single statement the two characteristics of wave motion discussed at the beginning of this chapter.

7.16. Difference in Phase Between Any Two Particles in a Wave Train—Phase Difference and Path Difference. Consider any two particles such as

x_1 and x_2 (Fig. 7.19), in a line along which a train of simple waves is traveling. The motion of x_1 is given by

$$y_1 = a \sin \left\{ 2\pi \left(\frac{t}{T} - \frac{x_1}{\lambda} \right) \pm \alpha \right\}$$

and of x_2 by

$$y_2 = a \sin \left\{ 2\pi \left(\frac{t}{T} - \frac{x_2}{\lambda} \right) \pm \alpha \right\}.$$

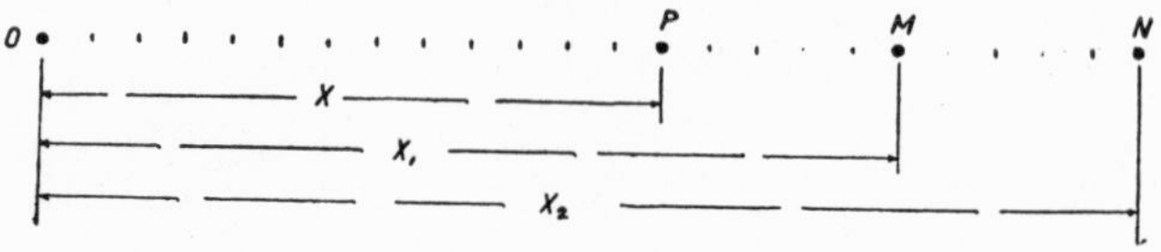

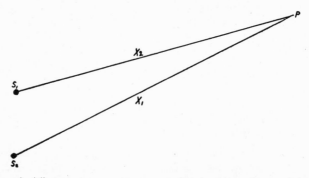

Fig. 7.19. *OPMN* represents a line of particles along which a S.H.M. wave disturbance is traveling.

Therefore, at any instant, the difference in phase for these two particles

$$= \left\{ 2\pi \left(\frac{t}{T} - \frac{x_1}{\lambda} \right) \pm \alpha \right\} - \left\{ 2\pi \left(\frac{t}{T} - \frac{x_2}{\lambda} \right) \pm \alpha \right\}$$

$$= \frac{2\pi}{\lambda} \cdot \left(x_2 - x_1 \right)$$

$$= \frac{2\pi}{\lambda} \cdot \text{path difference.} \tag{7.08}$$

This is a very important relation of which use will be made later. It is evidently applicable to express the difference in phase between two disturbances

Fig. 7.20. The path difference between two wave disturbances arriving at P from sources at S_1 and S_2 is $x_1 - x_2$.

coming to a single particle, such as P, Fig. 7.20, from two sources such as S_1 and S_2, provided the two sources execute the same S.H.M.

7.17. Plane and Spherical Waves. In section 7.16 we considered only a line of particles. Generally we have to do with a disturbance traveling through a medium of three dimensions and are concerned with wave-fronts. We now amplify somewhat the reference to wave-fronts given in section 3.1.

A *plane* wave-front is a plane surface through which a wave disturbance is passing and in which all vibrating particles are in the same phase. If, for example, the reader imagines a large number of lines of particles, all parallel to the one of Fig. 7.19, and all ending in points similar to O, which lie on a vibrating plane, a rough picture will be obtained of plane waves. In practice, plane waves are either a special case of, or derived from, spherical waves.

A *spherical* wave-front is a portion of a spherical surface through which a wave disturbance is traveling, and in which all vibrating particles are in the same phase.

Consider a vibrating source O, Fig. 7.21, so placed that a wave disturbance travels outward in a medium in *all* directions. If the medium is homogeneous, the wave velocity will be the same in every direction, and a portion of any sphere with center O will represent a spherical wave-front. If the sphere is sufficiently large and a relatively small portion such as MN is taken, this part will be approximately plane. When, therefore, we have to do with such a small part of a spherical surface, we may with little error treat

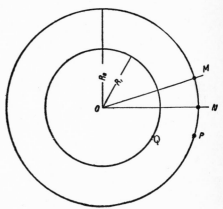

Fig. 7.21. Diagram used in proving the inverse square law for radiation emitted by a small source O.

it as a plane wave-front. For example, if we consider the light coming to an observer from a small region on the sun's surface, we are justified in treating the wave-fronts as plane.

It will be seen from their derivation that equations (7.07a) and (7.07b) are applicable to plane waves traveling in a direction parallel to the x-axis. They are also applicable to spherical waves traveling parallel to the x-axis, provided the fact that the amplitude changes is taken into consideration. How this can be done will be shown in the next section.

7.18. Change of Amplitude with Distance for Spherical Waves. If reference is again made to Fig. 7.21, it will be evident that (provided there is no absorption by the medium) the same amount of energy per second traverses the sphere of radius R_1 as the sphere of radius R_2.

Let E = energy radiated per second by the source; then $E/4\pi R_1^2$ = energy passing each second through each sq cm of the sphere of radius R_1, and $E/4\pi R_2^2$ = energy per second per sq cm for sphere of radius R_2. But the intensity of the disturbance (the brightness in light) at any point such as P depends on the rate at which a particle or particles in the neighborhood of P are receiving energy. Hence,

$$\frac{\text{intensity at } Q}{\text{intensity at } P} = \frac{\dfrac{E}{4\pi R_1^2}}{\dfrac{E}{4\pi R_2^2}} = \frac{R_2^2}{R_1^2},$$

from which we deduce that, in the case of spherical waves, the intensity falls off inversely as the square of the distance from the source.

To find out how the amplitude varies with the distance, it is necessary to know how the energy of a vibrating particle depends on its amplitude. That is essentially a problem in mechanics and it is left to the student to prove that *the energy is proportional to the square of the amplitude.*

Since, then, (1) the energy received by a particle per second from a distant source falls off inversely as the square of the distance from that source, and (2) the energy of a vibrating particle is proportional to the square of its amplitude, it follows that the amplitude falls off inversely as the first power of the distance. For spherical waves, we may write, therefore,

$$y = \frac{A}{x} \sin 2\pi \left(\frac{t}{T} - \frac{x}{\lambda} \right), \tag{7.09}$$

where A = amplitude at unit distance.

Relations (7.07a), (7.07b), and (7.09) are applicable only in the case of perfectly transparent media for which there is no falling off in intensity due to absorption. If absorption is to be considered, then the amplitude will gradually decrease on that account according to an exponential law, and relation (7.07b), for example, will now become

$$y = a e^{-\beta x} \sin 2\pi \left(\frac{t}{T} - \frac{x}{\lambda} \right), \tag{7.10}$$

where β may be defined as a coefficient of absorption.

7.19. Shape of a Train of Waves. In section 7.5 it was shown generally that the shape of a train of waves depended on the nature of the periodic motion of the source (or any other particle). We are now in a position to find the relation defining the shape when the periodic motion is S.H.M. Our problem is to express y, the displacement, as a function of x, at any instant, or, in general terms, to find out how the displacement of successive particles varies with their position *at any given moment.* In the case of water waves, we might do this by taking an instantaneous photograph. Generally, if we have plane waves defined by

$$y = a \sin 2\pi \left(\frac{t}{T} - \frac{x}{\lambda} \right),$$

we can find their shape by giving t any value we please. Take $t = T$, for example;

then, *at that instant,*

$$y = a \sin 2\pi \left(\frac{t}{T} - \frac{x}{\lambda} \right)$$

$$= a \sin \left(2\pi - \frac{2\pi x}{\lambda} \right)$$

$$= -a \sin \frac{2\pi x}{\lambda}. \tag{7.11}$$

Figure 7.22 is a graph of relation (7.11). Note that, although the curve has exactly the same form (although reversed) as that of Fig. 7.3, it represents something entirely different. From Fig. 7.22 we may read off the displacements of *successive particles* at the same instant, while Fig. 7.3 enables us to find the displacement of a single vibrating particle at any time. (See section 7.22.)

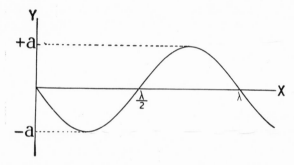

Fig. 7.22.   Graph of the wave form $y = -a \sin \frac{2\pi x}{\lambda}$.

7.20. Composition of Wave Trains · Stationary Waves.   When a medium is traversed by more than one set of waves, the principle of superposition may be applied to find the resultant wave form, in much the same way as for a single particle. An important example is found in the phenomenon of stationary waves.

Suppose a train of waves is meeting an exactly similar one traveling in the opposite direction (a condition which may readily be realized by reflection). At some instant which we may conveniently take as our initial time, the wave trains (if acting alone) will be represented as in *A*, Fig. 7.23. The continuous line represents a set moving to the right; the broken line, the set moving to the left. After a time equal to one-quarter of a period, each wave train will have advanced one-quarter of a wavelength ($\lambda/4$), and the position of each train will be as in *B*, Fig. 7.23. It will be noted that in the diagrams the distances $a1 = 1b = b2 = 2c = c3 = 3d = \lambda/4$. Similarly, after further time intervals of a quarter of a period, the wave train will occupy the positions shown in diagrams *C*, *D*, and *E*. Now let us apply the principle of superposition. In *A* a particle normally at *P* would be displaced an amount *PM* above its normal position due to one wave motion, while, due to the other, the displacement would be an equal amount PN in the opposite direction. The resultant displacement of P at this instant is, therefore, zero. Proceeding in this way with all the particles in each diagram, it is not difficult to see that the resultant wave forms will be as shown by the heavy lines in the diagrams.

The resultant motion is characterized by the following important features. (1) At certain instants, as in A, C, and E, all particles are in their normal positions. (2) Certain particles such as those marked 1, 2, and 3, exactly half a wavelength apart, *are always at rest*. They are said to be at *nodal points* or *nodes*. (3) Certain other particles such as a, b, c, and d, also half a wavelength apart,

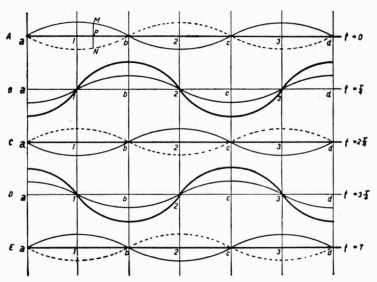

Fig. 7.23.   Graphical method of locating nodal points, at 1, 2, 3, and loops, at a, b, c, d, when two similar wave trains traveling in opposite directions are superimposed.

execute a periodic motion with double the amplitude caused by either of the wave trains acting alone. These particles are at *antinodes* or *loops*.

Waves with these characteristics are called stationary waves.

7.21. Analytical Proof of Nodes and Loops. In section 7.15 we saw that a train of simple waves traveling in a direction parallel to the x-axis is defined by the relation

$$y = a \sin 2\pi \left(\frac{t}{T} - \frac{x}{\lambda} \right).$$

This relation was derived on the supposition that the wave disturbance was advancing in the direction of increasing values of x. If we have an exactly similar set traveling in the opposite direction, it will be defined by

$$y = a \sin 2\pi \left(\frac{t}{T} + \frac{x}{\lambda} \right).$$

If two such sets are traversing a medium simultaneously, then the resultant disturbance will be given by

$$y = a \sin 2\pi \left(\frac{t}{T} - \frac{x}{\lambda} \right) + a \sin 2\pi \left(\frac{t}{T} + \frac{x}{\lambda} \right)$$

$$= 2a \sin \frac{2\pi t}{T} \cos \frac{2\pi x}{\lambda},$$

by trigonometrical expansion.

When $\qquad x = \dfrac{\lambda}{4}, 3\dfrac{\lambda}{4}, 5\dfrac{\lambda}{4}, \cdots$

$$y = 2a \sin \frac{2\pi t}{T} \cos \frac{n\pi}{2}, \text{ where } n = 1, 3, 5, \cdots$$

$$= 0, \text{ for all values of } t.$$

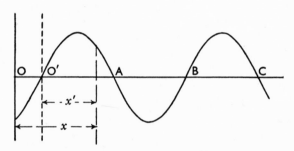

Fig. 7.24.   Diagram used in solving the problem in section 7.22.

In other words, there are certain particles half a wavelength apart, which are always at rest.   These are at nodal points.

Similarly, when $x = 2\dfrac{\lambda}{4}, 4\dfrac{\lambda}{4}, \cdots$

$$y = 2a \sin \frac{2\pi t}{T} \cos m\pi, \text{ where } m = 1, 2, 3, \cdots$$

$$= \pm 2a \sin \frac{2\pi t}{T}.$$

That is, there are certain other particles, also half a wavelength apart, and midway between the nodal points, which execute a S.H.M. with double the amplitude of that due to either of the original disturbances, when acting alone.   These particles are at loops.

7.22. We conclude this chapter with the solution of a problem which emphasizes the shape of a wave train.

PROBLEM. *Plane S.H.M. waves of wavelength 200 units and amplitude 10 units travel along an x-axis. Find the equation of the shape of the wave at such an instant that a particle at x = 40 has a phase angle of 180°.*

It is a simple matter to draw a picture of such a wave train, as in Fig. 7.24, where O is the origin, particles at O' and B have phase angles of 180°, and particles at A and C have phase angles of 0° (or any multiple of 360°).

Suppose now we shift the origin from O to O'. Then, if x' represents the ordinate of any particle P with respect to the new origin O', we can write down at once the equation giving the shape of the wave as

$$y = 10 \sin \frac{2\pi x'}{200}.$$

But, for any particle, $x' = x - 40$; hence, the required wave equation is

$$y = 10 \sin \frac{2\pi(x - 40)}{200}.$$

PROBLEMS

Note: In all questions, unless otherwise stated, assume that waves are plane.

1. A vibrating source executing a slow S.H.M. subject to the relation $y = a \sin \pi t$ causes waves to travel along a line of particles at a velocity of 40 cm per sec. (a) Find how many vibrations a particle P 70 cm from the source has made by the time the source has vibrated for 20 sec. (b) Find at this instant the phase angle of P.

2. A particle at the end of a long line of particles executes a S.H.M. given by the relation $y = 4 \sin 100 \pi t$ as a result of which waves are sent along the line. If the velocity of the waves is 6000 cm per sec, find the displacement of a particle 144 cm from the source 0.05 sec after the source began to vibrate.

3. A B C D E F
_____→

A train of S.H.M. transverse waves, of wavelength 200 cm and amplitude 10 units, traverses a line of particles in the direction of the arrow. At a certain instant a particle A has a phase angle of 0°. At this instant, find: (a) the direction of motion (to + or − side); (b) the phase angle; (c) the displacement of each of the particles A, B, C, D, E and F, where $AB = 25$ cm, $AC = 50$ cm, $AD = 75$ cm, $AE = 100$ cm, $AF = 110$ cm. Draw freehand a portion of the wave showing the actual positions of A, B, C, D, E and F at this instant.

4. A source executing S.H.M. of frequency 50 vps sends out waves of amplitude 10 units along a long line of particles at a velocity of 3000 cm per sec. At a certain instant the phase angle of the source is 180°. Find at this instant: (a) the phase angles; (b) the displacements of particles 10 cm, 30 cm, and 40 cm from the source.

5. A B C
_____→

A, B, and C are the normal positions of three particles in a line along which S.H.M. waves of amplitude 10 units are traveling. At a certain instant particle A has a displacement of $+3.42$ decreasing, B a displacement of $+5$ increasing, and C a displacement of -3.42 decreasing. The distance $AB = 13$ cm and is less than 1 wavelength. Find: (a) the phase angles of A, B, and C; (b) the wavelength; (c) the distance BC; (d) the position of two particles D and E, for each of which the displacement is zero. Draw a graph showing the actual positions of particles A, B, C, D and E.

6. A train of S.H.M. waves of amplitude 8 units traverses a long line of particles. (a) If the displacement of a particle A changes from $+4$ increasing to 4 decreasing in $1/50$ second, find the periodic time. (b) If the velocity of the wave disturbance is 500 cm per sec, find the nearest distance apart of two particles each of whose displacement is $+4$, one increasing, the other decreasing.

7. A source S executing S.H.M. according to the relation $y = a \sin 200\pi t$ sends out waves along a long line of particles. A particle P has made 998.2 complete vibrations when the source has vibrated for 10 sec. (a) If the distance $SP = 90$ cm, find the velocity of the wave disturbance. (b) Find the phase angle of P at this instant.

8. A source executing S.H.M. according to the relation $y = a \sin 200\pi t$ sends out waves along a long line of particles. If the velocity of the wave disturbance is 3000 cm per sec, find how long after the source first begins to vibrate, a particle P, 15 cm from the source, has, for the first time, a phase angle of $90°$.

9. Plane S.H.M. waves of amplitude 6 units, periodic time $1/100$ sec, travel along a line of particles with a velocity of 4000 cm per sec. At a certain instant the phase angle of a particle A is $+30°$, that of a particle B which is *farther* away from the source than A is $+60°$. Find: (a) the displacement of each particle; (b) the smallest distance which AB can be, to make these phase angles permissible.

10. A B
                 ———————————————————————→

A train of waves of amplitude 10 units travels along a line of particles in the direction of the arrow. At a certain instant a particle A has a displacement of $+4$ (decreasing) and a particle B has a displacement of $+10$ and a phase angle of $90°$, AB being less than 1 wavelength. Find: (a) the phase angle of A; (b) the wavelength if the distance AB is 33.21 cm. Plot *freehand* one wavelength of the wave curve at the above instant (including the particles A and B).

11. A train of S.H.M. plane waves travels along a line of particles. At a certain instant, the phase angles of two particles, A and B, 12 cm apart, are $70°$ and $10°$, B being farther away from the source than A. (a) If the phase angle of each particle increases $36°$ in $1/200$ sec, find: (i) the wavelength; (ii) the velocity of the wave disturbance. (b) If at a certain instant, the displacement of A is 9.4 units, find the displacement of B.

12. A source particle executing a S.H.M. given by $y = 10 \sin \pi t$ sends out waves which travel at the rate of 60 cm per sec. At a certain instance the source is displaced $+3.42$ decreasing, while a second particle, x cm, from it, is at the same instant displaced $+3.09$ cm increasing. Find two values of x.

13. Two S.H.M. disturbances acting in the same straight line, each of amplitude a units, are superimposed with a phase difference equal to (a) 90, (b) $180°$, (c) $360°$. For each phase difference find the resultant amplitude.

14. A particle is acted on simultaneously by three S.H.M. of the same period: the first of amplitude 3 units; the second of amplitude 4 units, with phase angle $45°$ behind that of the first; the third of amplitude 5 units, with phase angle $30°$ ahead of the first. Find the resultant amplitude.

15. Find the equation of the resultant motion when the following S.H.M. are superimposed. (Use method of section 7.12.)

(a) $\qquad y_1 = 6 \sin \dfrac{2\pi t}{T}; \quad y_2 = 8 \sin \left(\dfrac{2\pi t}{T} - 30° \right).$

(b) $\qquad y_1 = 6 \sin \left(\dfrac{2\pi t}{T} - 30° \right); \quad y_2 = 8 \sin \left(\dfrac{2\pi t}{T} + 30° \right).$

(c) $\qquad y_1 = 2 \sin \dfrac{2\pi t}{T}; \quad y_2 = 4 \sin \left(\dfrac{2\pi t}{T} + 45° \right);$

$\qquad\qquad y_3 = 6 \sin \left(\dfrac{2\pi t}{T} - 60° \right).$

16. Verify each case of problem 15 by plotting each S.H.M. separately and superimposing.

17. A particle is simultaneously acted on by the following three S.H.M.

$$ y_1 = 4 \sin \frac{2\pi}{T}\left(t - \frac{T}{10} \right); \quad y_2 = 6 \sin \frac{2\pi}{T}\left(t + \frac{T}{16} \right); \quad y_3 = 8 \sin \frac{2\pi}{T}\left(t - \frac{T}{4} \right). $$

Find graphically, by rule and protractor, or by calculation, (a) the resultant amplitude, (b) the equation of the resultant motion.

18. Six S.H.M., each of the same amplitude and period, acting along the same straight line, are superimposed. If the phase difference between each successive pair is the same, find one value of this phase difference for which the resultant amplitude is zero.

19. Prove graphically that when 2 S.H.M. of the same period, vibrating along lines at right angles, are superimposed, circular vibrations result if the amplitudes are equal and the phase difference between the two is 90°.

20. Prove graphically that when 2 S.H.M. of the same period, vibrating along lines at right angles, are superimposed, linear vibrations result when the phase difference between the two is 0° or any multiple of 180°.

21. When 2 S.H.M. of the same period, vibrating along lines at right angles are superimposed, find the amplitude of the resultant linear vibration if the individual amplitudes are 3 and 4 units and the phase difference is 180°.

22. A particle is acted on by 2 S.H.M. executed along lines at right angles. Find graphically the nature of the resultant motion for each of the following cases.

(a) $\qquad y = a \sin \dfrac{2\pi t}{T}; x = b \sin \left(\dfrac{2\pi t}{T} - \dfrac{\pi}{4} \right).$

(b) $\qquad y = a \sin \left(\dfrac{2\pi t}{T} - \dfrac{\pi}{3} \right); x = b \sin \left(\dfrac{2\pi t}{T} - \dfrac{\pi}{2} \right).$

(c) $\qquad y = a \sin \dfrac{2\pi t}{T}; x = b \sin \left(\dfrac{2\pi t}{2T} - \dfrac{\pi}{3} \right).$

23. A wave disturbance is given by the relation $y = 10 \sin 2\pi \left(\dfrac{t}{12} - \dfrac{x}{200} \right).$

(a) Plot graphs depicting the *motion* of particles at $x = 0$ and $x = 50$.
(b) Plot graphs depicting the *shape* of the wave train at $t = 0, 3,$ and 6.

24. At a certain instance the shape of a simple train of plane waves is

$$y = 12 \sin \frac{\pi x}{50}.$$

If the velocity of the wave disturbance is 100 cm per sec, in a direction away from the origin, find the equation giving the shape 0.25 sec later.

25. A train of S.H.M. waves of amplitude 10 units has a wavelength of 200 cm. Write down the equation giving the shape at the instant that the displacement of the particle at $x = 0$ is: (a) $+5$ increasing; (b) $+5$ decreasing.

26. Plane waves of amplitude 2 units and periodic time 1/100 sec traverse a medium at a velocity of 4000 cm per sec. Write down the equation, giving the shape of the waves at the following times: (a) when the particle at $x = 0$ is undisplaced, but moving in the direction of positive displacement; (b) when the particle at $x = 0$ has a positive displacement of 2 units. The waves are advancing parallel to the x-axis.

27. A plane wave disturbance which travels along an x-axis from a source executing the motion $y = 6 \sin \frac{2\pi t}{4}$, is represented by the equation

$$y = 6 \sin \left(\frac{2\pi t}{4} - \frac{\pi x}{200} \right).$$

(a) If at a certain instant the total phase angle of the particle at $x = 50$ cm is 1845°, find how long the *source* particle (at $x = 0$) has been vibrating at this instant. (b) Find the wavelength and the velocity of the disturbance. (c) Find the amplitude of the particle at $x = 25$, at a time $t = 4$.

28. Prove analytically the existence of nodes and loops when two S.H.M. trains of plane waves of equal amplitude and equal wavelength traveling in opposite directions are superimposed.

29. Plane S.H.M. waves of amplitude 10 units and wavelength 200 cm travel along an x-axis with a velocity of 40 cm per sec. Find the equation giving the shape of the wave: (a) at a time such that the phase angle of the particle at $x = 0$ is 180°; (b) at a time such that the phase angle of the particle at $x = 40$ is 180°; (c) at a time such that the displacement of the particle at $x = 40$ is $+5$ units increasing.

VIII

Interference

In Chapter I it was pointed out that the wave theory of light received general acceptance only after Thos. Young had demonstrated the phenomenon of interference. In Chapter VI use was made of the numerical magnitudes of wavelengths, but as yet no method has been described for actually measuring wavelengths. The purpose of this chapter is to show how a detailed consideration of interference leads us to various means of evaluating wavelengths, as well as to many other important applications.

8.1. Suppose S_1 and S_2, Fig. 8.1, are two sources vibrating with equal amplitudes, with the same periods, and sending out waves in any continuous medium. The figure has been drawn to represent, at a certain instant, the position of regions of maximum and of minimum displacement, that is, of what we may, by analogy with water waves, call crests and troughs. The maxima are represented by the unbroken lines, minima by dotted lines. An examination of the figure will show that at certain places, marked $\times$, crests and crests, or troughs and troughs occur simultaneously; at other places, marked 0, crests and troughs are superimposed. Now, if we apply the principle of superposition, it follows that at the former places the resultant displacement is double that due to either disturbance separately, whereas at the latter it is zero. Lines joining points marked $\times$ are, therefore, loci of particles for which there is a marked resultant disturbance, while lines joining the other set of points are loci of particles which are not displaced at all.

If S_1 and S_2 represent disturbances caused by the vibrations of the two prongs of a low-frequency tuning fork disturbing the surface of water or of mercury, the existence of such lines can readily be shown. If S_1 and S_2 are luminous sources, and a screen is placed at MN, it follows that on the screen we should have places of maximum displacement alternating with others of zero displacement—that is, alternately light and darkness.

For a quantitative discussion of this phenomenon we shall approach the question somewhat differently.

Consider any particle P, Fig. 8.2, which is disturbed as a result of wave motion coming from the two sources S_1 and S_2, vibrating with equal amplitudes, with the same period, and with no phase difference between them. Our problem is to find the resultant disturbance at P. This we shall do by two different methods, one graphical or semi-graphical, the other analytical.

Method I.—In this method we can make use of the proposition, proved in section 7.12, for, whatever the position of P, we have to do with the resultant of two S.H.M. of the same period. The resultant amplitude is, therefore, represented by $MN = A$, Fig. 8.3, where $MO = a = ON$ represents the amplitude of P due to each disturbance separately, and δ is the difference in phase of the two disturbances on reaching P. Obviously δ will depend on the position of P, in Fig. 8.2, and will continuously increase the greater the distance of P from the point M, where $S_1M = S_2M$, and PM is perpendicular to OM. The resultant amplitude, therefore, will also continuously change with the position of P, going through a cycle of values. Thus, when $\delta = 0$, A is a maximum $= 2a$; as δ increases, A decreases until when $\delta = \pi$, $A = 0$; for still greater values of δ, A increases, reaching a second maximum equal to $2a$, when $\delta = 2\pi$. The cycle is then repeated and we see that, if we had two such light sources as S_1 and S_2, the resultant disturbance at points on the screen should regularly alternate from maximum to minimum values, that is, from light to darkness.

By simple geometry,

$$A^2 = a^2 + a^2 + 2a^2 \cos \delta *$$

$$= 2a^2(1 + \cos \delta), \qquad (8.01)$$

which again tells us that whenever δ is increased by 2π, values of A^2 repeat, being equal to $4a^2$ when $\delta = 0, 2\pi, 4\pi, 6\pi \cdots$, that is, when $\delta = 0$ or $n \cdot 2\pi$, where n is integral.

Now, as already proved in section 7.17,

$$\text{phase difference} = \frac{2\pi}{\lambda} \cdot \text{path difference},$$

$$\therefore \qquad = \frac{2\pi}{\lambda} \cdot (S_2P - S_1P), \text{ for Fig. 8.2.}$$

* If the two disturbances are of unequal amplitudes, a and b,
$$A^2 = a^2 + b^2 + 2ab \cos \delta.$$

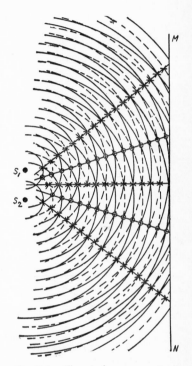

Fig. 8.1. The circles represent, at a given instant, two sets of wavefronts, half a wavelength apart, arising from two vibrating sources S_1 and S_2, of the same period and with zero phase difference. Along lines marked with x, the two displacements reinforce each other; along lines marked with o, annul each other.

∴   at maximum values of A^2,

$$n \cdot 2\pi = \frac{2\pi}{\lambda} \cdot (S_2P - S_1P)$$

or $S_2P - S_1P = n \cdot \lambda$

or $S_2P - S_1P = 0$, when $\delta = 0$.

In other words, whenever the path difference is equal to a whole number of wavelengths (or is zero) maximum values of the resultant disturbance exist. In

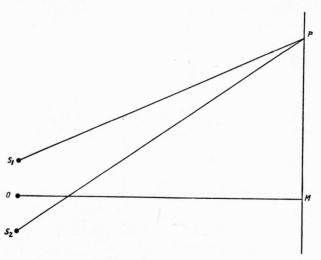

Fig. 8.2.   At P wave disturbances from the two sources S_1 and S_2 are superimposed.

the same way it can readily be shown that, for minimum values, the path difference is equal to an odd number of half wavelengths.

If the phase difference between S_1 and S_2 is not zero (although always a constant amount), the only difference in the foregoing solution is that the central maximum does not occur at M. Just as before, however, whenever the path

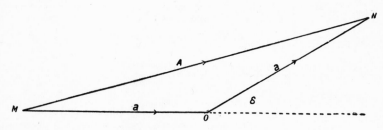

Fig. 8.3. MN is the resultant amplitude when two disturbances each of amplitude a, but with phase difference δ, are superimposed.

length is increased or decreased by one wavelength, we go from one maximum or one minimum to the next.

Since the intensity is proportional to the square of the amplitude, a plot of $2a^2(1 + \cos \delta)$ for various values of δ will show how the intensity varies as we go through maxima and minima values. Such a plot is given in Fig. 8.4. It should be noted that the width of bright regions (maxima) is about the same as that of dark places (minima).

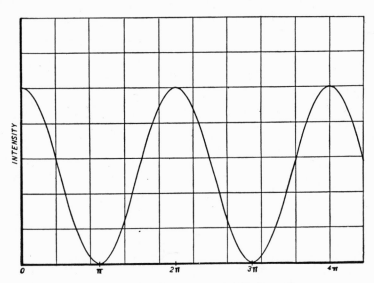

Fig. 8.4.   Plot of intensity $= 2a^2 (1 + \cos \delta)$.

Method II.—Let

$$y = a \sin \left(\frac{2\pi t}{T} - \alpha_1 \right)$$

represent the disturbance reaching P from S_1,

and

$$y = a \sin \left(\frac{2\pi t}{T} - \alpha_2 \right)$$

represent that reaching P from S_2.

It follows that $\alpha_1 - \alpha_2 = \delta$, the phase difference between the two disturbances.

The resultant disturbance at P is then given by

$$y = a \sin \left(\frac{2\pi t}{T} - \alpha_1 \right) + a \sin \left(\frac{2\pi t}{T} - \alpha_2 \right)$$

or $\quad y = a \left(\sin \frac{2\pi t}{T} \cos \alpha_1 - \cos \frac{2\pi t}{T} \sin \alpha_1 + \sin \frac{2\pi t}{T} \cos \alpha_2 - \cos \frac{2\pi t}{T} \sin \alpha_2 \right)$

or $\quad y = (a \cos \alpha_1 + a \cos \alpha_2) \sin \dfrac{2\pi t}{T} - (a \sin \alpha_1 + a \sin \alpha_2) \cos \dfrac{2\pi t}{T}$

or $\quad y = A \cos \theta \sin \dfrac{2\pi t}{T} - A \sin \theta \cos \dfrac{2\pi t}{T},$ $\hfill$ (8.02)

if we put $\qquad\qquad A \cos \theta = a \cos \alpha_1 + a \cos \alpha_2,$

and $\qquad\qquad\qquad A \sin \theta = a \sin \alpha_1 + a \sin \alpha_2,$

from which $\qquad\qquad \tan \theta = \dfrac{\sin \alpha_1 + \sin \alpha_2}{\cos \alpha_1 + \cos \alpha_2};$

and $\qquad A^2 = (a \cos \alpha_1 + a \cos \alpha_2)^2 + (a \sin \alpha_1 + a \sin \alpha_2)^2$

$\qquad\qquad = a^2(2 + 2 \cos \alpha_1 \cos \alpha_2 + 2 \sin \alpha_1 \sin \alpha_2)$

$\qquad\qquad = 2a^2[1 + \cos (\alpha_1 - \alpha_2)]$

$\qquad\qquad = 2a^2(1 + \cos \delta).$ $\hfill$ (8.01)

A and θ, therefore, can readily be found from the original constants a, α_1, and α_2.

Now returning to (8.02), we see that the resultant disturbance is given by

$$y = A \sin\left(\frac{2\pi t}{T} - \theta\right),$$

the equation of a S.H.M. of amplitude A and period T, which differs in phase from either of the original disturbances by an amount which depends on θ and which, therefore, can be found.

As far as amplitude is concerned, we have derived the same expression as by the previous method, and may apply all the results already discussed.

8.2. Realization of Interference. The realization of such regions of maximum and minimum intensity depends on our having two such sources as S_1 and S_2, and that is not quite as simple a matter as it may at first thought seem. For example, it would not do to place two sodium flames behind two narrow slits in an opaque screen, and to expect to obtain alternate regions of light and of darkness on a screen near them, for, since the flames are two absolutely independent sources, there can be no regular phase difference between the vibrations of the two slits. At any point P on the screen the phase difference between the two disturbances arriving there is constantly and irregularly changing, and no sustained maxima or minima are possible.

There are several means, however, of realizing the necessary *coherent sources* vibrating always with constant phase difference. Of these we shall consider the following.

(a) **Double Slit.** In Chapter I, where reference has already been made to the use of the double slit, it was pointed out that light must first of all spread out from a source slit S, as in Fig. 8.5. This means that, since well-defined wavefronts fall on the double slits S_1 and S_2, there will always be a constant phase difference (which may be and often is zero) between the vibrations in the separate slits. Interference, therefore, is possible between the two disturbances emerging from the slits, and consequently regions of maximum and minimum intensities (interference fringes) may be observed with this arrangement. Attention has

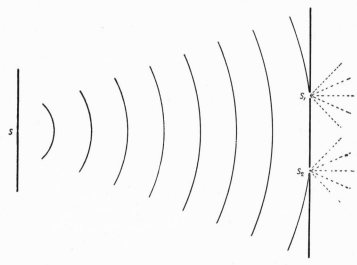

Fig. 8.5. Double slit. S is a narrow source slit illuminating the narrow apertures S_1 and S_2 of the double slit.

already been directed to Fig. 1, Plate IV (facing p. 153), an actual photograph of double slit interference fringes. (See also section 11.8.)

(b) **The Biprism.** By the use of a double prism such as LM, Fig. 8.6, with the refracting edge of one portion remote from that of the other, virtual images

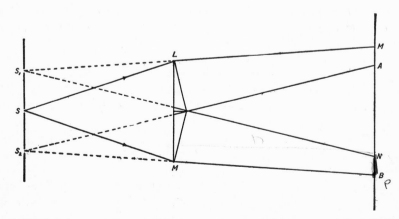

Fig. 8.6. The biprism. S_1 and S_2 are the two virtual sources after passage of the light from the narrow source slit S through the biprism LM.

S_1 and S_2 of a narrow source slit S may be obtained. A screen placed beyond the biprism, therefore, will receive light in the region MN apparently coming from S_1, in the region AB apparently from S_2. Since each of the apparent sources is the virtual image of the same slit, conditions are again suitable for interference, and

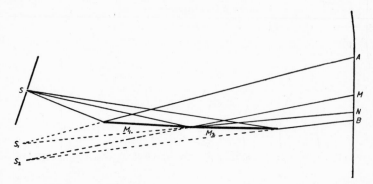

Fig. 8.7. Fresnel mirrors. S_1 and S_2 are the two virtual sources due to reflection of light from the narrow source S by the plane mirrors M_1 and M_2 slightly inclined to each other.

in the overlapping portion of MN and AB fringes are observed. Figure 2, Plate IV is a photograph of fringes obtained with the biprism arrangement.

(c) **The Fresnel Mirrors.** The virtual images of a narrow slit S, Fig. 8.7, formed by reflection at the surfaces of two mirrors M_1 and M_2, inclined at a slight angle, provide still another means of obtaining the necessary conditions

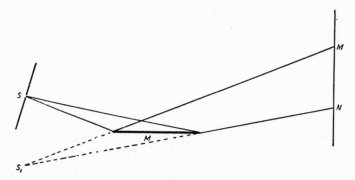

Fig. 8.8. Lloyd's single mirror. In the region MN direct light from a narrow source slit S and reflected light from the mirror M, from the virtual source S_1, are superimposed.

for the kind of interference we are discussing. No detailed explanation is necessary to show that in the region MN, Fig. 8.7, light is incident, coming apparently from both the sources S_1 and S_2, and interference fringes are obtained.

(d) **Lloyd's Single Mirror.** By using only one mirror, such as M, Fig. 8.8, and placing the source slit S near the plane of the reflecting surface, the actual source and its virtual image S_1 take the place of S_1 and S_2 in the simple diagram of Fig. 8.7. In this way a fourth method of realizing interference is obtained.

8.3. Still other methods may be used. We shall proceed, however, to show how simple linear measurements with any of the foregoing arrangements enable us to evaluate the wavelength of the light used.

Suppose, in Fig. 8.9, that M represents the position of the central maximum (bright fringe), P_1 that of the first to one side, P_2, the second, and so on. We then know that

$$S_2M - S_1M = 0$$

$$S_2P_1 - S_1P_1 = \lambda$$

$$S_2P_2 - S_1P_2 = 2\lambda.$$

Now in an actual arrangement such as the biprism, observation tells us that with a distance of the slit to the screen equal to one or two meters, the distance

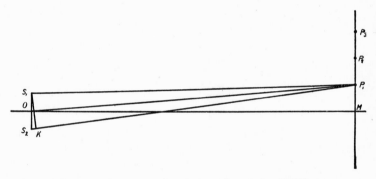

Fig. 8.9.   Diagram used in deriving the relation (8.03).

between bright fringes is invariably less than one millimeter. Angles such as $S_1P_1S_2$, $S_1P_2S_2$, are, therefore, very small, and the error is slight in putting the sine or the tangent of the angle equal to its measure in radians.

Consequently, if P_1K is taken $= P_1S_1$, so that $S_2K = \lambda$, with little error S_1K may be considered perpendicular to OP_1, where O is the midpoint of S_1S_2.

Also $\angle S_2S_1K = \angle P_1OM$, since OM is $\perp$ to S_1S_2, and OP_1 is $\perp$ to S_1K.

Now in $\triangle P_1OM$, $\qquad \tan P_1OM = \dfrac{P_1M}{OM}$

and in $\triangle S_2S_1K$, $\qquad \sin S_2S_1K = \dfrac{S_2K}{S_1S_2}.$

$\therefore$ since we are dealing with small angles,

$$\frac{S_2K}{S_1S_2} = \frac{P_1M}{OM}$$

or $$\frac{\lambda}{b} = \frac{x}{D},$$ (8.03)

where b = distance between S_1 and S_2,
$\quad\quad D$ = distance from O to screen,
$\quad\quad x$ = distance from central bright fringe to the next, that is, between any
$\quad\quad\quad$ two bright fringes.

Since each of these three quantities b, x, and D may be found by simple linear measurements, we have our first method of calculating wavelengths. In a certain biprism arrangement, for example, in which $D = 186.03$ cm, $b = 0.654$ cm, $x = 0.0184$ cm, the source of light was an arc lamp screened with a piece of red glass.

The mean wavelength of the light transmitted by this red light, therefore, equals

$$\frac{0.654 \times 0.0184}{186.03} = 6.46 \times 10^{-5} \text{ cm}.$$

In the preceding work we have considered the light approximately monochromatic. If white light is used, it is easy to see that the fringes are colored, except for one or two at the center, while the number will be very limited. For, since $x = \lambda \dfrac{D}{b}$, the width of the fringes is directly proportional to the wavelength.

Thus for $\lambda = 0.00006$ cm, the second bright fringe from the center will coincide with the third dark for $\lambda = 0.00004$ cm. Hence, after the first few fringes, the overlapping will be so great as to give approximately uniform illumination. At the center of the pattern, however, two or three black and white fringes are observed with colored ones on either side. In general, for a white light source, only a few fringes can be seen with any arrangement.

8.4. Wavelength and Double Slit. A simple and instructive, although not accurate measurement of the wavelength of light may be made by the use of a double slit and the following method. A source slit S, Fig. 8.10, is divided into

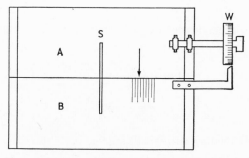

Fig. 8.10. A source slit S in which one half, A, may be shifted a measured amount with respect to the other half B.

PLATE IV. INTERFERENCE FRINGES

Fig. 1. Double
slit interference
fringes.

Fig. 2. Biprism
fringes.

Fig. 3. Lummer plate fringes.

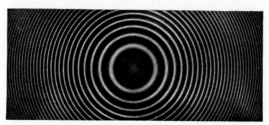

Fig. 4. Fringes obtained with Fabry and Perot Étalon.

Fig. 5. Interference fringes obtained with quartz
wedge and polarized light.

two portions by using two pieces of metal A and B, one of which may be shifted by the wheel W a measured amount with respect to the other. This source may conveniently be illuminated by a 250-watt lamp, with a piece of red glass, R, Fig. 8.11, to give approximately monochromatic light. When an observer focuses

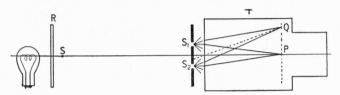

Fig. 8.11. Arrangement for using the source slit of Fig. 8.10, with a double slit S_1S_2 and telescope T to measure the wavelength of light.

a low-power telescope T on this source, placed at a distance of two or three meters away, and then inserts a double slit S_1S_2 (see, again, section 1.3) in front of the objective, good interference fringes are observed in the telescope because two beams are superimposed at points such as P and Q and they alternately reinforce and counteract each other.

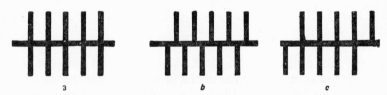

Fig. 8.12. Interference fringes: (a) in step, (b) exactly out of step, (c) in step after a shift of one fringe.

By adjusting the position of A until the two portions of the source slit are in line, the fringes appear somewhat as shown in a, Fig. 8.12. On shifting A the fringes at first gradually go out of alignment, as in b, Fig. 8.12, but eventually come into step again, as in c, Fig. 8.12. With continued shift of A, the fringes will of course again go out of alignment and a second time come into step.

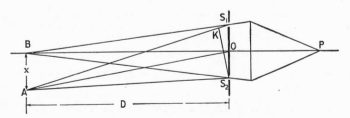

Fig. 8.13. Diagram used for deriving the expression for wavelength calculation to the arrangement in Fig. 8.11.

Let x = the shift of A, that is, the distance BA in Fig. 8.13, required to bring the fringes into realignment for the first time, as in c, Fig. 8.12. When this is the case, P, in Fig. 8.13, must represent either the central fringe for the fixed portion B of the source slit, or the first fringe to one side of the center for the movable slit A. This means that the ray paths BS_1P and BS_2P are equal, but that the path AS_1P must be greater than AS_2P by one wavelength. If then AK is taken equal to AS_2, it follows that KS_1 is one wavelength.

If O is the midpoint of S_1S_2, then with little error AO is perpendicular to S_2K, and

$$\angle KS_2S_1 = \angle AOB.$$

Putting this angle = ϕ, we can write

from $\triangle AOB$, $\tan \phi = \dfrac{AB}{BO} = \dfrac{x}{D}$,

and from $\triangle KS_2S_1$, $\sin \phi = \dfrac{KS_1}{S_1S_2} = \dfrac{\lambda}{b}$, where $b = S_1S_2$.

Since ϕ is small, $\tan \phi = \sin \phi$, and we have

$$\frac{\lambda}{b} = \frac{x}{D},$$

or $\lambda = \dfrac{xb}{D}$.

Here x is the shift of the movable slit A corresponding to a shift of one fringe; b is the width from center to center of the two apertures of the double slit; and D is the distance of the source slit to the double slit. All of these are easily measured quantities.

The following readings were taken by students when using the preceding arrangement:

Mean value of b for slit I = 0.0341 cm.

Mean value of x for slit I = 0.586 cm

when distance D = 317.9 cm.

Hence wavelength = 6.28×10^{-5} cm.

Mean value of b for slit II = 0.0875 cm.

Mean value of x for slit II = 0.227 cm

when distance D = 317.6 cm.

Hence wavelength = 6.25×10^{-5} cm.

8.5. One or two applications of interference will next be given, the first of which is illustrated by the following problem.

When a thin flake of glass, with index of refraction = 1.5, is introduced into the

path of one of the interfering beams in such an arrangement as the biprism, the posi-
tion of the central bright fringe becomes that normally occupied by the fifth. If the
wavelength used is 6×10^{-5} cm, find the thickness of the glass.

In the normal arrangement (that is, without the glass flake), if P_5, Fig. 8.14, is the position of the fifth bright fringe, then

$$S_2P_5 - S_1P_5 = 5\lambda, \text{ where } \lambda = \text{ wavelength in air.}$$

But with the glass flake present, since P_5 is the position of the central fringe, the optical path $S_2P_5 - S_1P_5 = 0$.

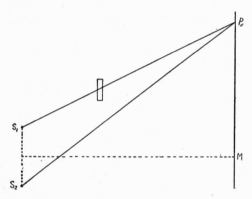

Fig. 8.14.   Diagram used in solving the problem in section 8.5.

Therefore, if t cm = required thickness of glass, *replacing t cm of air by t cm of glass must lengthen the optical path S_1P_5 by 5λ.*

But t cm of glass = 1.5 t cm of air,

∴   the path *change* = $(1.5 - 1)t$ cm of air.

Hence $(1.5 - 1)t = 5\lambda$

$$= 5 \times 6 \times 10^{-5},$$

from which $t = 6 \times 10^{-4}$ cm.

Hence, given the index of a thin piece of glass, and the wavelength of the light, we can find its thickness. Conversely, given the thickness and the wavelength, the index can be found.

8.6. Rayleigh's Refractometer.* Some interesting applications of interference are provided by the use of this instrument, which, in principle, is just a double slit placed before the objective of a telescope. When a distant *narrow* source, a star for example, is viewed through such an arrangement, fringes are observed in the focal plane of the objective.

* See also sec. 11.10.

Suppose the finite size of the star can be neglected, and that the parallel rays from it are incident on the telescope in a direction parallel to the axis of the instrument. Then, F, Fig. 8.15, the principal focus of the objective, is also the position of the central bright fringe. If P_1 is the position of the first bright fringe to one side of the central, then $S_2M = \lambda$, S_1M being $\perp$ to S_2M. Also, since

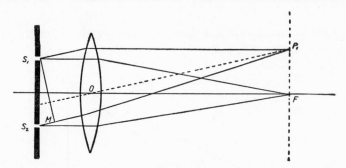

Fig. 8.15.   When a double slit S_1S_2, illuminated by light from a distant narrow source, is placed in front of the objective of a telescope, interference fringes are observed in the focal plane P_1F.

$\angle P_1OF = \angle S_2S_1M$, the angular separation of two bright fringes is measured by S_2M/S_2S_1 or λ/b, since $S_2M = \lambda$ and $S_1S_2 = b$. (If the student has difficulty in seeing this, he should re-read section 1.3(e), bearing in mind that in this arrangement the focal plane of the objective replaces the retina of the eye in Fig. 1.6.)

It follows at once that, if the distance between the two slits is adjustable,

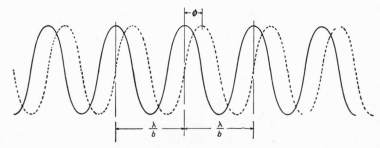

Fig. 8.16.   Plots of double slit fringes obtained from each of two distant sources so close together that fringes may be observed in the resultant pattern.

then the width of the fringes may be varied, being inversely proportional to b. The position of the central fringe, however, remains unaltered, since it is determined by the direction the incident light makes with the axis of the telescope, and, indeed, coincides with the image of the star formed by the telescope in the absence of the double slit.

Suppose, now, that a double slit telescope is directed toward two stars close together. Then, for each star, there is a system of fringes of angular width λ/b. The positions of the central fringes, however, are not the same, being separated by an angular distance ϕ, equal to the angle the two stars subtend at the telescope. (Recall again that the central fringe for each system coincides with the position of the image of the corresponding star in the absence of the double slit.) We then have two superimposed sets of fringes, somewhat as shown in Fig. 8.16. In this case, the resultant is a system of fringes. Now let the magnitude of b be increased. The angular width of the fringes then decreases, and, for a particular value of b, the maximum of one will fall on a minimum of the other, as in Fig. 8.17. The resultant illumination will then be uniform, no fringes being observed. When this is the case, we have

$$\phi = \frac{\lambda}{2b}.$$

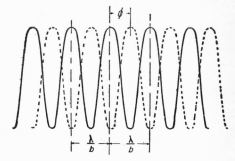

Consequently such an arrangement provides us with a means of measuring the angular separation of two close stars, from the observation of the value of b for which the fringes disappear.

Fig. 8.17. No double slit fringes are observed in the resultant pattern when two distant sources are separated such an amount that bright fringes due to one source coincide with dark fringes due to the other.

This work is based on the assumption that the dimensions of the star itself may be neglected. Now, although the angular width of a star is small, it is finite. It follows, therefore, that if we subdivide the surface of the star into a number of elemental strips, and consider each of these as a source of light, for each there will be a corresponding set of fringes with maxima in slightly different positions. In the case of a single star of finite width, therefore, we have a *slight* overlapping of a large number of systems of fringes. With small values of b, the fringes are so wide and the overlapping so slight, that no noticeable blurring of the fringes is observed. In that case the star may be treated as a point. That this is not always so, however, has been shown by a wonderful piece of experimental work done by Prof. Michelson of the University of Chicago. Using the star α Orionis, and very large values of b, he showed not only that the overlapping could not be neglected, but also that it could be used as a means of measuring the angular diameter of the star. Although the mathematical analysis dealing with the case of a single source of finite width is beyond the scope of this book, the student should not have difficulty in seeing, generally, that if the overlapping is sufficient the fringes disappear altogether, and that the condition for such disappearance depends both on b and on the angular diameter of the star. The analysis shows that the fringes disappear for a value of b given by

$$\text{angular diameter} = 1.22 \frac{\lambda}{b}.$$

In the case of α Orionis, Michelson found that when $b = 121$ in., the fringes disappeared, although they were sharp for other smaller stars. Taking $\lambda = 5750$ A, this gives 0.047 sec for the angular diameter of this star. To make this amazing measurement great skill and ingenuity were required. The large value of b was obtained by having a framework carefully constructed and attached to the telescope. By means of a system of adjustable mirrors carried by the framework, light was reflected somewhat as shown in Fig. 8.18.

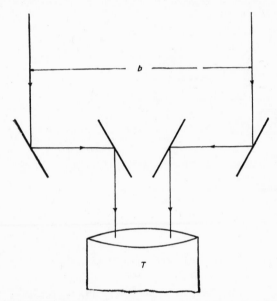

Fig. 8.18.   Michelson's arrangement of mirrors in front of a telescope, used in determining by an interference method, the angular width of the star α Orionis.

8.7. Index of Refraction of Gas.   When a narrow slit is placed in the focal plane of a good lens, conditions are essentially the same as if the slit was at infinity. For example, if a spectrometer is adjusted in the usual way and a double slit placed on the table (or immediately in front of the objective of the telescope) with its face normal to the beam emerging from the collimator, excellent interference fringes are observed in the telescope. Since, with this arrangement, the *angular* width λ/b of the fringes can be measured, although not accurately, an estimate of the wavelength of the light used may readily be obtained.

In one form of the Rayleigh's Refractometer the arrangement of Fig. 8.19 is used. This form is adapted for use in measuring the index of refraction of air or other gas by the principle of interference. Suppose two tubes, A and B, with good glass windows closing the ends, are placed side by side in the path of the parallel beam between the collimating lens L and the double slit, so that light incident on S_1 traverses one tube, that on S_2 the other. Then, if, by means of an outlet M attached to tube A, the density of the air (or other gas) in this tube is altered, the optical path of one of the interfering beams is altered and the position of the fringes will change. Technically it is said that there is a *shift* of the fringes, for, on viewing them, one observes a lateral motion as the position of a maximum (or minimum) changes. By observing the fringe shift for a given alteration in density (or pressure), it is possible to calculate the index of the gas in this tube. Again the principle of the method may be illustrated by the following example, which will be worked in three different ways.

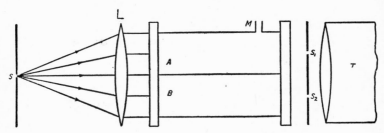

Fig. 8.19. When the pressure of the air is altered in *A*, one half of the double-barreled tube *AB*, the pressure in the other half *B* remaining constant, a shift of the fringes is observed in the telescope *T* of a Rayleigh Refractometer. From the amount of shift the index of refraction of air may be measured.

PROBLEM: *The removal of all the air from the tube A, Fig. 8.19, corresponds to a shift of 150 fringes. If the wavelength in air (at room temperature and the initial pressure) is 0.00004 cm and the tube is 20 cm long, find the index of refraction of the air.*

Method I.—In this problem it is necessary to distinguish carefully between air and vacuum. Thus, if n = the required index, then, the wavelength in vacuo = $0.00004n$ cm.

Since the fringe shift = 150, that is, since at a given place a bright fringe changes from bright to dark and back again to bright 150 times,

∴   the path change brought about by removing the air in tube A

$$= 150 \text{ wavelengths}$$

$$= 150 \times 0.00004 \text{ cm air}$$

$$= 150 \times 0.00004n \text{ cm vacuum.}$$

But, since the tube is 20 cm long,

the initial path in A = 20 cm air

= $20n$ cm vacuum,

the final path in A = 20 cm vacuum.

∴   the path change also = $20(n - 1)$ cm vacuum.

Hence, $20(n - 1) = 150 \times 0.00004n,$

from which $n = \dfrac{20.000}{19.994} = 1.0003.$

Method II.—The number of wavelengths in 20 cm air $= \dfrac{20}{0.00004}$; the number of wavelengths in 20 cm vacuum $= \dfrac{20}{0.00004n}$;

∴   the *change* in the number when the air is removed

$$= \frac{20}{0.00004} - \frac{20}{0.00004n}.$$

But every time there is a change in the number by 1, there is a fringe shift of 1.

$$\therefore \quad \frac{20}{0.00004} - \frac{20}{0.00004n} = 150,$$

from which $n = 1.0003.$

Method III.—Let

$$V = \text{velocity of light in vacuo,}$$
$$V_a = \text{velocity in air, so that}$$
$$V = n \cdot V_a.$$

Then, the time for light to travel 20 cm in air $= 20/V_a = 20n/V$; the time for light to travel 20 cm in vacuum $= 20/V.$

$$\therefore \quad \text{difference in times} = \frac{20}{V}(n - 1).$$

But the time difference is equal to that corresponding to a path difference of 150 wavelengths, and therefore $= 150T$, where T is the periodic time.

$$\therefore \quad \frac{20}{V}(n - 1) = 150T.$$

But $\lambda \text{ vacuum} = VT$

$$\therefore \quad \frac{20(n - 1)}{V} = \frac{150 \cdot \lambda \text{ vacuum}}{V}$$

$$\therefore \quad 20(n - 1) = 150 \times 0.00004n,$$

from which $n = 1.0003.$

As a matter of fact a fringe shift as great as 150 could not be obtained with such an arrangement. Actually, the fringe shift for a small pressure change is observed. In that case the index of air at $0°C$ and 760 mm pressure is found from the following relation:

$$n - 1 = f \cdot \lambda \cdot \frac{T}{273} \cdot \frac{76}{p_1 - p_2} \cdot \frac{1}{L}, \tag{8.04}$$

where f = fringe shift,

T = absolute temperature,

p_1 = initial pressure,

p_2 = final pressure,

L = length of tube path.

8.8. Measurement of Index of Refraction of Air. The following simple experiment, an adaptation of an arrangement described by Paul S. Delaup (United States), has been found to give excellent results for the index of refraction of air. The arrangement shown in Fig. 8.20 is essentially the same as

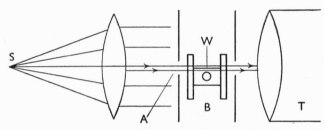

Fig. 8.20.   An arrangement for measuring the index of refraction of air by a small rectangular air cell B placed in front of the telescope of a spectrometer.

the Rayleigh Refractometer of Fig. 8.19, but use is made of an ordinary student's spectrometer and the double-barreled tube of Fig. 8.19 is replaced by the short air-cell shown in Fig. 8.20. This is a small rectangular box B, about 2 cm long, with a single chamber from which the air can be removed by a Hy-vac or similar pump. In the figure the small circle represents a piece of brass tubing soldered into the top of the box. The ends of the air-cell are closed by pieces of good-quality glass about 1/8 in. thick. When such a cell is placed in front of the telescope T and the collimated light is allowed to pass through a narrow rectangular aperture A cut in a piece of black paper and so placed that W, the thin side wall of the cell, divides the transmitted beam into two, narrow sharp interference fringes are observed in the telescope. The slit of the spectrometer should be very narrow and a monochromatic source such as a sodium flame or sodium lamp used. With such an arrangement, because of the short length of the cell, the value of L in relation (8.04) is so small that the change of pressure corresponding to a shift of one fringe is possibly 7 or 8 cm of mercury. By placing a simple U-tube mercury manometer in the exhaust system, readings of pressure changes can be taken, corresponding to a shift of 1, 2, 3, etc., fringes, and the index of refraction of the gas evaluated by the use of relation (8.04). An accuracy of 1 per cent can be obtained without difficulty.

IX

Interference (Continued)

THIN FILMS AND PLANE PARALLEL SURFACES

9.1. In the work of the previous chapter, interference fringes were obtained by superimposing two disturbances, each of which originally came from the same source, although by two different paths. In all the cases considered it was essential that a narrow source be used, for otherwise, as briefly indicated in the case of a star of finite magnitude, different parts of a broad source give rise to maxima in different places, and uniform illumination results. It is the purpose of this chapter to discuss in detail other ways of obtaining interference fringes, in all of which a *broad* source is necessary. The brilliant colors seen when light is reflected from a thin layer of oil on a wet pavement, and the entrancing colors every child has seen when blowing soap bubbles, are familiar examples of this kind of interference.

Suppose a film, formed by dipping a wire ring in a soap solution and illuminated with white light, is viewed directly with the naked eye, or, alternately, that an image of the film is cast on a screen by a projecting lens. If the film is in a vertical position, a series of beautifully colored horizontal bands are observed. If the illuminating source is made approximately monochromatic by placing a piece of red glass in the path of the light, a series of alternately red and black horizontal fringes are obtained.

In seeking the explanation of this experiment, it is necessary to remember that a soap film is, in reality, a thin layer of water enclosed between two surfaces —in this case, plane; in the case of a soap bubble, spherical. The film enclosed by the wire ring is wedge-shaped, gradually growing thinner and thinner at the top as the water falls because of gravity, and as it evaporates. Now when light falls on such a transparent film, part of the beam is reflected at the first surface, part is transmitted, of which a portion is reflected at the second surface, this portion eventually emerging from the first face. In the reflected light, therefore, there are two disturbances, both of which originally came from the incident beam, but one of which traveled a distance, approximately equal to twice the thickness of the film, greater than the other. Interference is then possible. Because of the changing thickness of the soap film, with monochromatic light regions of maxima and minima alternate and fringes are observed. If white light is used, then for any given thickness the resultant intensity will depend on the wavelength. It might be a maximum for one color, a minimum for another, so that, when all colors are present, certain portions of the original beam are either feebly present or absent altogether, and at all places the resultant is colored.

To discuss this type of interference more in detail, it is convenient to make use of individual rays of light. Suppose an eye is focused on the small region about P, Fig. 9.1, on the first face of a thin film illuminated with monochromatic light. The eye can then receive light by means of rays 1' and 1 from a *small* *source* S_1 so placed that, if PN is normal to the film, $\angle FPN = \angle NPS_1$. Another ray 2 may leave the source S_1, strike the first surface at a point Q near P, be

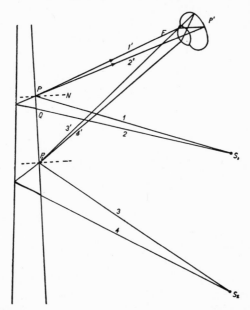

Fig. 9.1.   Interference fringes are observed at the surface of a thin film because of reflection from its two faces. S_1 and S_2 are points on a broad source of light.

refracted, then reflected at the second surface, and eventually emerge at P, traveling to the eye as ray 2'. The image of P on the retina, P', is formed, therefore, by means of two disturbances, both coming originally from S_1 but traveling by different paths. Consequently, the intensity at P' may vary all the way from a maximum to a minimum, depending on the magnitude of the path difference.

If a broad source of light is used, with the eye in the same position, the images of other places such as P_1 are formed by means of other pairs of rays, such as 3' and 4' which come originally from the small portion S_2 of the source. It follows, therefore, that if the thickness of the film gradually increases, the path difference between such pairs of interfering rays will do so also and consequently the face of the film will be alternately light and dark. That this is the case has already been pointed out in the soap film experiment. It may also readily be shown by forming a thin air wedge between two pieces of plate glass, touching at one end, slightly separated at the other, and viewing the reflected light from a yellow sodium flame.

Pairs of rays such as 1′ and 2′, 3′ and 4′ are called *congruent rays*. For any such pair we wish now to calculate the path difference. To do so, consider Fig. 9.2, bearing in mind always that, for the purpose of making the argument clear, in both this figure and in Fig. 9.1, the thickness of the film and the distance PQ are grossly exaggerated. Thus, in Fig. 9.2, PQ and LP are actually extremely small quantities compared with distances such as SP or SQ.

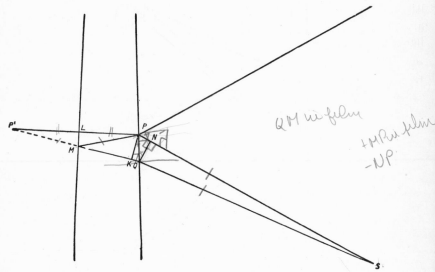

Fig. 9.2. Diagram used to find the path difference between the two interfering rays arising from reflection at the faces of a thin film.

The angle PSQ, therefore, is of small magnitude, and so if we draw $QN \perp$ to SP, SQ and SN are equal, to the first order of small quantities.

∴   the difference between the paths $SQMP$ and SP

$$= QM \text{ (in film)} + MP \text{ (in film)} - NP \text{ (in air)}$$
$$= n{\cdot}QM + n{\cdot}MP - NP \text{ cm of air,}$$

if n = index of the film material.

Now draw $PK \perp$ to MKQ.

Then since $\angle NQP$ = angle of incidence at P,
and $\angle KPQ$ = angle of refraction at Q,
                        $PN = n{\cdot}KQ.$

∴   required path difference

$$= n \cdot QK + n \cdot KM + n \cdot MP - PN$$
$$= n(KM + MP).$$

Produce KM to P', making $MP' = MP$, and join PP'.
Then, the path difference

$$= n(KM + MP)$$
$$= n(KM + MP')$$
$$= n \cdot KP'$$
$$= n \cdot PP' \cos PP'M.$$

By elementary geometry, it is easily seen that PP' must be perpendicular to the second face, and that $LP' = LP$.

∴ $PP' = 2t$, where t is the thickness of the film at P.

Also $\angle PP'M = \angle P'PM$
$$= (r + \theta),$$

where r is the angle the internal ray makes with the normal to the first surface at P, and θ is the angle of the wedge formed by the film.
Therefore, the path difference

$$= 2nt \cos (r + \theta). \tag{9.01}$$

Now we have to do only with films whose surfaces are almost parallel, that is, with those for which θ is such a small quantity that, with negligible error, we can put $\cos (r + \theta) = \cos r$.*
We have then, finally, path difference

$$= 2nt \cos r. \tag{9.02}$$

Several cases to which this important formula for the path difference is applicable are of interest.

When a film is viewed by light reflected in a direction approximately perpendicular to the surface, the path difference, with little error, is equal to $2nt$, or, if the medium is air, to $2t$. This simpler expression is useful in many problems.

9.2. Fringes of Equal Thickness.   If an observer views a piece of film a few centimeters in diameter at a distance of 25 cm or more, the variation in $\cos r$ in going from point to point on the film may be small compared with the variation in t. In that case the variation in t is largely responsible for the change from maximum to minimum, and the fringes are called *fringes of equal thickness* or

---

* The student who finds difficulty in steps of this sort will do well to take a concrete case. Thus, if a thin air wedge is formed by separating one end of two plate glass pieces, 10 cm long, by a thin piece of glass 0.04 mm thick, the angle θ has the value .0004 radian or a little over 1 min. Taking a case where $r = 30°$, we find $\cos 30° = 0.8660$, $\cos 30°1' = 0.8661$. Hence, in such a case, the error in putting $\cos (r + \theta) = \cos r$ is less than 0.015%.

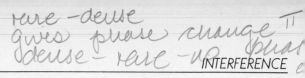

Fizeau fringes. This means, of course, that a bright fringe is the locus of points corresponding to places of equal thickness. The wedge-shaped soap film fringes, for example, belong to this class, as well as those in the Newton's Rings arrangement. (See section 9.5.)

9.3. Phase Change on Reflection. In thin film fringes if $t = 0$, the path difference is zero, and one might expect the resultant phase difference to be zero also. Now just before the soap film breaks, one can easily notice that at the top (where it is thinnest) it is dark, not bright. In other words, although the path difference is zero (for the two surfaces come together just at breaking), the two disturbances are out of step, and, therefore, there must be a phase difference between the two of 180°. Now when the question of reflection is considered mathematically, it can be shown that, when light after traversing a less dense medium is incident on a surface beyond which the medium is more dense, in the act of reflection there is a phase change of 180°, for perpendicular or near-perpendicular incidence. (Compare the change of phase when sound waves are reflected at the end of a closed organ pipe.) When, however, the light first traverses a more dense medium, no such change of phase takes place.

When, therefore, we are considering the superposition of the beams reflected, at near-perpendicular incidence, from both sides of a thin film, such as a soap film bounded on each side by air, or an air film between two plates of glass, the resultant phase difference between the two disturbances is equal to

$$\frac{2\pi}{\lambda} \cdot 2nt + \pi.$$

When the path difference is zero, the resultant phase difference = 180° and there is a dark fringe.

Since a phase difference of 180° corresponds to a path difference of $\lambda/2$, it is sometimes stated that the

$$\text{path difference} = 2nt + \frac{\lambda}{2},$$

but it should be kept in mind that the additional $\lambda/2$ is only a fictitious path difference. In many problems, where we are concerned only with the *change* in phase or in path difference as we go from one fringe to the next, it is not necessary to consider at all the phase change on reflection. One of the most useful as well as the most fundamental ideas in interference is that, *whenever in any arrangement we go from a bright (or dark) fringe to the next bright (or dark) one, the path difference changes by one wavelength.*

9.4. Nonreflecting Glass. The mathematical theory of reflection also shows that when light, traversing a medium of index of refraction n_1 is incident, approximately perpendicularly, on the surface separating this medium from a second one of index n_2, the following relation holds

$$\frac{\text{intensity of reflected light}}{\text{intensity of incident light}} = \left(\frac{n_2 - n_1}{n_2 + n_1}\right)^2.$$

In the case of reflection at an air-glass surface, $n_1 = 1$. If we take $n_2 = 1\cdot5$, simple arithmetic shows that the intensity of the reflected light is 1/25 or 4 per cent of the incident light. Thus, no matter how clean we make our spectacle lenses or shop windows or any glass surfaces we are using, 4 per cent of the incident light is reflected at a single surface, or 96 per cent is transmitted. With an achromatic objective of a telescope made of two lenses, with resulting four faces, only 85 per cent of the incident light is transmitted. With a combination of ten lenses, about 34 per cent is lost because of reflections.

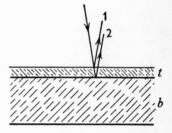

These reflection losses, extremely undesirable, especially under conditions of low luminosity, can be avoided by the use of so-called nonreflecting films deposited on the glass surfaces. In these the principle of interference is applied in a simple way. In Fig. 9.3, t represents a thin transparent layer of a substance like magnesium fluoride, of index n_1 and thickness $\lambda/4$, deposited by evaporation on the surface of a piece of glass b of index n_2.

Fig. 9.3. In nonreflecting glass a layer t of magnesium fluoride or other suitable substance is deposited on the surface of the glass.

It should be realized that, if Fig. 9.3 were drawn to scale and the thickness t represented by 2 mm, then, to represent accurately a 1-cm thickness of glass block, b would be more than 200 meters in length. Since t = the thickness of the film, then the phase difference* between the reflected rays = $(2\pi/\lambda)\cdot2t$, which, if $t = \lambda/4$, is equal to 180°. There is, therefore, annulment of the two beams and the intensity of the reflected light is a minimum. To obtain zero intensity, the two reflected beams† should have equal intensities. It can be shown mathematically that this condition is fulfilled when the index of the thin layer = $\sqrt{\text{index of glass}}$. Taking the index for glass as $1\cdot5$ gives $1\cdot23$ as the best index for the thin layer, a value somewhat lower than $1\cdot38$, the index for the magnesium fluoride. But even when this condition is not exactly fulfilled, the intensity of the reflected light approaches zero.

---

* Since the medium above the magnesium fluoride is air and since $n_1(1.38)$ is less than n_2, the index for glass, rays 1 and 2, Fig. 9.3, each suffer a phase change of 180° in the act of reflection. The resultant phase difference between the rays is, therefore, entirely due to path difference.

† Actually because of multiple reflections there are more than two beams but, with ordinary unsilvered surfaces of glass, second reflections are very feeble. Moreover, it can be proven that with a dielectric $\lambda/4$ in thickness, the resultant intensity, where multiple reflections are concerned, is also a minimum.

Perfect annulment can be obtained for one wavelength only. If, however, the wavelength chosen is 5540 angstroms, the frequency to which the eye is most sensitive, the over-all minimum approaches closely to zero, even when white light is used.

It is a natural question to ask, even if the two reflected beams annul each other, why is the energy added to the transmitted beam? The author knows of no physical picture to make clear why this is so. The same problem occurs in any system of interference fringes, where the energy corresponding to the superimposed beams giving rise to a minimum is added to the energy in a bright fringe. It is not difficult to prove this mathematically, and the student will have to accept it as a fact.

9.5. Newton's Rings. As stated in section 9.2, when fringes of equal thickness are viewed normally, the path difference $= 2t$ if the film medium is air. A good example is found in the Newton's Rings arrangement as represented in

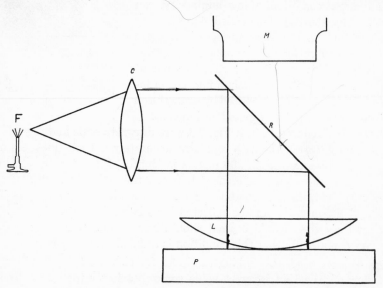

Fig. 9.4. A common arrangement for observing Newton's Rings by reflected light.

Fig. 9.4. In this figure L represents a plano-convex lens whose curved face rests on the plane face of a glass block P. A thin film of air whose thickness increases radially from the point of contact is then formed between the curved and the plane glass surfaces. Light from a sodium flame F, collected by the lens C, falls on a thin, inclined, transparent plate R and is reflected downward to the film. The light reflected back again from the faces of the film is viewed by a low-power traveling microscope M focused on the portion of the film about the point of contact. Interference fringes are then observed for exactly the same reason as

PLATE V

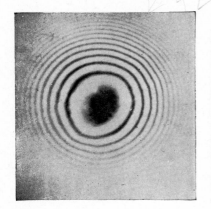

Fig. 1.   Newton's rings.

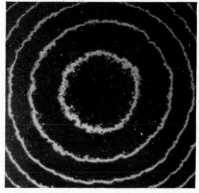

Fig. 2.   Newton's rings, with transmitted light and multiple reflection.   (Tolansky)

Fig. 3.   Interference pattern for highly convergent polarized light and quartz cut perpendicular to the optic axis.

has been explained for the soap film. In this case, since the path difference at any point $= 2t$ and since regions of equal thickness are obviously circular, the fringes observed are circular. Because of the different conditions of reflection at the two faces, the center of the fringe system is dark. A reproduction of a photograph of such fringes is given in Fig. 1, Plate V, facing p. 168.

Such an arrangement provides us with another means of evaluating the wavelength of light by measuring, (1) the diameter of any ring, (2) the radius of curvature of the upper curved surface. To find the necessary expression for the calculation, consider the nth dark ring. At the center (which again is dark), the path difference $= 0$, $(\pi$ rare $-$ dense$)$

$\therefore$ at the 1st dark ring, the path difference $= \lambda$,
at the 2nd dark ring, the path difference $= 2\lambda$.

and generally at the nth dark ring, the path difference $= n\lambda$.

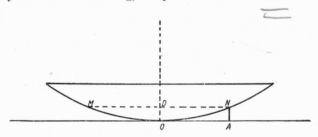

Fig. 9.5. Diagram used in deriving relation (9.04).

But the path difference anywhere $= 2t$,

$$\therefore \quad n\lambda = 2t. \tag{9.03}$$

Now, if DN Fig. 9.5, is the radius of the nth dark ring, then

$$AN = t = OD.$$

$(2R - OD)\,OD = ND^2$

But, by elementary geometry, as already proved in section 3.8,
$2R \cdot OD = DN^2$, where R is the radius of curvature of the curved face.

$$\therefore \quad OD = \frac{DN^2}{2R} = \frac{D_n^2}{8R},$$

where $D_n =$ diameter of the nth dark ring.
Finally, we have

$$2t = \frac{D_n^2}{4R},$$

or

$$\boxed{\lambda = \frac{D_n^2}{4nR}.} \tag{9.04}$$

$\dfrac{2u+1}{4}\lambda = \dfrac{D_u^2}{2\cdot 8R}$

$\lambda = \dfrac{D_u^2}{2R(2u+1)}$

Now it is a simple matter to measure D_n by means of the traveling micro-

$(u + \tfrac{1}{2})\lambda = 2t$

$t = \dfrac{2u+1}{4}\lambda$

scope, and R can easily be found by a spherometer; hence we have another, although again, not a particularly accurate method, of evaluating λ.

If the nth bright ring is used, it is left as an exercise for the student to prove that

$$\lambda = \frac{D_n^2}{2R(2n-1)}. \tag{9.05}$$

Since examples of the kind of interference we have been discussing are common in nature, it is not surprising that Newton and some of his contemporaries were familiar with the colors of thin films, and the rings to which the great Newton's name is given. To Hooke, who in 1664 published a book one chapter of which dealt with this phenomenon, we owe the statement—"In general wheresoever you meet with a transparent body thin enough, that is terminated by reflecting bodies of differing refractions from it, there will be a production of these pleasing and lovely colors." Indeed, while Newton explained the existence of fringes by applying ideas analogous to those involved in his theory of fits of easy reflection and easy transmission, in such a way that for certain thicknesses rays were transmitted, for alternate thicknesses reflected, Hooke's explanation almost anticipated the modern view, and that more than one hundred years before the pioneer work of Young on interference. According to Hooke, light was reflected at both the front and the rear surfaces of a thin film, colored phenomena resulting from the delay the latter beam suffers in crossing and recrossing the film.

9.6. Fringes of Equal Inclination. Suppose we have a thin film whose faces are parallel. Since t everywhere is constant, r is the only variable, and fringes can be observed only if the variation in $2nt \cos r$ over the face of the film is great enough to give path differences of a few wavelengths. In such a case, if a perpendicular is dropped from the eye to the film it is viewing, it is not difficult to see that the fringes obtained will be circular, with the foot of the perpendicular as center.

If t is large, that is, very many times the wavelength of light, fringes such as we have so far been discussing in this chapter cannot be obtained. To understand why this is so, it is first of all necessary to recall that the pupil of the eye has a finite aperture, of the order of 3 mm. That being the case, the eye can form an image of P, Fig. 9.6, by means of other pairs of congruent rays, for each of which the value of r is slightly different. Thus, for one pair the path difference is $2nt \cos r$; for another pair $2nt \cos (r + \Delta r)$, where Δr is a small fraction of r. Now if t is not more than a few wavelengths, the difference between these two values is a small fraction of a wavelength. If, therefore, P is bright as observed by one pair, it will be bright also for other pairs.

If t is large, a few millimeters or a centimeter or two, then the difference between $2nt \cos r$ and $2nt \cos (r + \Delta r)$ becomes sufficiently great that one pair of congruent rays may give rise to a maximum, another to a minimum, and so on. In such a case fringes cannot be obtained.

If, however, the surfaces are parallel and optically plane (that is, if the actual surface deviates from a geometrical plane by a small fraction of a wavelength), then fringes of another kind can be obtained even when the surfaces are separated many centimeters. This type of interference can be observed by the naked eye, or more usually by means of a telescope, provided each is focused for infinity, in which case parallel rays are brought together at a point on the retina, or in the focal plane of the telescope objective.

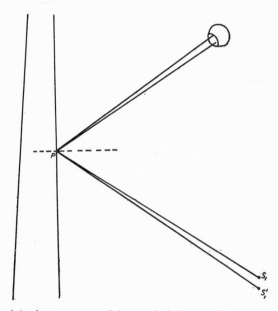

Fig. 9.6. Because of the finite aperture of the pupil of the eye, the point P is observed by interfering pairs of rays with slightly different path differences. In the figure, rays from the first surface only are shown.

Suppose AB, CD, Fig. 9.7, represent two such surfaces, plane and parallel to each other. Then, since at each surface, a partial reflection and a partial transmission are possible, an incident ray such as 1 can give rise to a reflected series of parallel rays a, b, c, d, e $\cdots$ as well as a transmitted series a', b', c', d', e' $\cdots$. If such a bundle falls on the objective of a telescope, a point image P is formed in its focal plane. Now between every two of these parallel rays there is the same path difference, which, by a method similar to that given above, may readily be shown to be equal to $2nt \cos r$, and which, therefore, since n and t are constants, varies only with r. It follows that the resultant intensity of the image at P varies with r, alternating from a maximum when $2nt \cos r$ is equal to a whole number of wavelengths, to a minimum when it is equal to an odd number of half wavelengths.* If then a beam incident on the face AB contains many rays striking the surface at different angles, and if either the reflected or the transmitted light is observed by a telescope focused for infinity, then a series of fringes is observed. Such fringes are called *fringes of equal inclination* or *Haidinger fringes*.

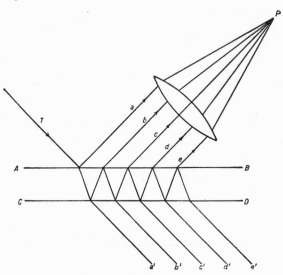

Fig. 9.7. a, b, c, d and e are interfering rays, superimposed at P, due to multiple reflections at the two parallel surfaces AB and CD of a transparent layer of uniform thickness.

To make the matter more concrete, a brief reference will be made to a simple instrument called the Fabry and Perot étalon, by means of which fringes of this kind are obtained using transmitted light. This instrument consists essentially of two glass plates, the inner adjacent surfaces of which, AB, CD, Fig. 9.8, are optically plane, accurately parallel, silvered although not opaque, and separated

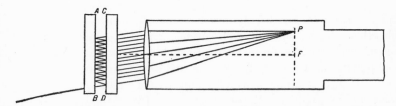

Fig. 9.8. Arrangement for viewing in a telescope fringes of equal inclination due to light transmitted through a Fabry-Perot étalon.

* This condition for a maximum or a minimum is correct only for the transmitted beam. In the case of the reflected beam, between rays a and b, there is always a phase difference of π in addition to the path difference. See again section 9.4.

by an air layer.   As explained in connection with Fig. 9.7, if a beam of light, fairly bright but *not* parallel, is incident on this arrangement, then, due to multiple reflections and transmissions, we have many emergent parallel bundles of rays, only one of which is shown in Fig. 9.8.   Since there is an infinite number of parallel bundles all of which make the same angle with the normal to the silvered surfaces, then, if *P* is a maximum (bright fringe), it follows that all

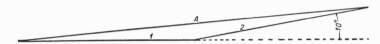

Fig. 9.9.   *A* is the resultant amplitude when two interfering rays 1 and 2 of equal amplitude, with phase difference 10°, are superimposed.

points on the circle passing through *P* with *F* as center, are also bright.   In other words we have circular fringes similar to those reproduced in Fig. 4, Plate IV, facing p. 153.

The fringes obtained by such an arrangement differ from those obtained by a biprism or a double slit, in respect to the distribution of intensity when one goes from one bright fringe to the next.   A comparison of Fig. 2, Plate IV (biprism fringes), or of Fig. 1, Plate IV (double slit), with Fig. 4, Plate IV (Fabry-Perot),

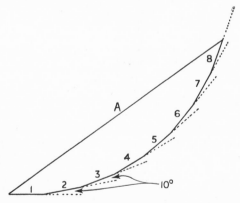

Fig. 9.10.   *A* is the resultant amplitude when interfering rays, 1, 2, 3 . . . 8, of equal amplitude, with phase difference between successive pairs 10°, are superimposed.

will show that in the latter case the maxima (bright fringes) are much narrower than in the others.   The reason for this is found in the fact that there are several interfering beams.   This will be evident if the student will apply the method of section 7.12, to find the resultant intensity, (1) of two disturbances differing in phase by 10°; (2) of eight, between every two of which there is a phase difference of 10°.   It will be found, by making diagrams similar to Fig. 9.9 and Fig. 9.10, that in the former case the intensity is more than 99% of the maximum, while

in the latter it has dropped to about 86% of the maximum.   This number has
been obtained on the assumption that all the beams are of equal amplitude,
whereas as a matter of fact the rays a', b', c', d', e', Fig. 9.7, steadily decrease in
intensity.   The general result, however, is not altered when this is taken into
consideration, for the complete analytical solution shows that the curve giving
the distribution of intensity for Fabry-Perot fringes is somewhat as illustrated
in Fig. 9.11.   If this is compared with the corresponding figure for two interfering
beams, Fig. 8.4, it will at once be evident that many interfering rays give rise
to narrow maxima.

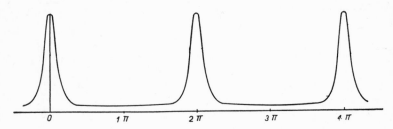

Fig. 9.11.   Intensity graph for fringe pattern due to the superposition of many interfering rays.
Note the narrow maxima composed with the broader maxima in Fig. 8.4. for two interfering rays.

Because of this fact, such an arrangement has several useful applications, two
of which are considered in sections 9.9 and 9.10.

9.7. Newton's Rings with Multiple Reflections.   Another excellent example
of the sharpening of bright fringes is shown in Fig. 2, Plate V, facing p. 168,
which is reproduced through the kindness of Professor S. Tolansky (Great
Britain).   This is a photograph of fringes obtained with a Newton's Rings arrangement using transmitted light, when the surfaces bounding the air film were
semi-silvered and so gave rise to many reflections.   The narrow bright fringes
in this photograph should be compared with the broad bright fringes shown in
Fig. 1, Plate V, to which reference has been made in section 9.5.

In Fig. 2, Plate V, it will be noticed that the fringes, although extremely
narrow, have a wavy appearance, a feature which is due to minute variations
in the surfaces.   The possibility of using multiple beam fringes to examine with
high precision the contours of crystal surfaces suggested itself to Tolansky, who
has carried out an important series of investigations on this subject.   For example, a sheet of mica with one face silvered was pressed against an optical flat
with a similar silver coating.   When this arrangement was illuminated with
monochromatic light at normal incidence, the fringe system observed "gave
contours of the topographical features of the crystal surface with very high
precision."   Since a fringe shift equivalent to $\lambda/100$ could be observed, such
features as extremely small discontinuous cleavage steps can be detected in this
way.

9.8. Interference Filters. In many experimental problems in optics it is necessary to use filters to transmit narrow bands of light, a hundred angstroms or less in width. For this purpose absorbing dyes have been used for many years. A recent development makes use of the principle of interference in so-called *interference filters.* In the simplest form, the arrangement, as shown in Fig. 9.12, is very similar to a Fabry-Perot étalon. In this figure, a and c represent *extremely thin* semi-transparent layers of a good reflecting material like silver, separated by a thickness t, equal to one or more half wavelengths, of a dielectric like magnesium fluoride. In the actual construction of the filter one layer of silver is deposited on a solid, transparent substrate like glass, then a coating of the dielectric (the spacer layer) is deposited on the silver, and finally the second layer of silver is added.

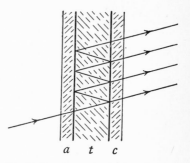

Fig. 9.12. In a simple interference filter a suitable thickness t of a substance like magnesium fluoride is enclosed between two extremely thin silvered reflecting layers a and c.

With such an arrangement, as in the étalon, corresponding to any incident ray (see again Fig. 9.8) because of multiple reflections a bundle of parallel rays emerges, the path difference between each successive pair being $2nt \cos r$. For light incident on the filter normally, this path difference $= 2nt$ and the emergent rays are all in phase when $2nt$ is equal to one wavelength λ_0 or a multiple of λ_0. If white light is used the intensity of the transmitted light will be a maximum for only those wavelengths which fulfill this condition. A plot of intensity of transmitted light against *wavelength* gives exactly the same type of graph as Fig. 9.11. The curve in this figure shows how the intensity varies either (1) when the incident light is monochromatic, with changing values of $\cos r$ (as in the Fabry-Perot étalon), or (2) when the incident light is white, with changing wavelength, for a fixed value of r, such as $r = 0$, in the case of the filter.

Hence, when white light falls on an interference filter, only narrow bands grouped around specific wavelengths are transmitted. If the thickness of the dielectric is such that $2nt = \lambda_0$ and $\lambda_0 = 5000$ A, then only a single narrow band in this region is transmitted because the other peaks in the graph would occur at 2500 A, 1250 A, etc. and these would be absorbed by the filter. If, however, $2nt = 4\lambda_0$ and $\lambda_0 = 1250$ A, then there would be transmitted bands in the visible region at 5000 A ($4\lambda_0$) and also at 6250 A ($5\lambda_0$).

By using silver layers with high coefficients of reflection, the peaks of the intensity curve may be made very sharp, widths as small as 20 angstroms having being obtained. Because of absorption by the silver layers, the intensity of the transmitted light is only from about 30 to 40 per cent of the incident. Compare this with the nonreflecting films discussed in section 9.4 where almost 100% is transmitted by the coated glass.

We have described the simplest type of filter. In some, the silver layers are replaced by multiple dielectric layers. For example, Polster (United States) has described a filter in which each silver film is replaced by a group of seven dielectric coatings, zinc sulphide alternating with cryolite. In between each group is the usual dielectric spacer layer. Because these coatings are of alternating high and low refractive indices, each group acts as a single reflecting layer with reflectivity exceeding 90 per cent. Polster states that a filter of this type transmits 80 per cent of the incident light, the transmitted band having a half-width of 65 A.

9.9. Comparison of Two Wavelengths. An important use to which the Fabry-Perot étalon has been put is in the accurate comparison of wavelengths. This is possible because the value of the radius of any fringe is a function of the wavelength. If now two wavelengths in a source are utilized, there are two systems of rings whose radii may be accurately measured. If one of these wavelengths is known to a high order of accuracy, then the wavelength of the other may be found to the same degree of accuracy by using a simple relation involving radii of corresponding rings.

9.10. Structure of a Single Spectral Line. An important use to which the Fabry-Perot étalon is often put is the analysis of a single spectral line. By placing the interferometer in the path of the beam of light between the collimating lens and the prism of a spectrograph (see section 6.2) we obtain not only the usual spectrum of the source but also part of a system of circular fringes crossing each spectral line. The appearance is then somewhat as shown by the heavy lines in Fig. 9.13, where AB represents the ordinary slit image of the spectral line, now, however, crossed with short interference fringes (which in reality are part of a circular system indicated by the dotted lines). Reproductions of actual photographs taken in this way are given in Figs. 3 and 4, Plate IX, facing p. 352.

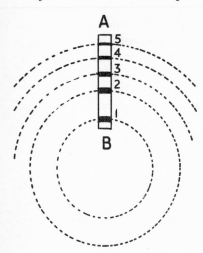

Fig. 9.13. AB is the appearance of a single spectral line when a Fabry-Perot étalon is combined with a spectrograph.

Now when the light corresponding to a spectral line is examined after this fashion it is generally found that the pattern obtained is not just a series of single fringes as in Fig. 9.13 or Fig. 3(a), Plate IX. More often the pattern consists of a group of two or more fringes regularly repeated. An excellent example of this is shown in Fig. 3(b), Plate IX, for which, together with Fig. 3(a),

the author is indebted to Dr. E. Gwynne Jones (Great Britain).   Fig. 3(b) clearly
shows that what in the ordinary spectrograph appears to be a single spectral line
(in this case, one due to bismuth, of wavelength 6600 A), in reality has three
components.   The reason they appear as a single line in the ordinary spectrograph is due to the fact that their wavelengths are too close together to be
separated by the dispersion of prisms.   Actually, in this case, the components
differ by 0.65 A and 0.53 A.

In Fig. 4, Plate IX, another example of this type of analysis is given.   In
Fig. 4(a), the interference pattern, that of the red hydrogen line H_a^1, of mean
wavelength 6562.79, shows that this line has at least two components and actual
measurement gives their separation as 0.14 A.   Fig. 4(b) is the interference pattern obtained with exactly the same optical arrangement as Fig. 4(a), but with
a luminous source containing a mixture of ordinary and of heavy hydrogen.   In

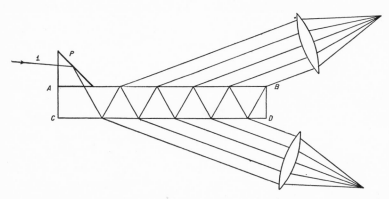

Fig. 9.14.   Ray paths due to multiple reflections in a Lummer plate arising from a single incident ray 1.

section 19.7 it will be explained that the red line emitted by heavy hydrogen,
that is, H_a^2 differs from the corresponding wavelength for ordinary hydrogen by
1.79 A.   The additional set of fringes which appears in Fig. 4(b) is then due to
this heavy hydrogen line.

Figure (a) of Plate I (frontispiece) shows the structure of the green line 5461
emitted by a discharge lamp containing ordinary mercury vapor.   In this example the complete ring system is used.   Both halves of this beautiful photograph, reproduced by the kind permission of Dr. E. C. Bullard, Director of the
National Physical Laboratory, England, were taken by Mr. H. Barrell of that
institution.   (See also section 9.12.)

Interferometers of high resolving power are also used for examining the
Zeeman effect (see section 17.7) when the component lines differ from each other
by a small fraction of an angstrom.   For example, in Fig. 4, Plate VIII, facing
p. 321, the two components there shown differ by only 0.07 of an angstrom.

9.11. Lummer Plate. Parallel bundles of interfering rays may be obtained by means of another comparatively simple device called the Lummer-Gehrcke plate, or sometimes the Lummer plate. While the essential part of the instrument is just a long narrow glass (or quartz) plate, its effectiveness lies in the fact that the sides AB and CD, Fig. 9.14, are optically plane and parallel. When, therefore, by means of a small reflecting prism P at one end, a ray 1 is introduced into the plate, multiple reflections give rise to bundles of parallel rays on either side of the plate, between every two of which there is the same path difference. For the same reason, and with the same general optical arrangement as in the Fabry-Perot étalon, interference fringes, such as shown in Fig. 3, Plate IV, facing p. 153, are obtained. Because of the great path difference, this instrument is also much used for the analysis of a single spectral line.

9.12. Michelson's Interferometer. At this stage the student will scarcely need to be told that an interferometer is an instrument which makes use of the

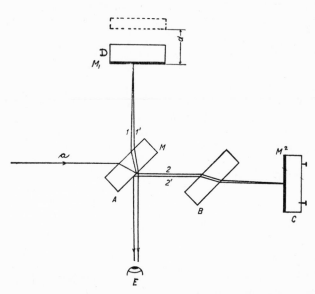

Fig. 9.15. Michelson's Interferometer. Because of reflection and refraction at the semi-silvered surface AM an incident ray a is broken into two rays 1 and 2 which, after reflection at the optically plane mirrors M_1 and M_2, are superimposed at the eye.

phenomenon of interference to make various measurements. One of the most interesting as well as one of the most useful of such instruments is one due to Michelson. In the standard form the arrangement is after the manner illustrated in Fig. 9.15, where A, B, C and D are glass plates, A and B with faces plane and parallel, the faces M_1 and M_2 of plates D and C being optically plane and well silvered. M_1 and M_2, therefore, are excellent optically plane mirrors, while, in addition, the surface M of plate A is frequently half silvered, although this is not necessary.

Suppose now that a represents a single ray from a broad source, which, on striking the surface M is partly reflected as ray 1, partly transmitted as ray 2. On striking mirror M_1, ray 1 is reflected as 1', subsequently falling on the eye at E, while ray 2 after traversing plate B and after reflection at mirror M_2, re-traces its path as ray 2', finally, after another reflection at M, traveling to the eye along with 1'. Since 1' and 2' originally came from the same disturbance, we once more have conditions suitable for interference. When, therefore, a broad source of light is used, in the whole field of view fringes are seen. For the proper adjustment and use of the instrument, the plane of mirror M_2 can be altered by adjusting screws, while the mirror M_1 can be moved parallel to itself over a con-siderable distance. The plate B, equal in thickness to A, is inserted between M and M_2 for the purpose of making the optical paths of the two interfering beams similar. It will be noticed that, without it, ray 1 and 1' after reflection at M would traverse a glass plate twice, ray 2 and 2' not at all, whereas, by the in-sertion of plate B, an equivalent thickness of glass is also traversed by ray 2' and 2.

Suppose, now, that such an instrument has been adjusted to give good fringes with an approximately monochromatic source, a sodium flame, for ex-ample. If, then, by means of a slow-motion screw the mirror M_1 is moved a small distance d cm, then the optical path of ray 1 is increased by $2d$ cm. Since, during the time that the path difference is increased by one wavelength, at any given place a bright fringe changes from bright to dark and back again to bright (a shift of one fringe), it follows that the slow motion of M_1 will cause a con-tinuous shift of the fringes. If the change from bright to bright takes place n times when the mirror is moved d cm, then

$$n\lambda = 2d. \qquad (9.06)$$

If, therefore, by means of a micrometer screw the distance d can be measured, we have from this simple relation another means of evaluating λ.

Conversely, and herein we have an important application of interference, if a source emitting a known wavelength is used, the same relation provides us with an exact means of measuring distances.

An important example of such an application is found in the work of Prof. Michelson on the measurement of the standard meter in terms of light wave-lengths. The standard meter, kept under lock and key at the International Bureau of Weights and Measures near Sèvres, France, and inspected only once in 10 years, defines the unit of length in terms of the distance between two scratches on a bar of platinum-iridium alloy. While there are secondary stand-ards, it is highly important that the length of the meter should be known in terms of an indestructible and permanent unit. Now a few sources emit highly mono-chromatic wavelengths which are reproducible and are constant in value to a high order of accuracy. For example, for many years the red line of luminous cadmium, whose wavelength in air at 15° C and 760 mm pressure is 6438·4696 A, was considered to be the most perfect source of monochromatic light which could be obtained. With this as a light source, Michelson found the length of the standard meter to be equal to 1,553,163.5 wavelengths.

Fundamentally the method used consisted in the measurement of the distance in terms of a count of fringes. As a count of such a large number would not only be very laborious, but also would increase the possible error of skipping a fringe or two, optical sub-units somewhat as illustrated in Fig. 9.16 were used. In each of these, blocks A and B were placed with silvered faces M_1 and M_2 plane and parallel, while their distances apart were made 10 cm, 10/2, $10/2^2$ ··· $10/2^3$ cm, or 0.390625 mm. By actual count of fringes the smallest distance was measured. This was then used as a unit of length by means of which (again by the use of the interferometer) the second distance was measured. Proceeding in this way,

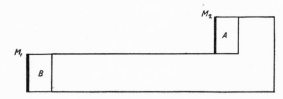

Fig. 9.16. M_1 and M_2 are reflecting optically plane mirrors on the face of blocks used by Michelson in measuring the standard meter in terms of light waves.

the 10-cm unit was accurately known in terms of a number of wavelengths. Finally the length of the standard meter was measured, using the decimeter piece as unit, with the result already given. For full details the student should consult Michelson's "Light Waves and Their Uses" or his "Studies in Optics."

Since Michelson carried out this investigation in 1893–1895, in association with Benoît (France), several other similar determinations have been made. Indeed, in 1923 and in 1927 the International Committee on Weights and Measures gave its approval to the principle of using the wavelength of light as the ultimate standard of length, the value of the meter at that time being provisionally expressed as equal to 1,553,164.13 wavelengths of the red cadmium line 6438.4696 A. The source of light was a cadmium lamp run at low temperature, low pressure, low current density, and at moderate voltage.

The need for the most careful measurements was obvious and, as Table VIII shows, a number of important investigations have been carried out. The fourth column in this table gives the wavelength of the red cadmium line when the meter is treated as the known quantity. It should be noted that the mean of all the observations 6438·4696 is exactly the same as the number used in defining the International Angstrom. (See section 6.3.)

But the story does not end here. A standard, especially such an important

one as the fundamental standard on which length is to be based, must be reproducible to an extremely high order of accuracy and even the red line of
cadmium is not absolutely free from objections.   For example, it has been found
that its wavelength increases *slightly* with increasing current through the cadmium lamp.   It is fortunate that nuclear physics has come to the rescue with
an even better source.   In section 19.12 it is pointed out that a spectral line has
components (and so departs from monochromatism) for two reasons: (a) because
of the presence of different isotopes in the element emitting light; and (b), even
for a single isotope, because of the spin of the nucleus of the atom.   A spectral
line emitted by an element consisting of a single isotope of zero nuclear spin is
free from components and highly monochromatic.   Such an isotope is found in
mercury, atomic weight 198, which can be manufactured by the bombardment
of gold by neutrons.   Moreover, as will be pointed out in section 17.9, because

Table VIII.

Date	Observers	Country	Wavelength
1892–3	Michelson & Benoît	France	6438.4691
1895–6	Benoît, Fabry and Perot	France	6438.4703
1927	Watanabe and Imaizumi	Japan	6438.4682
1933	Sears and Barrell	England	6438.4713
1933	Kösters and Lampe	Germany	6438.4689
1934–5	Sears and Barrell	England	6438.4709
1934–5	Kösters and Lampe	Germany	6438.4690
1937	Kösters and Lampe	Germany	6438.4700
1940	Romanova, Varlich, Kartashew and Batarchukova	Russia	6438.4687
	Mean Value		6438.4696

of its high atomic weight, any wavelength emitted by this element is an extremely small fraction of an angstrom in actual width, provided the temperature
of the vapor is low enough.

In recent years a number of observers, notably Meggers (United States) at
the Bureau of Standards and Barrell of the National Physical Laboratory, have
investigated the radiations emitted by discharge lamps containing mercury 198.
Barrell's photograph in Plate I (frontispiece), to which reference was made in
section 9.10, shows in part (b) how completely free from structure wavelength
5461 is, when emitted by such a source.   Meggers has shown that a water-cooled
electrodeless lamp of this kind "yielded wavelengths with probable errors less
than 0.0001 angstrom" and that the green line 5460.7532 is "a practically perfect
standard of length."   In June 1951, the National Bureau of Standards and the
Atomic Energy Commission announced that suitable lamps are now available
for qualified laboratories.   The announcement states that "present measurements show that 1,831,249.21 wavelengths of the green radiation from mercury
198 equal one meter".   (Dr. B. W. Sargent, Canadian neutron expert, states that
extreme care is necessary to make sure that mercury 198 is not contaminated

with mercury 199.   Work in progress in 1951 suggests that gold 198, the first product when gold 197 is bombarded by neutrons, captures neutrons readily to form gold 199 which transforms to mercury 199.)

Considerable work is also being done regarding the possible use of krypton 84 as a suitable source instead of or as an alternative to mercury 198.   Krypton 84, being a gas, has the advantage that it can be excited to luminosity at a much lower temperature than mercury 198, but the higher atomic weight of mercury gives it the advantage as a source of highly monochromatic radiation.   (See section 17.9.)

9.13. Difference in the Wavelengths of Sodium D_1 and D_2.   If a sodium flame is used as the source of light in a Michelson Interferometer and the fringe pattern observed over a wide range of path differences, it is found that the fringes disappear and reappear periodically.   For example, in some early measurements it was observed that, starting from zero path difference (when clear, distinct fringes were visible), the fringes disappeared when the path difference was increased by 0.289 mm.   Thereafter, they reappeared and disappeared periodically, the path change corresponding to two successive disappearances being 2×0.289, or 0.578 mm.   The explanation is due to the fact that a sodium flame emits two wavelengths λ_1 and λ_2 separated by a few angstrom units.   Whenever the path difference contains a whole number of wavelengths of λ_1 and a whole number plus $\frac{1}{2}$, or $\frac{3}{2}$, or $\frac{5}{2}$, of λ_2, bright fringes for λ_1 occur at the same place as dark fringes for λ_2 and uniform illumination results.

This experiment can be used to evaluate the difference between λ_1 and λ_2. As noted previously, whenever the path difference is changed by 0.578 mm, we go from one disappearance to the next.   It follows that this path difference must contain exactly one more wavelength of λ_2 than of λ_1 or that

$$\frac{0.578}{\lambda_2} - \frac{0.578}{\lambda_1} = 1,$$

or

$$0.578 \frac{\lambda_1 - \lambda_2}{\lambda_1 \lambda_2} = 1,$$

or

$$\Delta\lambda = \frac{\lambda^2}{0.578},$$

where $\Delta\lambda$ is the difference between λ_1 and λ_2 and λ is the mean value 5.89×10^{-5} cm of these two wavelengths.   Substituting, we find $\Delta\lambda = 0.60$ A.

This method of observing the change in the visibility of fringes with changing path difference was used with great skill by Michelson to analyze the spectral structure of other sources.   For example, by means of it he showed that the 6438 red line of cadmium was highly monochromatic.   This method, however, requires high experimental skill and was superseded by the more accurate method to which reference is made in section 9.10.

9.14. Before leaving the subject of interference a brief summary of its significance may not be amiss. First and foremost, we have been dealing with phenomena which can only be explained in terms of a wave theory of some kind. Moreover, these very phenomena provide us with various methods of measuring the actual wavelengths of light emitted by a source. Again, once wavelengths have been evaluated, instruments or optical arrangements by which interference fringes are obtained, enable us to make a great variety of measurements such as the determination of the index of refraction of a gas, the accurate measurement of small distances, the trueness of surfaces, and the analysis of the structure of a single spectral line. Finally, in the next chapter we shall see how the principle of interference helps us to meet one of the great objections made against the wave theory by the adherents of the corpuscular.

PROBLEMS

1. Two beams, as in a double slit or similar arrangement, are superimposed at a point where the phase difference between them is 60°. Find the ratio of the resultant intensity at this point to the resultant at a point where the two beams have no phase difference.

2. In an arrangement like the biprism, prove that the resultant intensity at a point where each ray has an intensity of a^2 is equal to $2a^2(1 + \cos \delta)$, where δ = phase difference between the interfering rays.

3. Interference fringes are formed because of the superposition of two interfering beams (as in a biprism) of equal intensities. Find the ratio of the intensity at the center of a bright fringe to the intensity at a point one-quarter of the distance between two fringes from the center.

4. At a certain point on a screen, the path difference for the two interfering rays (in an arrangement such as the biprism) is one-eighth of a wavelength. Find the ratio of the intensity at this point to that at the center of a bright fringe.

5. Light of wavelength 6.4×10^{-5} cm emerging from two narrow slit sources, 0.4 mm apart, is superimposed at points on a screen 50 cm from the sources. (A constant phase difference of zero degrees exists between the sources.) Find: (a) the distance between the central and the first bright fringe on either side of the center; (b) the phase difference between the two superimposed beams at a point P which is 0.1 mm from the center of a bright fringe (along a line running at right angles to the fringes); (c) the ratio of the intensity of the light at P to the intensity at the center of a bright fringe.

6. A double slit, with distance between the centers of its slits 0.324 mm, is placed in front of the objective lens of the telescope of a spectrometer. The slit of the collimator, which has been adjusted so that parallel rays emerge, is illuminated with light of wavelength 4.86×10^{-5} cm. If the focal length of the objective is 100 cm, find the ratio of the intensity at F, the center of the central bright fringe, to the intensity at a point P which is 0.5 mm from F, the line PF being in the focal plane of the objective.

7. A spectrometer is adjusted with a very narrow slit so that parallel rays leave the collimating lens. The telescope of the spectrometer has an objective of focal length 30 cm. Find the linear separation of two successive bright interference fringes observed in the focal plane of the objective when a double slit with distance between the centers of the slits = 0.5 mm is placed in front of the objective. Take $\lambda = 6.24 \times 10^{-5}$ cm,

8. Parallel rays of monochromatic light of wavelength 6000 A fall normally on a double slit, with separation between the centers of the slits = 0.3 mm, placed in front of a converging lens of focal length 50 cm. The emergent light is observed in the focal plane of the lens. Find the difference in phase between the two beams superimposed at a point P in the focal plane 0.25 mm. from the principal focus.

9. The telescope of a spectrometer is replaced by a camera, with a lens of focal length 60 cm, and the collimator is adjusted, with a narrow slit and monochromatic light, so that parallel rays emerge from the collimating lens. When a double slit, with distance from center to center of the two openings equal to 0.32 mm, is placed before the camera lens, fringes of width 1.2 mm are observed in the focal plane of the camera lens. Find the wavelength of the light.

10. A spectrometer, whose slit is illuminated with monochromatic light of wavelength 5461 A, is adjusted in the usual way, and then a double slit, with distance from center to center of each opening = 0.5 mm, is placed before the objective of the telescope. Find the angular width of the fringes observed.

11. Find by how many wavelengths of monochromatic light of 5461 A the path length is increased when a flake of glass of thickness 0.0428 mm and index of refraction 1.524 is placed in the path of the light.

12. An air-cell, such as is illustrated in Fig. 8.20, is placed in front of the objective of the telescope of a spectrometer and its position adjusted so that sharp interference fringes are observed with light of wavelength 5.89×10^{-5} cm. When all the air is exhausted from the cell, a shift of 10 fringes is observed. If the cell is 2.02 cm long, find the index of the air at room temperature and pressure.

13. If the index of refraction of a gas at 0° C and 76 cm pressure is 1.000292, find its value at 20° C and 75 cm pressure. (Assume the law that $n - 1$ is directly proportional to the density of the gas.)

14. A Fabry-Perot étalon is adjusted so that interference fringes for wavelength 5461 are observed in a telescope focused for infinity. The étalon, of thickness 1.01 cm, is enclosed in a box with transparent windows from which the air can be exhausted. It is found that there is a shift of one fringe when the pressure is changed by 6.46 cm Hg. Find the index of refraction of the air at room temperature and the original pressure which was 77 cm Hg.

15. If the temperature in problem 14 is 15° C find the index of refraction of the air at 0° C and 76 cm Hg pressure.

16. A telescope is focused on a narrow source slit, illuminated by D light, and the resulting interference fringes observed when a double slit, with distance between the centers of its component slits 0.324 mm, is placed in front of the objective. The source slit is divided into two parts, one fixed, the other movable, as in Fig. 8.10. If the two parts are originally exactly in line, find through what distance the movable part has to be moved until the resulting two sets of fringes are first exactly out of step. Distance from source slit to double slit = 5.00 meters.

17. A large telescope is focused on a double star and the interference pattern is observed when an adjustable double slit is placed in front of the objective. The distance between the centers of the components of the double slit is gradually increased until the fringes disappear. If this distance is 57.5 cm, find the angular separation of the two components of the double star. (Take mean $\lambda = 5.55 \times 10^{-5}$ cm.)

18. The slit of a spectrometer which is illuminated by 5461 A, is made in two halves, one fixed, the other movable. A double slit, with separation between the centers of its components 0.300 mm, is placed in front of the objective of the telescope and the movable half of the source slit adjusted until the two sets of fringes are exactly in line. If the focal length of the collimator lens is 20 cm, find through what distance the movable half must be shifted until the fringes are in line again.

19. A spectrometer with a very narrow slit is illuminated with monochromatic light. When a double slit, with separation between the centers of its components 0.314 mm, is placed in front of the objective of the telescope, the angular width of 8 fringes is 54 minutes. Find the wavelength of the light.

20. In a certain Rayleigh refractometer, the focal length of the objective of the observing telescope is 120 cm. When the narrow source slit is illuminated with monochromatic light and a double slit is placed in front of the objective, interference fringes 0.072 mm apart are observed. The source slit and collimating lens are then removed and the telescope (plus double slit) directed to a source, illuminated with the same light, consisting of two very narrow parallel slits at a distance of 480 cm from the objective. If the fringes have now disappeared, find the separation of the two narrow slits.

21. If a thin piece of glass, thickness = 3.6×10^{-4} cm, is placed in the path of one of the interfering beams in a biprism arrangement, it is found that the central bright fringe shifts a distance equal to the width of 4 fringes. Find the index of refraction of the piece of glass.
Wavelength of light used = 5.46×10^{-5} cm.

22. When the movable mirror of a Michelson's interferometer is shifted a certain distance, 200 fringes are observed to pass a given point in the field of view. If light of wavelength 6.24×10^{-5} cm is used, find how much the mirror was moved.

23. When the light from a sodium flame is viewed by reflection from a thin wedge-shaped air layer, formed between two pieces of good quality glass, interference fringes are observed. If, when looking perpendicularly, 10 fringes (bright to bright) are observed in a distance of 2 cm, find the angle of the wedge. (Wavelength is given.)

24. An air wedge is formed between two strips of plate glass by separating the plates at one end by a wire of thickness 0.036 mm, the plates being in contact at the other end. The distance from the line of contact to the wire is 17.9 cm. When the plates are held in a vertical position and viewed, approximately normally, by reflected yellow light, interference fringes 1.4 mm apart (dark to dark) are observed. Find the wavelength of the light.

25. An air wedge is formed as in problem 24, the plates being separated by a wire of unknown thickness and viewed by reflected green light of wavelength 5461 A. In going from the edge of contact to the wire, 84 dark and 84 bright fringes are counted (not including the dark region at the place of contact). Find: (a) the thickness of the wire; (b) the distance from the place of contact to the wire, if the angle of the wedge is 17.3 secs.

26. Monochromatic light emitted by a broad source of wavelength 5.89×10^{-5} cm falls normally on two plates of glass which enclose a thin wedge-shaped air film. The plates touch at one end and are separated at a point 20.2 cm from that end by a wire 0.042 mm in diameter. Find the width between any two bright fringes observed by reflected light.

27. In problem 26, if the air space is filled with water, whose index of refraction is 1.33, find the distance between the fringes.

28. A thin air film is formed by resting the spherical surface of a plano-convex lens on a flat plate of glass, the surfaces being in contact where they touch. The film is viewed perpendicularly by reflected green light of wavelength 5.46×10^{-5} cm. (a) Find the thickness of the air film (i) at the 10th bright ring; (ii) at the 8th dark ring. (b) If the radius of curvature of the spherical surface is 50.2 cm, find the diameters of the 10th bright and the 8th dark rings. (c) Find the diameter of the 10th bright and the 8th dark rings if the air space is filled with sulphuric ether, with index of refraction = 1.36.

29. A spherical glass surface resting on a plane glass surface forms a typical Newton's Rings arrangement (center black). Prove that the difference of the squares of the diameters of any two successive bright rings is a constant.

30. In a certain Newton's Rings arrangement the central spot is bright, not dark. If the thickness of the air film at the center is the smallest for which the center can be bright, find the diameter of the nth dark ring in terms of n, λ the wavelength, and R the radius of curvature of the curved surface.

31. A particle is disturbed by eight superimposed beams, each of the same intensity, and every successive pair of which differ by 12°. Apply the method of Fig. 9.10 to find the ratio of the resultant intensity to that when the phase difference between each pair is 0°.

32. Two optical arrangements are used to obtain interference fringes with monochromatic light. In the first there are two interfering beams of equal amplitude. In the second there are 37 beams and the arrangement is such that the phase difference between each successive pair is the same.

Find, in each case, the ratio of the intensity at the center of a bright fringe to the intensity at a point to one side of the center, when the point is so chosen that the phase difference between the two interfering beams, or between each successive pair, is 5°. (Apply the method of Fig. 9.10, and assume that the lines representing the 37 beams, when each successive pair differs in phase by 5°, form an arc of a circle.)

33. Prove that, for the multiple beam arrangement in problem 32, the same ratio is obtained for 73 beams with phase difference between successive pairs = 2.5°, or 145 beams, with phase difference = 1.25°.

34. Two interfering rays of equal intensity unite to form a resultant whose intensity is (a) 75 per cent; (b) 88.3 per cent of the resultant intensity when there is no phase difference between the rays. In each case find the phase difference between the rays.

35. In a Newton's Rings arrangement, find, for $\lambda = 5.44 \times 10^{-4}$ mm, the *resultant* phase difference between the two interfering rays, at a place where the thickness of the air film is 2.244×10^{-3} mm.

36. Monochromatic light of wavelength (in air) 6.40×10^{-5} cm is reflected approximately normally from the two plane faces of glass plates enclosing a thin film of water. If the index of water for this wavelength is 1.33, find (in degrees) the phase difference between the two interfering rays at a point on the face of the film where the thickness is 3.2×10^{-3} mm.

37. The thickness of a fourth-order interference filter (path difference = 7λ) is chosen to transmit a narrow band at 4000 A. Find, neglecting dispersion, what other bands are transmitted in the visible region.

38. A first-order interference filter, chosen to transmit a narrow band at 5500 A, is tilted through a small angle. Toward what end of the spectrum is the transmitted band shifted because of the rotation?

39. A source of light emits two wavelengths $\lambda_1 = 5890$ A, $\lambda_2 = 5896$ A. Interference fringes are observed with a certain arrangement when the paths of the interfering beams are exactly equal. How much will the path difference have to be increased so that a bright fringe for λ_1 coincides with a dark fringe for λ_2? (See section 9.13.)

X

Diffraction

10.1. In Chapter I it was pointed out in some detail that the *apparent* impossibility of explaining rectilinear propagation on a wave theory was so serious an obstacle to its acceptance that Newton and many other scientists gave their support to the corpuscular theory. In the preceding chapter we have given convincing evidence that a wave theory of some kind is necessary for the interpretation of interference phenomena, but as yet no explanation has been given of the fact that light for all practical purposes travels in straight lines.

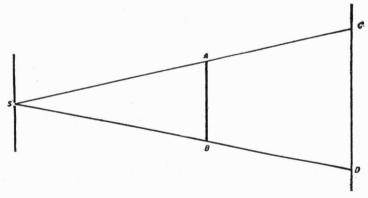

Fig. 10.1. If light travels in straight lines, *CD* is the shadow of an obstacle *AB* cast by a small source *S*.

In the present chapter we shall endeavor to show, (1) that, strictly speaking, light does *not* travel in straight lines, (2) that by combining a modification of Huygens' Principle with the principle of interference, after the manner of Fresnel, approximate rectilinear propagation results *for a wave motion in which the wavelengths are very small in comparison with the dimensions of ordinary obstacles and openings.*

Phenomena which make it evident that light, in certain circumstances, is not traveling in straight lines are said to be examples of diffraction, a name we owe to Grimaldi (Italy, 1618–1663), its discoverer. When an opaque obstacle such as *AB*, Fig. 10.1, is placed in the path of a beam of light emerging from a small hole S, Grimaldi showed not only that the width of the shadow cast on a screen is larger than the width CD it would have if light traveled in straight lines, but also that this wider shadow is bordered by colored bands. The pioneer work of Grimaldi was repeated and extended by Newton, who tried to explain the phenomenon in terms of the repulsion of light corpuscles by the obstacle, without realizing that it was something to be expected on a wave theory.

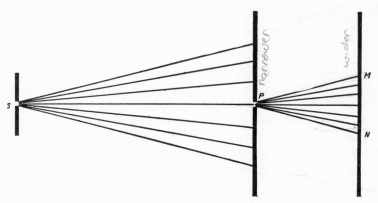

Fig. 10.2. Contrary to rectilinear propagation, light spreads out from a narrow aperture P illuminated by a small source S.

There are many other ways of showing that light does not travel in straight lines. If, for example, an adjustable slit P, Fig. 10.2, is placed in the path of a beam emerging from a narrow source slit S, and the light pattern on a screen is observed, it is found, after a certain width of P is reached, that the *narrower* P is made, the *wider* the band of light MN becomes. For a very narrow slit,

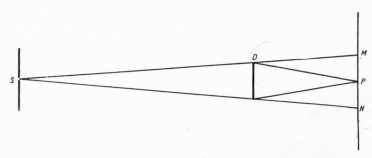

Fig. 10.3. Contrary to rectilinear propagation, when a small source of light is used, a bright spot P is observed at the center of the shadow MN of a small circular object D.

although the emergent light is faint, it covers an area hundreds of times greater than that which would be illuminated if light traveled in straight lines from the source to the screen.

Again, if a small perfectly circular object D, Fig. 10.3, is placed in the path of the beam from a point source S, instead of having a uniformly dark shadow MN, there is a *bright* spot at the center of the circular shadow. A photograph of the appearance will be found in Fig. 2, Plate VI, facing p. 209.

Later we shall have occasion to discuss other illustrations of the point we are trying to emphasize, but these should be sufficient to make it clear that it is not difficult to show by simple arrangements that light does not always even apparently or approximately travel in straight lines. It is natural then to ask, What are the general conditions necessary for making diffraction phenomena evident, and, once again, why is it that, generally speaking, light does appear to travel in straight lines?

10.2. A suggestive fact which will help in the answer to these questions is found when the slit P, Fig. 10.2, is made very wide, as represented in Fig. 10.4. It is then observed that the light patch on the screen has just about the width to be expected from the laws of geometrical optics (which postulate rectilinear propagation), although here again a close examination shows that at the edges M

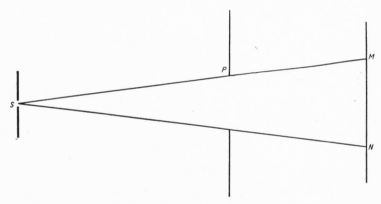

Fig. 10.4. When an aperture P is large, the size MN of the light patch on a screen due to a small source S is that to be expected from rectilinear propagation.

and N one or two narrow light and dark bands can be seen. Experiment then suggests that the larger an opening (or obstacle), the more nearly may we expect rectilinear propagation. Let us see what can be deduced about the matter from theoretical considerations.

Suppose we postulate again, as in section 3.2, that every particle in a wavefront is the source of a secondary wavelet, which, however, we shall now consider to be effective over the whole of its wave-front, and not simply at the small area tangent to the enveloping surface.

If, then, the small circle in Fig. 10.5 represents a wavelet starting from particle 1 on a wave-front which originally came from the source S, we are assuming that the wavelet is effective not only at P, where CPD is the enveloping surface representing a later position of the wave-front, but also at other points such as M. We shall postulate further that the *amplitude* of the disturbance at points on the wavelet is less the greater the angle $1M$ makes with the ray $1P$, in other words, that it varies with the obliquity.

Bearing these things in mind, we see that if well-defined wave-fronts from a small source S fall on an opening P, Fig. 10.6, the intensity at any point Q on a screen receiving the emergent light will be the resultant of all the elementary disturbances coming to it from all the sources in the plane of the opening sending out wavelets. The problem, then, becomes one of superimposing a large number

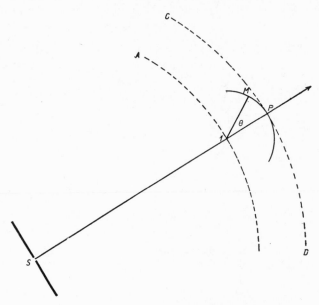

Fig. 10.5.   In Fresnel theory of diffraction the wavelet originating at particle 1 is effective in the direction $1M$ as well as $1P$; but the greater θ, the less the effect.

of disturbances, and therefore is one to which we can apply the principle of interference. The solution is not always easy, and fairly extended mathematical analysis is needed for treating the problem generally with any attempt at exactness. Much, however, can be learned by confining our attention to simple cases and by making use of graphical methods.

10.3. Half-Period Elements.   First of all, then, let us consider that the point source S is sufficiently far away that we are concerned with plane wave-fronts of monochromatic light. Then let us find the resultant amplitude at a point P, Fig. 10.7, due to an aperture limiting the exposed part of the wave-front to AB. As a first step in the solution it is convenient to subdivide the wave-front into a number of elemental areas. To do so, drop a perpendicular $PM_0 = b$, from P

to the wave-front; then with M_0 as center draw on the wave-front a circle of radius M_0M_1, the magnitude of M_0M_1 being such that the distance $PM_1 = b + (\lambda/2)$. Next, describe a second circle of radius M_0M_2, such that $PM_2 = b + 2 \cdot (\lambda/2)$, and so on. In this way the whole of the wave-front is subdivided into areas called *half-period elements* or *zones*, of such a size that the

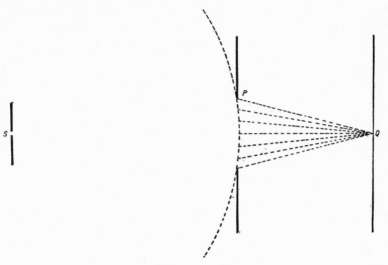

Fig. 10.6.   The intensity of the light at Q is the resultant of all the disturbances coming from elementary parts of the exposed wave-front P.

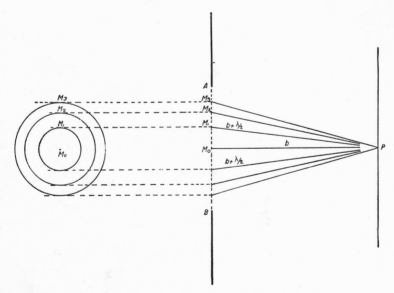

Fig. 10.7.   Diagram used to explain half-period elements.

distance from the outer edge of any one to the point P is greater than that from the outer edge of the preceding one by half a wavelength.

The areas of these half-period elements are equal *when the wavelength in question is small in comparison with the distance b in Fig. 10.7.*

$$\text{Area of first elemental area} = \pi M_0 M_1{}^2$$

$$= \pi (PM_1{}^2 - PM_0{}^2)$$

$$= \pi \left\{ \left(b + \frac{\lambda}{2} \right)^2 - b^2 \right\}$$

$$= \pi b \lambda + \frac{\pi \lambda^2}{4}$$

$$= \pi b \lambda,$$

if λ is small compared with b.

Again, the area of the first and the second elements

$$= \pi M_0 M_2{}^2$$

$$= \pi (PM_2{}^2 - PM_0{}^2)$$

$$= \pi \left\{ (b + \lambda)^2 - b^2 \right\}$$

$$= 2\pi b \lambda.$$

$$\therefore \quad \text{area of the second element} = \pi b \lambda.$$

Proceeding in this way, we see generally that, if λ is sufficiently small compared with b, we may with little error neglect λ^2, and the area of each half-period element $= \pi b \lambda$. For $\lambda = 6 \times 10^{-5}$ cm and $b = 50$ cm, it is easy to show that the error in using this expression for the area is 0.00003 per cent for the first element and 0.006 per cent for the 100th.

Actual Size of Half-Period Elements. Suppose we are dealing with light for which $\lambda = 5 \times 10^{-5}$ cm, and that the screen is placed at a distance of 50 cm from the aperture; then the area of each element

$$= \pi b \lambda$$

$$= 3.14 \times 50 \times 5 \times 10^{-5} \text{ sq cm}$$

$$= 0.00785 \text{ sq cm}.$$

As ordinary areas go, therefore, half-period elements are extremely small. A circular aperture whose radius is 1 cm contains 400 in this particular case.

The student must not fail to realize, however, that the actual area of these hypothetical elements depends both on the wavelength and on the distance of the screen or eyepiece from the wave-front.

Although the area of each element may be taken as $\pi b \lambda$ to a high order of accuracy, in considering the various factors which affect the resultant amplitude at P, in Fig. 10.7, one ought not to neglect the very slight increase in the areas of the elements as we go out from M_0. Let us examine this question carefully. The amplitude at P due to a single half-period element depends on: (1) the area of the element; (2) its mean distance from P; and (3) the obliquity, that is, the angle between the line joining the element to P and a perpendicular to the plane waves incident on AB, in Fig. 10.7.

(1) As far as area is concerned, it is reasonable to assume that the amplitude at P is directly proportional to the area. The greater the area, the greater the number of particles sending out wavelets in accordance with the modification of Huygens' Principle we are discussing.

(2) As far as distance is concerned, we know from the work discussed in section 7.18, that the amplitude falls off inversely as the distance.

If we consider the *combined effect* of both area and distance, it is easy to show that the contribution of each element is *exactly the same*. Here is the proof.

From the foregoing, we can state that the amplitude at P due to a single element is proportional to area/distance.

But the area of the nth element

$$= \pi \left\{ \left(b + n\frac{\lambda}{2} \right)^2 - b^2 - \left(b + \overline{n-1}\,\frac{\lambda}{2} \right)^2 + b^2 \right\}$$

$$= \pi\lambda \left\{ b + \left(2n - 1 \right)\frac{\lambda}{4} \right\}.$$

Also, the mean distance of the nth element from P

$$= \frac{1}{2}\left(b + n\frac{\lambda}{2} + b + \overline{n-1}\,\frac{\lambda}{2} \right)$$

$$= b + \left(2n - 1 \right)\frac{\lambda}{4}.$$

Hence,

$$\frac{\text{area}}{\text{distance}} = \frac{\pi\lambda \left\{ b + \left(2n - 1 \right)\dfrac{\lambda}{4} \right\}}{b + \left(2n - 1 \right)\dfrac{\lambda}{4}}$$

$$= \pi\lambda, \text{ a constant for all values of } n.$$

(3) There is left the obliquity factor (see section 10.2). As already postulated, the amplitude at points in a wavelet originating in a secondary source decreases with increasing obliquity. We conclude, therefore, that, as we go outward from M_0 in Fig. 10.7, the amplitude due to each successive element decreases steadily, although extremely slowly because of the scarcely detectable difference in the obliquities of two neighboring elements.

In considering the *resultant* amplitude due to all elements making their contribution at P, differences in phase are of primary importance. Because of the way in which the half-period elements are constructed, the phase difference between any two successive zones is π radians or 180°. Our original problem, therefore, may now be re-stated as follows:

Find the resultant amplitude for n S.H.M., all in the same straight line, whose amplitudes decrease extremely slowly and between every successive two of which there is a phase difference of π.

Let d_1 = amplitude of disturbance at P due to the first element alone,

d_2 = amplitude of disturbance at P due to the second element alone,

or, in general,

d_n = the amplitude due to the nth element.

As we have seen, d_1 is *slightly* greater than d_2, d_2 than d_3, d_n than d_{n+1}. Moreover, the difference between any two successive d's becomes less and less the higher the numbers of the elements, because of their increasing narrowness as we go out from the first.

In solving this problem we apply the proposition of section 7.12, obtaining the result that all the amplitudes (because of the phase difference of π) lie on the same straight line, as in a, Fig. 10.8. For the purpose of clearness we have separated the individual amplitudes as in b, Fig. 10.8 and c, Fig. 10.8, but it must not be forgotten that they all lie along the same straight line. The resultant amplitude is represented by BA, and it will be noted that b, Fig. 10.8 applies to odd values of n, c, Fig. 10.8 to even.

Fig. 10.8.   *AB represents the resultant amplitude when n disturbances, whose amplitudes steadily decrease and between every successive pair of which the phase difference is 180°, are superimposed. In (b) n is even; in (c) odd.*

The actual value of BA, the resultant, which we shall henceforth represent by D, will be found in a few special cases.

Case I. **Circular Aperture Containing Only a Few Elements.** Suppose the aperture AB, Fig. 10.7, is circular and is so small that $n = 1$ (the student should find its actual radius for particular values of b and λ). In that case, $D = d_1$.

When $n = 2$, $D = d_1 - d_2$, or is practically zero. In other words, the intensity of the light at P when the opening contains two half-period elements is a minimum, or P is dark.

When $n = 3$, $D = d_1 - d_2 + d_3$, that is, is very nearly equal to d_1 or d_3. In this case, the intensity at P is a maximum, or P is bright.

We see then, generally, that if a small circular opening contains a few elements the number of which is odd, the intensity at P is a maximum, whereas if the number is even, the intensity is a minimum. The truth of this can readily be verified by direct experiment, if a circular opening, of diameter 1 or 2 mm is illuminated with light coming from a distant pin-hole source and the emergent

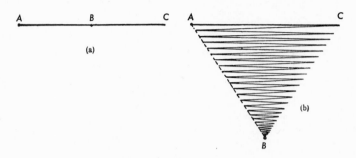

Fig. 10.9.   *AB is the resultant amplitude when the number of disturbances superimposed as in Fig. 10.8 is large.*

light is received on a screen or viewed in an eyepiece. By gradually altering the distance b from the eyepiece to the aperture, it will be found that the center of the light pattern is alternately bright and dark. Since the area of a half-period element depends on b, as b is altered the opening of fixed area must contani

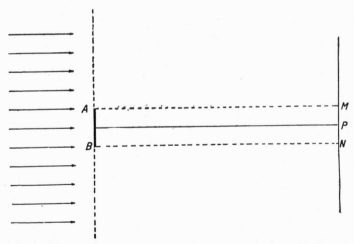

Fig. 10.10.   *P is a point at the center of the shadow MN cast by a circular object AB illuminated by parallel rays. P is bright if the object covers only a few half-period elements.*

alternately an odd and an even number of elements. Actual photographs of the appearance are reproduced in Fig. 1, Plate VI, facing p. 209, where Fig. *b* shows a bright center, Fig. *a*, a dark one.

Case II. **Large Aperture Containing Very Many Zones.**   If the number of exposed elements is sufficiently large, then ultimately the value of d_n will become negligibly small, and the figures corresponding to a, and b or c, Fig. 10.8, will be as shown in a and b, Fig. 10.9.   This figure shows at once that

$$D = \frac{d_1}{2}. \tag{10.01}$$

This important result tells us that when the exposed portion of the wave-front contains a very large number of half-period elements, or, in other words, when the dimensions of an opening are large compared with the wavelength, the resultant intensity at a point such as P is the same *as if* the light came directly from an opening smaller than the first half-period element.

Case III. **Circular Obstacle.**   Consider the intensity at a point P at the center of the geometrical shadow MN, Fig. 10.10, cast by a circular object AB illuminated by plane waves of monochromatic light.   According to the view we are presenting, disturbances from all the particles in the exposed portion of the wave-front arrive at P.   What is the resultant in this case?

Let the object cover k elements.   Then, since the $(k + 1)$ element is the first from which P receives light, the problem is exactly the same as the one we have

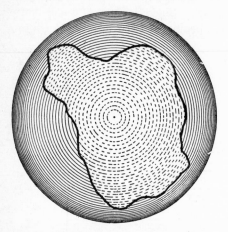

considered for a large opening, except that d_{k+1} replaces d_1. The figure for finding the resultant otherwise will be exactly the same as Fig. 10.9.   It follows, therefore, that the resultant amplitude at P for this case is

$$\frac{d_{k+1}}{2}.$$

If now the object is so small that only a few elements are covered, this resultant amplitude cannot be neglected.   This means that there is then a bright spot at the center of the shadow MN.   That this is actually the case has already been pointed out when reference was made to Fig. 2, Plate VI. If the object is small and not circular, no such spot will be seen because, in the case of an irregular object, irregular

Fig. 10.11. The dotted circles represent half-period elements covered by an irregularly shaped obstacle. In this case whether the object is small or large, no light is received at points within the shadow cast by the object.

portions of a number of elements will be "exposed" in a random fashion, as Fig. 10.11 suggests, and no maximum at P is possible.

Case IV. **Large Obstacle.**   If an object is large, that is, if it is one which covers a large number of elements and therefore has dimensions large compared with the wavelength, then k is so great that the value of $d_{k+1}/2$ may be neglected.

This means that for the majority of ordinary objects (whose dimensions fulfill this condition) points such as P are completely screened. The reason again is *not* because light travels in straight lines from the distant point source, but because *the application of the principle of interference shows that the resultant of all the disturbances from the various parts of the exposed wave-front is practically zero.* Conditions, however, are the same *as if* light traveled in straight lines from the distant point source and the "direct" rays were cut off by the obstacle.

Approximate rectilinear propagation, then, results from the fact that ordinary openings and ordinary objects have dimensions many times the mean wavelength of light. The screening action of obstacles depends on the wavelength of the disturbance; consequently in the case of sound, where we have to do with wavelengths of a foot or two, it is not surprising that we do not observe shadows. To obtain shadow effects, objects of great dimensions are necessary.

10.4. Diffraction effects prove that light does "bend around corners," and in general behaves in this respect like any other kind of wave motion, the difference being in degree, not in kind. But even diffraction effects are not observed unless the object or aperture is properly illuminated. In the examples we have given, the distant source was always so narrow that we were able to consider well-defined wave-fronts in the plane of the aperture or opening. If, however, a broad source is used, or if we are dealing with the general illumination due to diffuse light, no such effects are observed even in the case of small objects. The reason is much the same as has been given to explain why double slit fringes cannot be obtained with a broad source. Every elemental source into which the wide one may be subdivided will give rise to its own diffraction pattern. The superposition of all these makes the formation of maxima or minima impossible.

10.5. Zone Plate. An interesting example of diffraction, as well as a confirmation of the foregoing theory, is found in the zone plate. This is a simple device whose construction is based on the fact that, since the areas of the half-period elements are equal, their radii are in the ratios $1 : \sqrt{2} : \sqrt{3} : \sqrt{4} :$ etc.

Suppose, then, that a set of circles, whose radii increase according to this law, are drawn on a sheet of white paper, and that every second area is blackened. If this pattern is then photographed, the resulting plate will give a system of areas corresponding to the half-period elements, every second one of which is opaque. If this zone plate, as it is now called, is placed in the path of plane waves of monochromatic light and the emergent light allowed to fall on a screen, there will be a certain position of the latter (that is, a certain value of b) for which the hypothetical half-period elements coincide with the actual areas of the zone plate. In that case, when the even numbers are opaque,

$$D = d_1 + d_3 + d_5 + \cdots,$$

since the phase difference between every successive exposed area is 2π. Again the graphical solution gives a straight line but this time the lines representing individual amplitudes all point in the same direction, lying end to end. A maximum of such great intensity results that the zone plate is sometimes spoken of as having a focal length equal to this particular value of b.

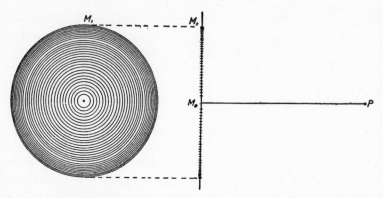

Fig. 10.12.   The subdivision of a single half-period element into a large number of sub-elements.

10.6. More General Treatment.   Hitherto we have dealt with only the resultant amplitude due to each half-period element. Actually, as we go from particles just on the inner edge of a single element to the outer edge of the same element, the phase difference must gradually change. It is our purpose now to take into consideration this gradual change of difference in phase between disturbances from particles in a single element. To do so, consider the first element

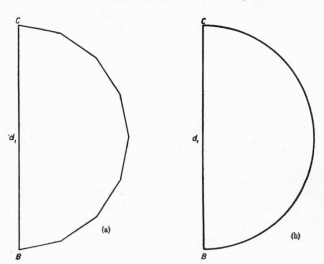

Fig. 10.13.   The sub-elements of Fig. 10.12 combine to give a resultant at P, Fig. 10.12, represented by BC.

and imagine it subdivided into a large number of very small elemental ring areas subject to the condition that the distance to the point P, Figs. 10.7 and 10.12, from the edge of any ring differs from the distance of the corresponding edge of the next by the same amount. There will then be the same phase difference between the disturbances from any two successive elemental areas. Moreover, it may readily be proved, just as we did for the half-period zones themselves, that all these sub-areas are equal. Therefore, if a is the amplitude at P due to the first of these elemental areas about M_0, the amplitude of the last (in the neighborhood of M_1) will differ from a by a negligibly small amount.

Suppose, now, we have n of these sub-areas in a single half-period element such as the first, and we wish to find the resultant disturbance. Since the phase

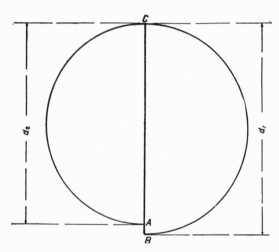

Fig. 10.14.   The sub-elements of two half-period elements combine to give a resultant represented by AB, which in practice is negligibly small.

difference between any successive two is the same, since the phase difference between the first and the last is π, and since the individual amplitudes are practically equal, the polygon from which the resultant is found, Fig. 10.13(a), will approach a half circle more and more closely, as the number of sub-elements (which may be as large as we please) is increased. In the limit, then, Fig. 10.13(b), is the graphical solution from which we see that the resultant of the first half-period element $= BC$, that is, d_1 in the above notation. Moreover, $d_1 = 2na/\pi$, since na is the length of half the circumference of a circle of diameter d_1. (See section 10.7.)

If we proceed in similar fashion to find the resultant of the first two zones, then a second half-circle will be added to Fig. 10.13(b), whose diameter $CA = d_2$, Fig. 10.14, practically could not be distinguished from BC. Theoretically, since there is a very slight falling off in amplitude even in going out from the center a distance equal to two zones, the half-circles are not perfect and the point A does not quite coincide with B. Once more, however, the resultant of the two zones,

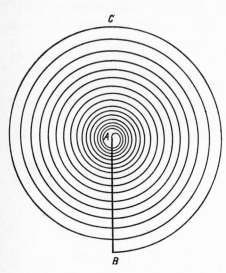

equal to BA, that is, $d_1 - d_2$, is negligibly small, the length BA being grossly enlarged in the figure.

When a large number of elements is considered it is not difficult to see that the graphical solution by this method is given by Fig. 10.15. The final resultant is then AB, Fig. 10.15, which is equal to $BC/2$ or $d_1/2$, just as in the other method.

Fig. 10.15. The sub-elements of a very large number of half period elements combine to give a resultant AB, equal to $BC/2$. Compare Fig. 10.9.

10.7. PROBLEM. *Plane waves of monochromatic light fall normally on an opaque screen containing an adjustable circular aperture. The size of the aperture is altered so that, with respect to a point P on the axis the aperture successively contains: (a) $1\frac{1}{2}$ half-period elements (H.P.E.); (b) 1 H.P.E.; (c) $\frac{1}{2}$ H.P.E.; (d) $\frac{1}{4}$ H.P.E. If the resultant intensity at P in case (b) is taken as 1, find the intensity at P in each of the other cases.*

In Fig. 10.16 let $BC = d_1$ represent the resultant amplitude at P due to the first H.P.E. Since, as we have seen before, the arc in Fig. 10.14 is proportional to the *area* of the small opening, then in Fig. 10.16 the arc $BFEC$ is proportional to the area of the first H.P.E. Hence, the arc $BECD$ is proportional to $1\frac{1}{2}$ H.P.E.; the arc BFE to $\frac{1}{2}$ H.P.E.; and the arc BF (where $BF = FE$) to $\frac{1}{4}$ H.P.E.

The corresponding amplitudes are BD, for $1\frac{1}{2}$ H.P.E.; BE for $\frac{1}{2}$ H.P.E.; and BF for $\frac{1}{4}$ H.P.E.

Since $OB = \dfrac{BC}{2} = \dfrac{d_1}{2}$, by simple geometry, using the $\triangle BOD$, it follows at once that $BD = d_1/\sqrt{2}$. Also $BE = d_1/\sqrt{2}$, and using the $\triangle BOF$,

$$BF = d_1 \tan 22.5°$$
$$= 0.414 d_1.$$

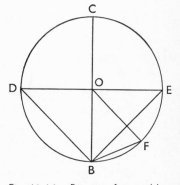

Fig. 10.16. Diagram for problem solved in section 10.7.

Hence, since the intensity varies as the square of the amplitude, and we are given that $d_1{}^2 = 1$, the four required intensities are: (a) 0.5; (b) 1; (c) 0.5; (d) 0.17.

10.8. Other Examples of Diffraction. Some very interesting, as well as beautiful, examples of diffraction are obtained when a pin-hole distant source is replaced by a very narrow slit, and narrow rectangular apertures, or objects such as wires and needles are used. For example, Fig. 5, Plate VI, facing p. 209, is a photograph of the diffraction pattern of a narrow aperture, with width and screen distance such that the center is dark. On the other hand Fig. 3, Plate VI, shows the pattern obtained with a narrow wire, conditions being such that there is a bright line down the center of the shadow.

In considering diffraction problems where we have to do with a narrow source slit, we may adopt a graphical method very similar to the one we have used for a pin-hole source. In the former case, however, if the slit is sufficiently long, we must consider cylindrical wave-fronts rather than spherical. When, therefore,

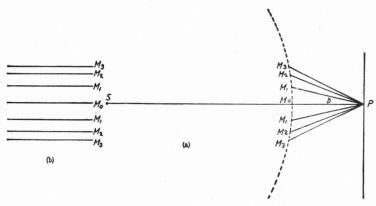

Fig. 10.17.   Cylindrical half-period elements.

the resultant intensity is wanted at points along a line running through the point P, Fig. 10.17, and parallel to the slit, we subdivide the wave-front into strips rather than zones. To do so the same general method is followed as for half period zones. Thus, $PM_0 = b$ is drawn perpendicular to the wave-front; a line through M_1 defining the outer edge of the first strip in the upper half of the wave-front is drawn subject to the condition that $PM_1 = b + (\lambda/2)$; the upper edge of the second strip is defined by a line through M_2 such that $PM_2 = b + (2\lambda/2)$, and so on for the others. The lower half is subdivided similarly so that looking at the wave-front "face on," the very exaggerated appearance is somewhat as shown in b, Fig. 10.17.

Now while these strips are extremely narrow, their areas, unlike those of the half-period zones, are not equal, but decrease, at first fairly rapidly, as the distance from M_0 increases. The result of this is that, when we find the resultant at P by a graphical method similar to that exemplified in Fig. 10.15, we obtain for the solution a diagram like that given in Fig. 10.18. While mathematical analysis is needed to determine the exact nature of this figure, called *Cornu's*

Spiral, its general features should be clear enough by analogy with the solution for a pin-hole source. Thus, since the difference in phase between disturbances from the corresponding edges of two successive strips is π, OM represents d_1, the amplitude contributed by the first strip in the upper half, OM' the correspond-

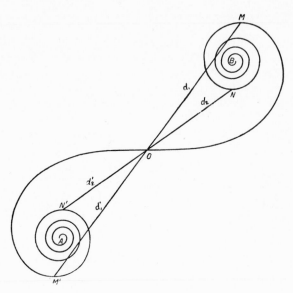

Fig. 10.18.   Cornu's Spiral.

ing d_1' for the first strip of the lower half; ON, d_2 for the first and second strips of the upper, ON', d_2' for the first and second of the lower, and so on.

If, then, the whole wave-front is exposed, the resultant amplitude is represented as always (see again section 7.12) by the line joining the beginning and end of the figure formed by the individual amplitudes—in this case, by AB. If,

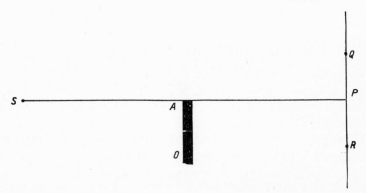

Fig. 10.19.   *S* represents a narrow slit; *AO* an object with a straight edge at *A* parallel to the slit.

however, a narrow aperture is used covering only the first strip in each half, then the resultant amplitude is $MM'(2d_1)$. If such an aperture is widened so that it now includes two strips in each half, then the resultant is equal to $NN'(2d_2)$. Thus, for this second width, the intensity at P, the center of the diffraction pattern, is considerably less than for the first one.

An interesting example of this type of diffraction has to do with a straight edge. Suppose S, Fig. 10.19, represents a long narrow source slit running perpendicular to the plane of the paper, AO an obstacle whose straight edge A is parallel to the slit, and QPR a screen, P being the line which separates light from darkness according to the laws of geometrical optics (that is, exact rectilinear propagation). Consider now the intensity, (a) at the point P (in reality

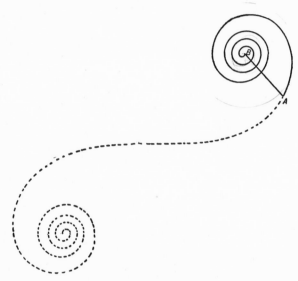

Fig. 10.20. AB represents the amplitude at points such as R in the region below P in Fig. 10.19.

at points along a line running through P and parallel to the slit); (b) at points such as R in the shadow region below P; (c) at points such as Q in the light region above P.

Since at P the lower half of the spiral is covered by the obstacle, exactly the upper half of the wave-front being "exposed," the resultant amplitude at P is represented by OB, Fig. 10.18.

For all points such as R, it will be seen that not only the whole of the lower half of the spiral is covered, but that smaller and smaller portions of the upper half are exposed, the farther R is taken from P. The resultant amplitude, therefore, which in Fig. 10.20 is represented by BA, is steadily decreasing as points are taken farther and farther into the shadow region.

Turning next to points such as Q, Fig. 10.19, above P, we note first of all that all of the upper half of the wave-front is exposed, together with a portion of the lower whose magnitude increases the farther Q is taken from P. Thus, when Q is in such a position that the first strip of the lower is added to the upper half, the resultant is represented by BM', Fig. 10.21, while when Q is sufficiently far removed from P that the first two strips of the lower are added, the resultant is BN' in the same figure. We see, then, that, as points are taken farther and farther away from P in the light region, we have alternately maximum and minimum values for the resultant amplitude. A careful use of Cornu's Spiral

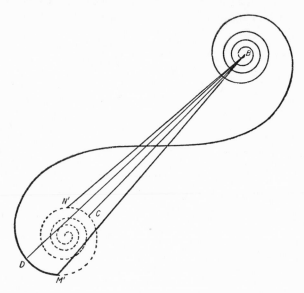

Fig. 10.21. At points above P in Fig. 10.19, the amplitude alternates between maxima and minima values. In this figure BD is the amplitude at the first maximum above P, BC at the first minimum.

in this way enables one to plot an intensity curve of the general nature shown in Fig. 10.22, where AB corresponds to the square of AB in Fig. 10.20; OB to the square of OB in Fig. 10.18; and BC', BD' to the squares of BC, BD in Fig. 10.21. The actual appearance of such a diffraction pattern is reproduced in Fig. 4, Plate VI, facing p. 209.

The following problem is given as a further illustration of the use of the spiral.

Using an arrangement like that of Fig. 10.19, prove that the intensity at P, if the obstacle AO is removed, is four times the intensity at this point with the obstacle in the position shown.

With the obstacle removed, the whole wave-front is effective, and the resultant amplitude at $P = AB$, in Fig. 10.18.

As already noted, with the obstacle in position, the resultant amplitude at $P = OB$, in Fig. 10.18.

Hence, the required ratio

$$= \frac{AB^2}{OB^2} = \frac{4OB^2}{OB^2} = \frac{4}{1}.$$

10.9. Fresnel and Fraunhofer Diffraction. There are two general classes into which diffraction phenomena may be divided. In the first, to which the name Fresnel is applied, the intensity at any point is the resultant of disturbances coming directly to that point from all parts of the exposed wave-front. This is the kind we have been considering in this chapter. In the second, designated

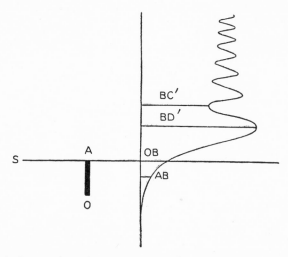

Fig. 10.22.   Graph showing how the intensity varies from point to point in the region *RPQ*, of Fig. 10.19.   In this figure *OB* represents the amplitude at *P*, Fig. 10.19.   See Plate VI, Fig. 4, facing p. 209.

by the name Fraunhofer, a lens is placed beyond the aperture or obstacle, and the diffraction pattern is examined in the plane where a sharp image of the source would be formed in the absence of the aperture or obstacle. Since the source is generally a distant one, this plane is never far from the focal plane of the lens, and in all cases which we shall consider in the next chapter, is identical with that plane.

Although there is no real fundamental difference between the two classes, it is worth noting the following. In Fresnel diffraction, except for regions close to the center of the half-period elements into which the wave is divided, the phase changes rapidly as we go from point to point on the wave-front and the only really effective part is that portion of the wave-front near the center. For example, in the case of a straight edge, this means the region near the edge.

In Fraunhofer diffraction, however, at a focal point the disturbance from *all* parts of the exposed wave-front arrive in phase, and so *the whole wave-front is effective.* The next chapter should make the difference clear. Since the Fraunhofer diffraction pattern is to be observed in the focal plane of a lens, we may use either a *distant* narrow source of light or a collimating lens with the source in its focal plane.

XI

Fraunhofer Diffraction

11.1. Three important cases of this type of diffraction will be discussed: (1) a single opening, (2) two openings (the double slit), (3) many openings (the grating). In all cases we shall assume that plane waves fall on the openings, and hence that the diffraction pattern is observed in the focal plane of a lens. It follows that, for visual observation, a spectrometer (adjusted in the usual way described in section 6.2) provides an excellent arrangement if the aperture is placed in the parallel beam leaving the collimator.

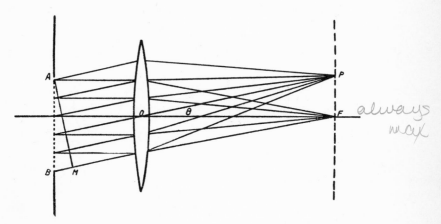

Fig. 11.1.   At *P* all rays parallel to *OP* diffracted at the rectangular aperture *AB* are superimposed by the lens.

Single Rectangular Aperture.   Suppose, then, that a narrow rectangular aperture is placed in the path of plane waves before the objective of a telescope. Applying the same ideas as in the last chapter, we see that there will be a resultant disturbance at points such as *P*, Fig. 11.1, in the focal plane of the objective.   There will be this difference, however, that for each point such as *P* we have to deal with a large number of *parallel* rays incident on the lens, and not, as in Fig. 10.6, for example, with rays going directly to *Q* from the elemental sources in the plane of the opening.   For this reason, two important conclusions at once follow.   (1) Since the path length for all rays parallel to the axis of the

207

lens and focused at F is the same, the center of the diffraction pattern is always a maximum, and not sometimes bright, sometimes dark, as in Fresnel phenomena. (2) Since, as already noted, for every point such as P the rays incident on the lens have all the same obliquity, the amplitude contributed by each elemental disturbance is exactly the same.

To find the resultant amplitude at P, we can subdivide the aperture into as many elemental sources as we like, and apply the same graphical method as already has been used so frequently. In the case we are considering, since the amplitude contributed by each elemental source is the same, and since there is always the same phase difference between disturbances from any two successive sources, the figure from which the resultant amplitude is obtained is always an

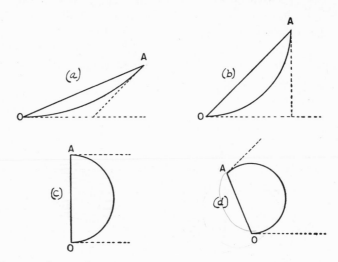

Fig. 11.2.   Diagrams showing how the amplitude at P, Fig. 11.1, at first decreases the farther P is from F.   In these diagrams OA represents the amplitude at P.

arc of a circle. Thus, if the path difference between the disturbances coming to P from the two edges of the aperture, that is, if BM, Fig. 11.1, is $\lambda/8$, the resultant amplitude at P is represented by OA, Fig. 11.2(a); if $BM = \lambda/4$, by OA, Fig. 11.2(b); if $BM = \lambda/2$, by OA, Fig. 11.2(c); and if $BM = 5\lambda/8$ by OA, Fig. 11.2(d). It will be noted that, as we go out from F, where, again, the intensity is always a maximum, the resultant must at first steadily decrease, becoming zero when the arc closes to form an exact circle. For this result to be obtained, the phase difference between the disturbance from one edge must differ from that coming from the other by 360°, or the corresponding path difference BM must be exactly one wavelength.

If, then, θ_1 is the angular distance from F to P when the intensity has dropped to zero, since in Fig. 11.1 $\angle POF = \angle BAM$, we have the important result

PLATE VI. DIFFRACTION PATTERNS

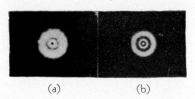

(a)   (b)

Fig. 1. Diffraction pattern for circular aperture. (a) center dark, (b) center bright.

Fig. 2. Shadow of circular object, showing bright center.

Fig. 3. Diffraction pattern for narrow obstacle, showing center bright.

Fig. 4. Diffraction pattern for straight edge.

Fig. 5. Fresnel diffraction pattern for rectangular slit, showing center dark.

Fig. 6. Fraunhofer diffraction pattern for narrow rectangular aperture.

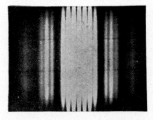

Fig. 7. Fraunhofer diffraction pattern for double slit, showing single slit diffraction fringes with double slit interference fringes.

$$\sin \theta_1 = \frac{\lambda}{AB} = \frac{\lambda}{a}, \qquad (11.01)$$

where a = width of the narrow aperture.

As we take points still farther away from P, since the phase difference between successive elemental disturbances becomes steadily greater, it is easy to see that the arc forms more than a whole circle, the resultant amplitude OA at first increasing, then decreasing to a second zero, after the manner shown in

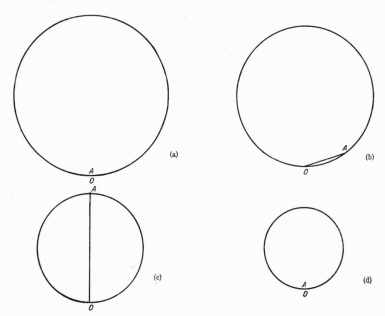

Fig. 11.3. Further examples of the change in amplitude as the point P, Fig. 11.1, is taken farther and farther from F. In this figure, in (a) the amplitude OA is zero; in (b) it has increased to OA; in (c) it has reached a maximum; in (d) fallen to zero again. See plot in Fig. 11.4.

(a), (b), (c), and (d) of Fig. 11.3. The second zero in intensity is reached when the arc forms exactly two circles, for which condition the path difference between the edge disturbances must be two wavelengths.

If θ_2 is the angular distance of the second minimum from F, it will be evident that

$$\sin \theta_2 = \frac{2\lambda}{a}.$$

Generally, then, the diffraction pattern for an aperture placed before the objective of a telescope consists of a bright center, bordered on either side with regions of zero intensity, between which, of course, there are other maxima. Thus OA, in Fig. 11.3(c), represents the amplitude of the maximum between θ_1 and θ_2.

The curve showing the changes in intensity for this pattern is given in Fig. 11.4, while an actual photograph of the appearance is reproduced in Fig. 6, Plate VI, facing p. 209. The pattern may easily be observed if the student will look at a single-filament incandescent lamp a few meters away, through the narrow aperture formed by holding two fingers in front of an eye.

It will be noticed that the intensity of the central bright band is much greater than that of the maxima on either side of it. The reason for this follows at once from the explanation which has been given of the whole phenomenon. For, if the aperture is subdivided into n elemental sources, each contributing an amplitude s at F, then the resultant amplitude at F is ns. Now, after we pass the first minimum at θ_1, we reach the first maximum on one side when the figure forms

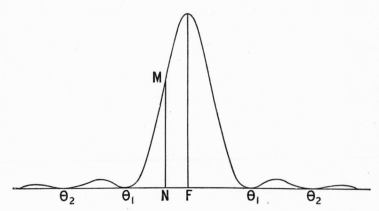

Fig. 11.4.   Plot of intensity in Fraunhofer diffraction pattern for a rectangular aperture. θ_1 corresponds to (a), Fig. 11.3; θ_2 to (d).   See Plate VI, Fig. 6, facing p. 209.

(approximately) a circle and a half,* as shown in Fig. 11.3(c). Since, however, there are still n elemental sources and since the amplitude contributed by each will differ very slightly from s (unless the obliquity is great, which is not usually the case), it follows that the total length of the arc must always differ very slightly from ns. OA, then, in Fig. 11.3(c), representing the amplitude of the first maximum to one side, is the diameter of a circle, three halves of whose circumference are equal to ns.

$$\therefore \quad \frac{3\pi}{2} OA = ns$$

or
$$OA = \frac{2}{3\pi} ns.$$

* Actually this maximum is reached when the figure forms a little less than one and one-half circles; or, to be exact, when the phase difference between the disturbances from the two edges of the rectangular aperture is 2.86 π rather than 3.00 π.

Hence,

$$\frac{\text{amplitude of central maximum}}{\text{amplitude of first maximum}} = \frac{ns}{\dfrac{2ns}{3\pi}} = \frac{3\pi}{2}.$$

Therefore, since, as we have seen in section 7.18, the intensity varies as the square of the amplitude,

$$\frac{\text{intensity of central maximum}}{\text{intensity of first maximum}} = \left(\frac{3\pi}{2}\right)^2,$$

a number which exceeds 22.

We have proved, therefore, that the intensity at the center of the central maximum is more than twenty times greater than that at the center of the first bright band on either side, and obviously still greater than that at the center of the other maxima. *Most of the light, therefore, is concentrated into the central band* whose angular width is $2\theta_1$, where

$$\sin \theta_1 = \frac{\lambda}{a}.$$

11.2. Rectilinear Propagation.   When the aperture is many times the wavelength of light, θ_1 is very small—indeed, so small, that with ordinary apertures the diffraction bands on either side are not seen at all.   Sharp images are then formed, and the laws of geometrical optics hold—in other words, rectilinear propagation results.

As a becomes smaller, however, θ_1 becomes greater.   Thus when the eye looks at a narrow bright source through an aperture 1/10 mm wide, if we take 5×10^{-5} cm as a mean value for λ, we have

$$\sin \theta_1 = \frac{5 \times 10^{-4}}{0.1} = 5 \times 10^{-3},$$

or

$$\theta_1 = 17'.$$

Again, if plane waves fall on an aperture 1/1000 mm wide, we find $\theta_1 = 30°$, which means that there is an unbroken band of emergent light about 60° in width.

11.3. Limit of Resolution and Resolving Power of a Telescope.   It follows from all this that the laws of geometrical optics can be applied to the formation of images by a telescope only when apertures of fair width are utilized—and even then with some limitation, as we shall presently see.   The narrower the aperture, the wider the central band, and the less sharp the image.   This means that the ability of a telescope to separate two distant objects close together, that is, what is called its *resolving power*, depends on the aperture of the objective.   The question of resolving power is so important that we shall here digress to point out that the phrase is used in two senses: (1) when the purpose, as in the case just mentioned, is to examine two objects close together; or when the fine structure of an object is observed through a microscope; (2) when one has in mind the ability of an instrument to separate two spectral lines (two wavelengths) close together. Concerning the latter some mention will be made in connection with the diffraction grating. At present we are concerned with the former.

Suppose S_1 and S_2, Fig. 11.5, represent two small luminous objects, either very distant (two near stars, for example) or in the focal plane of the collimating lens of a spectrometer. Then, if the light emerging from the collimator falls on a telescope, images I_1 and I_2 are formed in the focal plane of the objective. If the aperture of the objective is large, I_1 and I_2 are tolerably sharp, and there is no difficulty in recognizing two distinct images. Suppose, however, that a *rectangular* adjustable aperture is placed before the objective and that its width

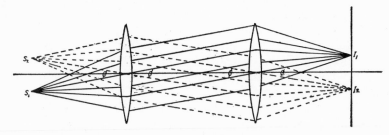

Fig. 11.5. I_1 and I_2 are the images in the focal plane of the objective of a spectrometer when two narrow sources S_1 and S_2 replace the usual spectrometer slit.

is gradually decreased. The images I_1 and I_2 then begin to spread out in accordance with Fig. 11.4, and sooner or later the two central bands will merge into each other. When this is the case, it is not possible to distinguish two images and, therefore, to tell that there are two sources. The resolving power of the telescope has become less with the more narrow aperture.

Now, obviously, there must be an aperture of critical width when an observer is just ceasing to be able to distinguish two images or, technically, when the *limit of resolution* has been reached. The magnitude of this critical aperture will depend on how close together the two sources are, for evidently the closer I_1 and I_2, the sooner the central bands will merge together. What, then, is the relation between the separation of the two objects and the corresponding limiting aperture, beyond which it is impossible to tell that there are two?

The answer to this question will be explained with reference to Fig. 11.6 and Fig. 11.7. To begin with, if ϕ is the angular separation of the two sources, this is also the angular separation of the *centers* of the two images, *regardless of their total widths*. When, therefore, ϕ is much greater than θ_1, as represented in Fig. 11.6, there is no difficulty in seeing two distinct images. As the aperture narrows, θ_1 becomes greater, ϕ remaining constant, and, for a normal eye, the limit of resolution has been reached when θ_1 has increased to such an extent that the first minimum for one image falls on the center of the central maximum for the other, somewhat as shown in Fig. 11.7. While different observers may differ slightly in stating just when the two images fuse, it is agreed to adopt as a

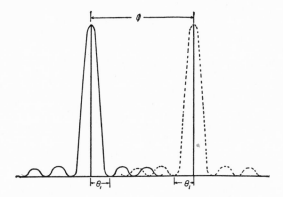

Fig. 11.6.   Intensity distribution in each of the images I_1 and I_2 of Fig. 11.5, when the diffraction patterns are widely separated.

measure of the limit the criterion (sometimes called the Rayleigh criterion) just given, that is, that it is reached when θ_1 becomes equal to ϕ.*

Conversely, if we are dealing with a fixed aperture, the angular separation between two objects which a normal eye is just ceasing to distinguish as two is

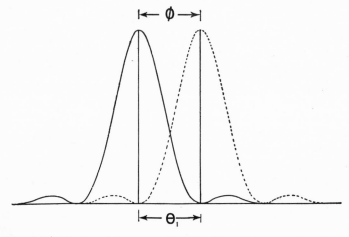

Fig. 11.7.   Intensity distribution of the images I_1 and I_2 of Fig. 11.5, when the diffraction patterns are beginning to merge, that is, when the limit of resolution has been reached.

* This criterion applies only for visual observation. When two near images are observed photographically and a microphotometer trace made, it is possible to detect two sources separated by a smaller angular distance.

given by $\phi = \theta_1$, or, since $\sin \theta_1 = \lambda/a$ and since θ_1 is small, for ordinary apertures by

$$\phi = \frac{\lambda}{a}. \tag{11.02}$$

This, then, is a measure of the limit of resolution of a telescope with a rectangular aperture of width a. For a circular aperture of diameter a, the same general ideas apply, and the more extended mathematical theory shows that the limit is then defined by

$$\phi = 1.22 \frac{\lambda}{a}. \tag{11.03}$$

An interesting qualitative, and approximately quantitative, illustration of the truth of the foregoing theory is obtained if the slit of a spectrometer is replaced by a piece of fine wire gauze illuminated by some monochromatic source such as a sodium flame. With full aperture of the telescope a very sharp image of the pattern of the gauze is seen. If, however, with one set of wires vertical, an adjustable rectangular vertical aperture is placed before the objective, it is found that, starting with a wide opening, when a certain critical width is reached, the vertical wires of the gauze have disappeared altogether. When this is the case, the images of the narrow vertical sources (between each pair of wires) have become so wide that they fuse into one another, in accordance with the explanation already given. A more exact quantitative test may be made by replacing the slit of the spectrometer by two very narrow slits close together.

When it is desired, therefore, to detect distant objects which are close together, that is, to increase the resolving power of a telescope, it is necessary to increase the aperture. For that reason, as well as to increase the amount of light collected, the diameters of the objectives of telescopes used in observatories are very large. At the famous Yerkes Observatory of the University of Chicago, the telescope* objective has a diameter of 40 in. or approximately 100 cm. With this telescope, therefore, objects with an angular separation as small as $\dfrac{1.22 \times 5 \times 10^{-5}}{100}$ radian or about one-eighth of a second can be resolved.

Since a normal eye can detect only an angular separation of 1 or 2 minutes, distant objects would not be seen as two unless the magnifying power of the telescope was sufficiently high. Thus, in the case of the Yerkes telescope, taking 1.5 minute as a mean value for the limit of resolution of the eye, a magnifying power of $\dfrac{1.5 \times 60}{\frac{1}{8}}$, or 720, is necessary.

It will be recalled that in section 5.4, it was pointed out that high magnifying powers should go along with wide apertures for another reason—in order to keep the diameter of the eye ring no bigger than that of the pupil of the eye.

* This type of telescope is sometimes called a refractor. In section 11.4 reference is made to reflecting telescopes.

11.4. Reflecting Telescopes. Large apertures not only increase the resolving power of a telescope, but they also increase its light-gathering power. If the diameter of a lens is doubled, the intensity of the light entering it is increased fourfold. It is not surprising, therefore, that astronomers have built bigger and bigger telescopes for exploring the heavens in greater and greater detail. Because of the difficulty of manufacturing huge lenses free from flaws, no refracting telescope has been built with an objective lens larger than the one in the 40-in. Yerkes instrument. Greater apertures are obtained by the use of reflectors, that is, telescopes in which the objective is a large concave mirror. Of these the largest in the world is the famous 200-in. reflector at Mount Palomar, California. The surface of its mirror is paraboloidal, because mirrors of this shape produce images *near the axis* free from the spherical aberration so pronounced in spherical mirrors.

The Palomar reflector has the disadvantage that good definition and high resolution fall off rapidly away from the axis, the field of view having a width of only about half a degree. For this reason it is used in conjunction with a much smaller reflector, usually called a Schmidt camera, a type of instrument which has become of great importance in photographic astronomy. It is the invention of Schmidt, a craftsman at Hamburg, who over twenty years ago showed that it was possible to use spherical surfaces in reflectors. Aberration defects are corrected by the addition of a "thin lens of small but complicated curvature" with such success that in the Schmidt arrangement wide fields are obtained in good focus. It has the further advantage that it can be used with a focal length only twice the diameter of the mirror, instead of some five times, as in most standard reflectors. Consequently, there is increased brightness of the image and, hence, shorter exposures. At Mount Palomar, a Schmidt camera, 48 in. in diameter, with a 72-in. mirror, is used for preliminary exploration of the heavens, special details revealed by it being examined later by the big instrument.

11.5. Resolving Power of a Microscope. When the term numerical aperture (N.A.) was introduced in section 5.8, it was stated that this quantity was of importance chiefly in connection with the resolving power of a microscope. We are now able to discuss this question.

In the previous section we have shown that the smallest *angular* separation of two distant objects which a telescope can resolve is $1.22\lambda/a$, where a is the aperture of the objective. When we use a microscope, the corresponding problem is to find the smallest *linear* separation which two neighboring small objects can have and be seen as two in the instrument. Fundamentally the two problems are the same because in each case the resolving power depends on the effect of diffraction, and in each case the limit of resolution is reached when two neighboring images overlap to the extent shown in Fig. 11.7.

Suppose, in Fig. 11.8, that K is the position of the center of the image of the small object R formed by an objective, represented by the lens AB. For reasons discussed in section 11.1, as we go out from K toward the edge of the image, the intensity of the light falls to zero at a point M for which the path difference $BM - AM = 1.22\lambda$.

Since AB represents the objective of a microscope, OK is many times greater than RO. Hence, by making $DM = AM$ and joining OM and AD, we can show, by exactly the same method as was used in section 8.3, that, with little error,

$$\frac{BD}{AB} = \frac{KM}{OK}.$$

Therefore, MK, the radius of the central bright portion of the image

$$= \frac{BD \cdot OK}{AB},$$

$$= \frac{1.22\lambda}{2 \tan \alpha_1},$$

where $\alpha_1 =$ image slope angle AKO.

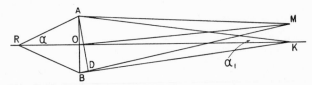

Fig. 11.8. Diagram used in finding the linear separation of the two closest objects which can be resolved by a microscope.

If we are dealing with two small neighboring objects, the limit of resolution is reached when M represents both the place of zero intensity at the edge of the image of one object and the center of the image of the other. In other words, MK is also the linear separation of the centers of the two images when the limit of resolution has been reached.

Therefore, d, the linear separation of the two closest objects which can be resolved, is found at once from the relation

$$d = \frac{MK}{\text{initial magnification}},$$

$$= \frac{1.22\lambda}{2m \tan \alpha_1},$$

where m is the symbol previously used for the initial magnification of an objective. From the sine condition we have

$$m = \frac{n \sin \alpha}{n_1 \sin \alpha_1},$$

$$= \frac{\text{N.A.}}{\sin \alpha_1},$$

since in the microscope the image medium is always air. Hence,

$$d = \frac{1.22\lambda \cdot \sin \alpha_1}{2 \tan \alpha_1 \cdot \text{N.A.}}.$$

Since OK is many times greater than AB, α_1 is small, and hence, with little error $\tan \alpha_1 = \sin \alpha_1$, and we have finally

$$d = \frac{1.22\lambda}{2 \text{ N.A.}}. \tag{11.04}$$

The resolving power of a microscope may be increased, therefore, by using as short a wavelength and as large a N.A. as possible. The dependence on wavelength is just what we should expect, because the shorter the wavelength the less the diffraction. For visual observation there is not much leeway in the choice of wavelength since we are more or less restricted to the use of white light, for which the brightest part of the spectrum is around 5300 angstroms. In photomicrography, however, there is a very distinct gain in resolving power by using the shortest wavelength possible. For example, with a N.A. of 1.00, some 78,600 lines to the inch can be resolved if $\lambda = 5300$, whereas, if $\lambda = 4000$, about 104,000, or well over 30 per cent more are resolvable.

When the object medium is air, 0.95 is the highest value of N.A. which is available. With an objective of this N.A., relation (11.04) shows that we cannot resolve a structure in which details are separated less than approximately $\lambda/2$. By the use of an oil immersion objective, the value of the N.A. may be increased to a maximum of 1.4, with a corresponding gain in resolving power.

In photomicrography the real image Q_1KP_1, Fig. 5.12, is projected on a photographic plate by using the eyepiece (or any other suitable lens) as a projecting lens. In this case, the magnification necessary to make full use of the resolving power depends on the size of the grains of the photographic plate. Although 0.01 mm may be taken as a mean value of grain size for an average plate, according to B. K. Johnson (Great Britain) it is desirable that the distance between the centers of the images of the nearest two small objects which can be resolved be equal to ten times that value, that is, 0.1 mm. Hence, for an instrument using a wavelength of 2000 A, with a N.A. of 0.75, if m is equal to the magnification necessary to utilize the full resolving power,

$$\frac{0.61 \times 2 \times 10^{-4}}{0.75} \times m = 0.1,$$

or

$$m = 615.$$

In photomicrography, further increased resolving power is obtained by using ultraviolet light. An intense radiation emitted by a mercury lamp in the neighborhood of 3650 A is particularly useful because, for wavelengths longer than about 3200 A, glass lenses and prisms may be used as in the visible region. Since glass absorbs wavelengths shorter than 3200 A and quartz transmits down to 1950 A, a further gain in resolving power is obtained by using quartz lenses and a quartz prism, and a source emitting radiation in the region between 3200 and 2000. A mercury lamp is again a suitable source, provided it is built of quartz. Since, until recently, an achromatic objective could not be made for wavelengths in this region, it has been necessary to use monochromatic light with instruments designed for this range.

Below 1850 A, quartz cannot be used, but it can be replaced by lithium fluoride which transmits to about 1100 A. In this region of very short wavelengths a further difficulty arises because the oxygen in the air absorbs the radiation, and hence an evacuated instrument or one with a chamber filled with a suitable gas must be used.

11.6. The Reflecting Microscope. With ordinary lens systems there are certain practical difficulties in using ultraviolet light for photomicrography. For

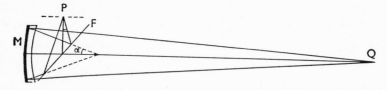

Fig. 11.9. Reflecting microscope. Light from an object *P* after reflection at the inclined transparent plate *F* falls on the lens-mirror *M* which forms an image at the conjugate point *Q*. (Adapted from diagram by B. K. Johnson.)

example, accurate focusing is not easy because it is extremely difficult to design a lens system to give an image in focus for both visible and ultraviolet light.

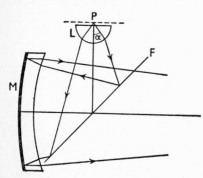

Fig. 11.10. Reflecting microscope. By placing the object *P* at the aplanatic point of a hemispherical lens *L*, the N.A. is greatly increased. (Adapted from diagram by B. K. Johnson.)

Moreover, when focusing has been made for visible light, it is not easy to shift mechanically to the right position for the ultraviolet. For these and other reasons work has been done by Burch (Great Britain), Johnson (Great Britain), and others, on the construction of reflecting microscopes, the position of images formed by reflection being independent of the wavelength. A brief reference is made to a satisfactory instrument, designed by Johnson, in which the reflecting surface has the big practical advantage of being spherical.

Light from a small illuminated object *P*, Fig. 11.9, on either a transparent or an opaque surface, after reflection at the first face of a transparent plate *F* falls on the lens-mirror *M*. A reflected image of *P* is formed at the conjugate point *Q* about 40 in. from the mirror. If visible light is used, this image may be viewed in an eyepiece, or for both visible and ultraviolet it may be projected on a photographic plate. The lens-mirror is a meniscus, made of lithium fluoride, with its back surface silvered. To avoid a double reflection, the rear surface of plate F is coated with a nonreflecting film.

With this simple arrangement the N.A. is small, being about 0.4, but by placing the object P at the aplanatic point of a hemispherical lens L (made of quartz), as in Fig. 11.10, its value is raised to 0.84. Note the increased size of the angle α in Fig. 11.10, compared with that in Fig. 11.9. By placing a meniscus lens, also of quartz, in front of the hemispherical one, a N.A. as high as 1.27 is obtained.

11.7. Microscope Condensers. Since the objects examined by a microscope are not self-luminous, they must be properly illuminated. The full value of the

N.A. of an objective cannot be utilized unless the illuminating cone of light has a sufficiently great angular width. To ensure this, a good microscope is provided with one or more substage *condensers*, that is, with a combination of lenses which collects the illuminating rays of light and throws a highly convergent beam on the small object. The method is illustrated by Fig. 11.11, a diagram taken from literature of the Bausch and Lomb Optical Company.

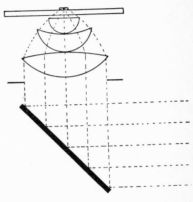

Fig. 11.11. A microscope condenser with associated reflector.

11.8. Magnifying Power and Resolving Power. Although the resolving power depends entirely on the objective, the eyepiece plays an important part in visual observation. The details of the real image formed by the objective may be well resolved, but this detail cannot be observed by the eye unless there is sufficient magnification. The point is illustrated by a concrete example.

Suppose a microscope has an objective with N.A. equal to 0.95, which, as we have seen, will resolve small objects $\lambda/2$ apart. Two neighboring objects separated by this distance when viewed directly by the eye at 25 cm subtend at the eye an angle of about $\dfrac{5.3 \times 10^{-5}}{2 \times 25}$ or approximately 10^{-6} radian. Now a normal eye can separate neighboring images on the retina only if their angular separation is at least 1 or 2 minutes. Using $1\frac{1}{2}$ minutes as a mean value, we find, since $1\frac{1}{2}$ minutes $= 4.5 \times 10^{-4}$ radian, that the magnifying power necessary to see the resolved images of the two objects $\lambda/2$ apart must be at least $\dfrac{4.5 \times 10^{-4}}{10^{-6}}$ or about 450.

In section 5.8 we have shown that, for a N.A. of 1.00, the normal M.P. is only 200, or possibly 250. In the same section it was pointed out that the use of higher than normal M.P. cuts down the size of the exit pupil. The full N.A. of the objective is used, however, and hence the increased M.P. does not involve a loss of resolving power. At this stage we again point out that, if M.P. less than normal are used, the N.A. of the objective is not fully utilized and there is a consequent loss in resolving power.

11.9. Electron Microscope. In section 21.6 it is pointed out that an essential feature of wave mechanics is that moving particles have a wave aspect, the associated wavelength being shorter the higher the speed of the particle and the smaller its mass. In the case of an electron moving along an evacuated tube under a potential difference of V volts, the associated wavelength λ is given by

$$\lambda = \frac{12.26}{\sqrt{V}} \text{ angstrom.}$$

For $V = 15,000$ volts, this gives $\lambda = 0.1$ A. It follows that, if practical use could be made of such electron waves, resolving powers 10,000 times greater than for the ultraviolet wavelength 1000 A could be obtained. In the *electron microscope* a practical application of electron waves is made, with both high magnification and resolving power.

In this instrument a pencil of electrons in a vacuum replaces the visible or ultraviolet light used in an ordinary microscope, focusing of the beam being accomplished by the use of magnetic (or electrostatic) lenses. Electrons emitted from an electron gun G, Fig. 11.12, in which the primary source is a heated tungsten wire W, for example, are focused by means of a magnetic lens L_1 on a

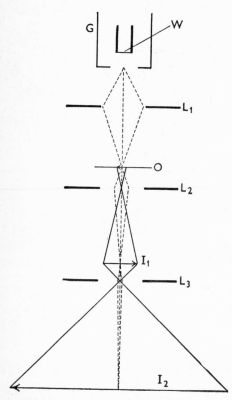

Fig. 11.12. The electron microscope. The dotted lines represent electrons emerging from a small portion of the heated filament W of an electron gun G. L_1, L_2, and L_3 are magnetic (or electrostatic) lenses. I_1 and I_2 are the first and second images of a small object at O.

very small portion of an extremely thin object, O, whose detail is to be examined. The object is mounted on a thin layer of a substance like cellulose supported by a wire mesh. This stage corresponds to the illumination of the object in an ordinary microscope by the condenser. The electron beam emerging from an element of the object is focused by the objective, a magnetic lens L_2, to form a magnified image at I_1, as in the first stage of the ordinary microscope. A final further magnified image I_2 is projected on a screen or photographic plate by the magnetic lens L_3. By coating a screen with a suitable fluorescent material, the final image may be viewed visually. In the figure the dotted lines represent a beam of electrons passing through the central element of the object.

Although in such an instrument the numerical aperture is small, being of the order of 0.01, if we apply relation 11.04 to 15,000-volt electrons with their associated wavelength of 0.1 A, we find that objects as close as $\dfrac{0.61 \times 0.1}{0.01} \times 10^{-7}$ mm,* or about 6 A, should be just separable. In the actual instruments, the resolving power is considerably less than the theoretical value, many electron microscopes having the limit of resolution at 100 A. As low as 20 A, however, has been obtained. It is interesting to note that this has reached the value necessary for observing many individual molecules.

To make full use of the resolving power, correspondingly high magnifications are, of course, necessary. For example, if, using a N.A. = 0.01 and λ = 0.1 A or 10^{-8} mm, we make an estimate of the necessary magnification, as has been done in section 11.5, we find that m exceeds 80,000. Values comparable with this are actually used.

Unlike the ordinary microscope, where the initial or first stage magnification due to the objective is greater than the second stage due to the magnifier or eyepiece, in the electron microscope the higher magnification is in the second stage. If the student will recall the simple relation that

$$\text{linear magnification} = \frac{\text{image length}}{\text{object length}},$$

he will realize that high magnification means long image lengths, and he will understand why many electron microscopes are of the order of 6 ft in length. An actual photograph, reproduced through the kindness of Prof. G. I. Finch formerly of the Imperial College, London, is given in Plate VII, Fig. 1, facing p. 224.

11.10. Two Narrow Apertures (The Double Slit). In Chapter VIII we have shown that, when a double slit is placed before the objective of a telescope, interference fringes are observed in its focal plane. In the discussion of that problem it was more or less assumed that each of the slits was extremely narrow and that we had to do only with the superposition of two interfering beams. Now, as a matter of fact, when interference fringes are obtained in this way, the width of the slits is often quite comparable with that of the opaque region be-

* 1 angstrom = 10^{-7} mm.

tween them. Although no objection need be made to the statements made in the previous discussion, for a complete understanding of the problem consideration must be given to the diffraction of a single opening.

Suppose, then, that we have two apertures of equal width, AB, CD, Fig. 11.13, and that we wish the resultant amplitude at any point P in the focal plane

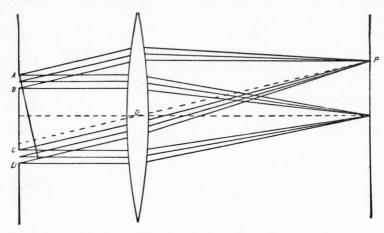

Fig. 11.13. In the double slit, parallel diffracted beams from the narrow apertures $A\,B$ and $C\,D$ are superimposed at P.

of the objective lens of a telescope. For each aperture separately we can find the resultant amplitude in the manner already described. Thus the resultant for each slit alone might be represented by MN in the curve of Fig. 11.4. When the two slits are acting together, therefore, the final general resultant at P is found by combining two amplitudes, each equal to MN, but differing in phase

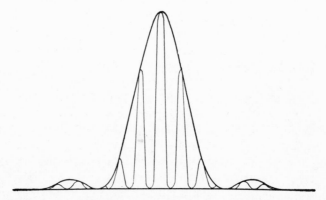

Fig. 11.14. Graphs showing the relation between double slit interference fringes, represented by the narrow maxima and minima, and the diffraction pattern for a single aperture, represented by the outer enveloping curve. See Plate VI, Fig. 7, facing p. 209.

by an amount which depends on the position of P, Fig. 11.13. The problem, therefore, is essentially one of interference.

Since for any particular position of P the path difference between any ray in one slit and the corresponding ray in the next is always the same (for example, the ray from edge A differs in path from the ray from edge C by the same amount that a ray from B differs from a ray from D), the difference in phase between the two resultant disturbances meeting at P can be found from any such pair of rays. Thus, if the central rays differ in path by half a wavelength, the resultant phase difference will be π, and P is dark; if this path difference is a whole wavelength, P is bright; and so on, just as we have already seen in the work on interference. We see now, however, that the interference fringes are superim-

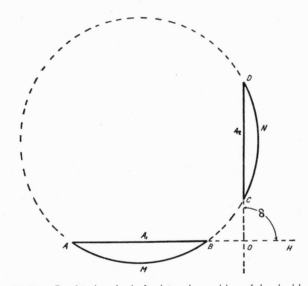

Fig. 11.15. Graphical method of solving the problem of the double slit.

posed, as it were, on the diffraction pattern of a single slit, the intensity distribution being somewhat as represented in Fig. 11.14. That this is the case is clearly shown in the photograph reproduced in Fig. 7, Plate VI, facing p. 209. To obtain the double slit fringes of Fig. 1, Plate IV, facing p. 153, a weak source of light and a shorter exposure were used, so that the fringes there seen are only the more intense ones in the central band of the single slit pattern.

The problem of the double slit may also be discussed by making use of the same graphical method as was used for the single aperture. The solution is indicated by the diagram of Fig. 11.15, where A_1 represents the amplitude at some point such as P, Fig. 11.13, due to the first slit, alone; A_2 that due to the second slit, while the angle COH $(= \delta)$ is the difference in phase between A_1 and A_2. It is not difficult to see that this angle is also equal to the difference in phase between the disturbances at P from the central elements of each opening, M and N, or from any other corresponding portions of the two openings.

11.11. Many Apertures (The Transmission Grating). Although the methods we have been considering may be extended to a consideration of three, four, five, or any number of apertures, we shall confine our discussion to the case of a large number of narrow rectangular apertures, alternating with opaque regions. Such an arrangement constitutes a *transmission grating*, although in the gratings

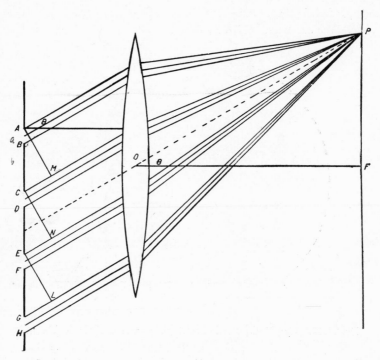

Fig. 11.16.   In a transmission grating, parallel diffracted beams from many openings such as *AB, CD, EF, GH,* are superimposed at *P*.

in actual use the openings are not quite so sharply defined as we have represented in Fig. 11.16. The fundamental principles, however, may be arrived at by a consideration of the more or less ideal grating, a portion of which is depicted in the figure.

In the first place, it should be evident that, just as in the case of two openings, at any point such as P, Fig. 11.16, there is a resultant amplitude due to each aperture alone, which is the same for all apertures, at the same point. To find the general final resultant at P, then, we must combine a large number of such amplitudes, between every two of which there is the same difference in phase.

PLATE VII

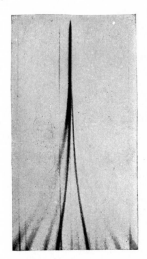

Fig. 2.   Stark effect.
(J. S. Foster.)

Fig. 1.   Electron microscope.   (G. I. Finch)

Fig. 3.   Photoelastic strain test.
(Polaroid Corporation)

Moreover, this difference in phase, just as in the case of the double slit, is that existing between the rays from any two corresponding portions of any two successive openings. When, therefore, the path difference between rays from points such as A and C $(= CM)$, or C and E $(= EN)$, or E and G $(= GL)$ is exactly one wavelength, or two or three, etc., the disturbances at P arising from all apertures are in the same phase, and for such directions, very bright maxima are obtained.

If θ_1 is the angular distance from F of the first bright maximum, θ_2 of the second, or generally θ_n, of the nth, then since Δs POF and ACM (or CEN or EGL) are similar, we have $\angle POF = \angle CAM$ (or $\angle ECN$ or $\angle GEL$), and hence

$$\sin \theta_1 = \frac{CM}{AC},$$

or
$$\lambda = AC \sin \theta_1,$$

and similarly
$$2\lambda = AC \sin \theta_2,$$

or generally
$$n\lambda = AC \sin \theta_n. \tag{11.05}$$

AC, the width of one opening and one opaque region, is called the *grating element*. We shall designate the magnitude of the element by $a + b$, a for the width of the aperture, b for that of the opaque part. The value of $a + b$ can be found by means of a high-power traveling microscope, or frequently it is provided when the grating is manufactured.

11.12. Width of Maxima. When CM or EN or GL, Fig. 11.16 is equal to an odd number of half wavelengths, the disturbances from successive openings differ in phase by π and the resultant is a minimum of zero intensity. It is important for the student to realize, however, that in the ordinary grating with many apertures the intensity does not *gradually* fall from a maximum to a minimum giving broad bright bands separated by dark, but, on the contrary, that there are extremely narrow bright lines separated as a rule by wide dark regions. While the general reason for this has been indicated in the discussion of the Fabry-Perot interferometer fringes, the problem is somewhat different in the case of a grating where we have to do frequently with several thousand fine openings.

Suppose we have N openings and that A is the amplitude due to a single one, at a value of θ where a maximum occurs. The final resultant amplitude at this maximum is then NA and is represented by the line OB, in Fig. 11.17(a). If now we consider points corresponding to values of θ *slightly* greater than that of the maximum, there exists a phase difference between every two successive openings and the general resultant is represented by OB, in Fig. 11.17(b), the total length of the polygon being still NA. (If N is large, as is generally the case, the figure will form an arc of a circle.) Now, applying the same ideas as were used in the case of a single slit, we see that the figure will close, that is, the total resultant intensity will drop to zero, when the phase difference between the disturbances from the first and the *last* openings has increased by 2π. (More exactly by $[(N - 1)/N] \cdot 2\pi$, but for very large values of N, the error is slight and does not affect the point under discussion.) The corresponding phase difference between disturbances from the first and the *second* openings, or any two successive ones, is, therefore, $2\pi/N$, while the path difference for these two disturbances is λ/N. We have shown, then, that the intensity drops from a maximum to zero when the path difference between disturbances from the first and second openings has changed by λ/N. Since at the maximum itself, this path difference is either λ or 2λ or $3\lambda \cdots$, it follows that the *change* in the value of θ

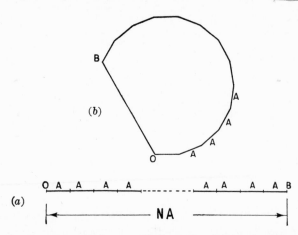

Fig. 11.17.   Graphs to show that in a transmission grating the intensity at the center of a diffraction maximum, represented by *NA*, rapidly falls to small values on either side of the center.

giving what we may call half the width of the maximum, must be extremely small when N is as large as it is in ordinary gratings. Thus, dealing with the first maximum, if α is one-half its angular width, we have

$$\sin \theta_1 = \frac{\lambda}{a + b}$$

$$\sin (\theta_1 + \alpha) = \frac{\lambda + \dfrac{\lambda}{N}}{a + b},\tag{11.06}$$

from which
$$\frac{\sin (\theta_1 + \alpha)}{\sin \theta_1} = 1 + \frac{1}{N}.$$

For large values of N, therefore (and N may be 10,000 or 20,000 etc.), α must be a very small angle compared with θ_1. Consequently when a transmission grating of many elements is placed on the table of a spectrometer in the path of the parallel beam of monochromatic light leaving the collimator, and the diffracted light is observed in a telescope, one observes in addition to the central image at F, Fig. 11.18, *narrow* maxima at I_1 and I_1' at an angular distance of θ_1 from the center; other maxima (not shown) at I_2 and I_2', at a distance of θ_2 from the center and possibly still others.   These maxima, which are usually called spectral *orders*, are so sharp that they appear as images of the slit of the collimator, just as (but for a very different reason) in the case of a prism.   It can be shown by analysis beyond the scope of this book that, in between these orders, there are secondary maxima.   In the case of an ordinary grating, however, these are so numerous and so faint, that they are not visible.

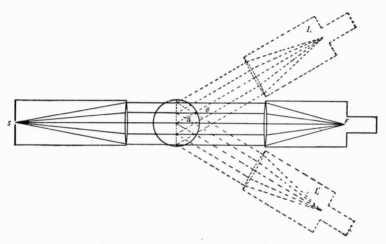

Fig. 11.18. A common arrangement of using a transmission grating with a spectrometer.

11.13. Measurement of Wavelength.   Since the angles θ_1 and θ_2 can be measured with a fair degree of accuracy by the spectrometer, the wavelength of the light used can be calculated (from relation 11.05) more accurately than by any of the other methods which were discussed under interference.

It follows, also, that when a source which is not monochromatic is used, for each wavelength present the corresponding maximum for any order occurs in a different position. We thus obtain, in each order, a spectrum of the source. It will at once be evident from the fundamental relation (11.05) connecting wavelength and angular deviation that all grating spectra, unlike prismatic, are rational.   The relative displacement of corresponding lines is always the same.

11.14. Number of Orders.   The number of orders which can be observed depends both on the width of a single aperture and on the size of the grating element.   The larger the grating element, the smaller the angular separation between orders, and, therefore, the greater the number of orders visible—*provided the diffracted light spreads out over a sufficiently large angle.*

To illustrate: if the grating element = 0.01 cm, and light for which $\lambda = 5 \times 10^{-5}$ cm is used, we have

$$\sin \theta_1 = \frac{5 \times 10^{-5}}{10^{-2}} = 0.005,$$

or $\theta_1 = $ about $17'$.

Similarly θ_2 is about $34'$; θ_3, $52'$; and so on.

Again, if, for the same wavelength, the element = 0.001 cm, we find that $\theta_1 = 2° 52'$; $\theta_2 = 5° 44'$; $\theta_3 = 8° 38'$.

But the angular width over which light is spread out depends on the width of a single opening, the central band (which as we have seen represents almost the whole of the light) having an angular width 2θ, where $\sin \theta = \lambda/a$. In the first example, therefore, if a, the width of the *opening*, is 0.004 cm, light of appreciable intensity would be confined to a band one-half of whose total angular width does not exceed $\sin^{-1} \dfrac{5 \times 10^{-5}}{0.004}$ or about $43'$. Since, with this grating we have found the orders to be separated about $17'$, it follows that only two of appreciable intensity could be observed on either side of the central image.

If, however, *for the same grating element*, each opening had a width of 0.001 cm, then one-half of the angular width of the central band would be approximately $\sin^{-1} \dfrac{5 \times 10^{-5}}{0.001}$ or $2° 54'$. In this case, then, as many as $2°54'/17'$, or 10 on each side, are theoretically possible.

In the laboratory, transmission gratings are frequently used which have about 14,000 grating elements or "lines" to 1 in. With such a grating, we have, for $\lambda = 5 \times 10^{-5}$ cm,

$$\sin \theta_1 = \frac{5 \times 10^{-5}}{2.54} \times 14,000 = 0.276$$

or $\theta_1 = 16° 2'$.

Also $\theta_2 = 33° 32'$,

and $\theta_3 = 57°$.

We see, then, that, even if the openings of this type of grating were sufficiently small to spread out the light the whole 90° on either side of the center, at the most not more than three orders could be observed. Actually two are generally visible with good intensity.

11.15. Examples of grating spectra can often be observed with the simplest means. If one views a narrow white source of light through half-closed eyelashes, the pupil of the eye is crossed with a coarse grating, and colored bands corresponding to successive orders are seen on either side of the central image. The same phenomenon is observed if vision is through a piece of fine wire gauze, with this difference, however, that there are now two sets of diffracted orders, one for the wires running in one direction, the other for those at right angles.

Instead of the wire gauze, suitably "ribbed" semi-transparent cloth goods, such as is sometimes found in umbrella covers, may be used. It may not be amiss to point out that the grating was first used to obtain spectra and to measure wavelengths by Fraunhofer, who in 1821 read a paper on this subject. It is interesting to note that his first gratings, by means of which he made surprisingly accurate measurements, consisted of regularly spaced silver wires of various sizes and at varying distances apart.

11.16. Phase Contrast Microscope. It is sometimes necessary to reveal structural details in thin, *transparent* specimens which, when viewed unstained by the ordinary microscope, reveal little or no structure. In the phase contrast microscope, first suggested by Zernike (Holland), an application is made of principles of interference and diffraction whereby details of such objects are readily revealed. To understand the changes incorporated in this form of microscope the student should realize that any fine transparent structure diffracts light, giving rise, if regular in structure, to a central and diffracted beams of light as in the transmission grating. Moreover, an exact image of such a structure can be obtained only if use is made of both the direct and the diffracted light. At any elemental area in the image, the amplitude of the light is the resultant of the diffracted and the undiffracted beams. When the original specimen is transparent, since no light is absorbed, the resultant amplitude, for uniform illumination of the object, is the same for all elemental areas of the image.

But, if the object varies slightly in thickness or in refractive index, the ampli-

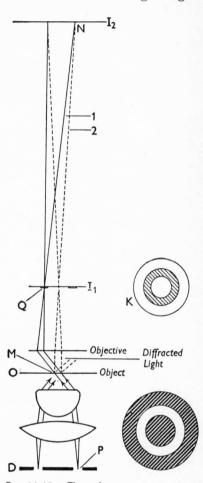

Fig. 11.19. The phase contrast microscope. D is a uniformly illuminated annular source so placed that parallel rays leave the condenser, falling on a thin transparent object O. A transparent phase plate K, with an annular layer coated with a transparent substance of thickness either one-quarter or three-quarters of a wavelength, is placed to coincide exactly with I_1, the real image of the source formed by the objective. The retardation of 90° or 270° in the phase of the light passing through the coated layer causes a difference in intensity between two adjacent elements in the image I_2 of corresponding elements on the object.

tudes at these elemental areas will differ slightly in phase. Structure is not revealed, however, because the intensity of light at any given place depends solely on the amplitude, which we have seen does not change. *In the phase contrast microscope a factor is introduced whereby changes in phase give rise to corresponding changes in intensity.* The essential features of the instrument can be understood by reference to Fig. 11.19, which is a simplification of a diagram in Bausch and Lomb literature and reproduced by permission. The source of light is a uni-

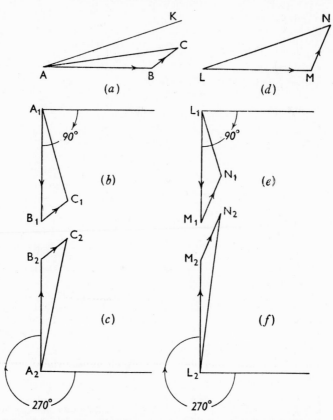

Fig. 11.20. Vector diagram to explain how the phase plate in the phase contrast microscope causes a difference in intensity between two adjacent elements of the image.

formly illuminated diaphragm D which has an *annular* aperture as shown in cross-section at the lower right-hand side of the figure. Since the diaphragm is placed in the front focal plane of the *condenser* of the microscope, parallel rays emerge. These fall on the objective and a real image I_1 of the diaphragm is formed in its rear focal plane.* Q, for example, is the image of a point P in the center of the annular opening.

* For simplicity the objective is represented by a single lens as in Fig. 5.12.

Now suppose we introduce a thin, transparent specimen O in the usual place in front of the objective so that a real image I_2 is formed by the objective, this image being viewed in the ordinary way by an eyepiece (not shown in the figure). Because of the fine structure of the object, not only does a direct beam of parallel rays emerge, but also diffracted beams, as indicated by the dotted lines. A glance at the diagram will show that, whereas the direct beam in its passage through the image I_1 is limited to the annular region, the diffracted beams (one of which is represented by the dotted lines) are not, and some diffracted light will pass through the central area of I_1. On the other hand, a direct beam, represented in the figure by the single line marked *1*, which emerges from a small elemental area in the neighborhood of the point M on the object (and which passes through the annular region of I_1) and a diffracted beam *2* originating also at M (and passing inside the annular region of I_1) are superimposed at the elemental area N on the final image. In Fig. 11.20(a), AB represents the amplitude at a certain elemental area in the image plane I_2 due to the direct beam, BC the amplitude at the same place due to the diffracted light, the two being combined by the method of section 7.12 to give the resultant amplitude AC. Similarly, for a different adjacent elemental area, LM and MN, the respective amplitudes of the direct and diffracted beams combine to give the resultant LN in Fig. 11.20(d). Since the original specimen does not absorb light, the intensity of light is the same at all points of the image, that is, $AC = LN$. Note, however, that in general there is a difference in phase between these two amplitudes, being equal, for the two elemental areas we have chosen, to the angle KAC, Fig. 11.20(a), where AK is parallel to LN. By a means immediately to be explained, use is made of this difference in phase to bring about a difference in intensity.

A *phase plate*, with an annular area whose size equals that of the annular area of the image at I_1, is introduced in the instrument so that it coincides *exactly* with this image. In Fig. 11.19 the phase plate K is shown in cross-section to the right of the image I_1. On the annular area of the plate there is a deposit of a transparent material whose thickness, for a given light, usually green, is either one-quarter or three-quarters of a wavelength. The direct beam, therefore (which passes through this annular area), is retarded in phase by either 90° for the $\lambda/4$ thickness, or 270° for the $3\lambda/4$ thickness. The effect of such a retardation can be seen by an examination of the diagrams in Fig. 11.20. Take first the case of 90° retardation shown in (b) and (e). In (b) AB has been rotated through 90° to A_1B_1 and, when A_1B_1 is combined with B_1C_1 (equal and parallel to BC), the resultant amplitude is now A_1C_1. Similarly, because of the rotation of LM through 90° to L_1M_1, the resultant amplitude, shown in (e), is now L_1N_1. Moreover, although CA and NL are equal, C_1A_1 is now greater than L_1N_1 and hence, *when the phase plate is used, the two elemental areas under consideration have different intensities in the image and contrast is observed.*

Diagrams (c) and (f) are the corresponding figures when the thickness of the phase-altering deposit is $3\lambda/4$ or when CA is retarded through* 270°.   Note that again the resultant amplitudes, A_2C_2 and L_2N_2, are unequal, but that in this case L_2N_2 is the greater.   When there is a retardation of 270° (or acceleration of 90°), microscopists describe the image as *positive* or *dark contrast*, the terms *negative* or *bright contrast* being used when the phase plate retards 90°.

Since the intensity of the direct beam is normally considerably greater than that of the diffracted light, a further improvement in contrast is obtained by combining a metallic absorbing film (an Inconel deposit) with the phase annular element.   This film makes the intensity of the direct beam more nearly equal to the diffracted.

11.17. Dispersion and Resolving Power of a Grating.   In the previous chapter it was shown that the ability of a telescope to separate distant objects close together depends on the aperture of the objective, and it was there pointed out that we sometimes are interested in another kind of resolving power, namely, the ability of an instrument to separate two wavelengths close together.   Now a grating, as we have just seen, is an excellent means of obtaining the spectrum of a source of light, and therefore in connection with it, as with any instrument which analyzes light into a spectrum, we wish to know two things: (1) the dispersion it produces, (2) the resolving power.

Strictly speaking, as we have already pointed out in Chapter VI, dispersion refers to the change in velocity in a medium with changing wavelength, as a result of which a prism gives a spectrum.   The term, however, is also used in the sense with which we are at present concerned, and that is, with reference to the separation of wavelengths produced by any instrument.   When so used (see again section 6.6), it is measured by the value of $d\theta/d\lambda$.

In the case of a transmission grating, therefore, since for the first order we have

$$\sin \theta_1 = \frac{\lambda}{a + b},$$

by simple differentiation, we obtain

$$\frac{d\theta}{d\lambda} = \frac{1}{(a + b) \cos \theta_1}.$$

More generally, for the nth order, we have

$$\frac{d\theta}{d\lambda} = \frac{n}{(a + b) \cos \theta_n}. \tag{11.07}$$

The dispersion, therefore, increases with the order, and is greater, the smaller the grating element.

Dispersion must not be confused with resolving power, which refers to the

---

* Since a retardation of 270° is the same as an advance in phase (counter-clockwise rotation) of 90°, in this case the phase is said to be accelerated.

degree of closeness two spectral lines can have and still be distinguished as two. The point will perhaps be clear by comparing (a) with (b), in Fig. 11.21. In these diagrams, where images of two wavelengths λ_1 and λ_2 are represented, and where in each MN, the angular separation, is equal, the dispersion is the same for each. It should be evident, however, that with the wider images as represented in (b), the two images would fuse into each other much sooner than would be the case with the sharper images of a, and that, consequently, the resolving power in the former case would be much less.

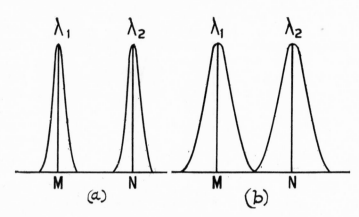

Fig. 11.21. In (a) and (b) the dispersion is the same. Because of the narrower images in (a), the resolving power in (a) is greater than in (b).

To measure the resolving power we make use of a criterion similar to that given in section 11.3. According to this the images of two spectral lines can just be distinguished as two when the center of one falls on the edge of zero intensity of the other. Suppose, now, that this critical state is reached when λ_1 and λ_2 differ by $\Delta\lambda$. Then, from relation (11.07), the corresponding angular separation $\Delta\theta$ of the centers of the two lines, in the first order, is given by

$$\Delta\theta = \frac{\Delta\lambda}{(a + b)\cos\theta}.$$

When $\Delta\theta$ becomes equal to α (the angular distance from the center of either image to the edge of zero intensity), as in Fig. 11.22, the limit of resolution has been reached. Now α we can find from relations (11.05) and (11.06).

Thus, we have
$$(a + b)\sin\theta_1 = \lambda,$$

and
$$(a + b)\sin(\theta_1 + \alpha) = \lambda + \frac{\lambda}{N},$$

or expanding,

$$(a + b)\sin\theta_1 \cos\alpha + (a + b)\cos\theta_1 \sin\alpha = \lambda + \frac{\lambda}{N}.$$

Since α is a very small angle, with slight error we may put $\cos \alpha = 1$ and $\sin \alpha = \alpha$, and, therefore, the last relation becomes

$$(a + b) \sin \theta_1 + (a + b) \cos \theta_1 \cdot \alpha = \lambda + \frac{\lambda}{N},$$

or

$$(a + b) \cos \theta_1 \cdot \alpha = \frac{\lambda}{N},$$

or

$$\alpha = \frac{\lambda}{N(a + b) \cos \theta_1}. \tag{11.08}$$

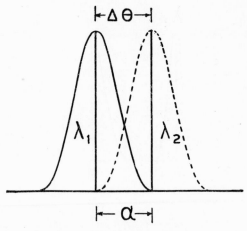

Fig. 11.22.   Intensity distribution in images of two spectral lines at the limit of resolution.

Hence, we have the following condition which obtains when $\Delta\lambda$ is the smallest difference in two wavelengths which can be detected.

$$\frac{\Delta\lambda}{(a + b) \cos \theta} = \frac{\lambda}{N(a + b) \cos \theta},$$

or

$$\frac{\Delta\lambda}{\lambda} = \frac{1}{N}.$$

The magnitude of $\lambda/\Delta\lambda$ is taken as a measure of the resolving power. Thus, if 10,000 elements of a grating were utilized, it follows that in the neighborhood of 6000 A, one could just distinguish, in the first order, two wavelengths as close as λ/N or 6000/10,000 or 0.6 A.

When we deal with the nth order, the same type of proof leads to the more general expression

$$\text{resolving power} = \frac{\lambda}{\Delta\lambda} = n \cdot N. \tag{11.09}$$

The student who finds difficulty in following the mathematical development should be able to see generally (from section 11.9) that the greater the number of elements, the finer the spectral orders, and, therefore, the closer two wave-lengths can be, and still be separated.

11.18. Hitherto we have assumed that the incident beam of light strikes a grating normally. This, however, need not be the case, for, if the beam is incident, as in Fig. 11.23, making an angle i with the normal to the grating, there will be a diffracted beam in any direction making an angle ϑ with the normal. In such a case the path difference between rays from corresponding points such as A and C is now $AN + AM$, or $(a + b)(\sin i + \sin \theta)$. The same general considerations as have already been given still apply and we have

$$\lambda = (a + b)(\sin i + \sin \theta_1) \text{ at the first order}$$

and

$$n\lambda = (a + b)(\sin i + \sin \theta_n) \text{ at the } n\text{th order.} \tag{11.10}$$

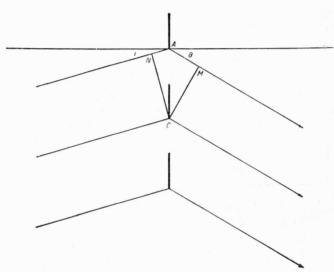

Fig. 11.23. Diffraction from a transmission grating when light is incident at an angle.

If the diffracted beam is on the side of the normal opposite to that of the incident beam, we have

$$n\lambda = (a + b)(\sin i - \sin \theta_n). \tag{11.11}$$

11.19. Reflection Grating. Spectra are also obtained when diffracted reflected light is utilized. Here again the same general considerations hold and it is not difficult to prove that there are diffraction orders subject to the relation

$$n\lambda = (a + b)(\sin i \pm \sin \theta), \tag{11.12}$$

where i is the angle the incident beam makes with the normal, θ that of the reflected beam. While reflection spectra may be observed with the ordinary transmission gratings so frequently used in the laboratory, good plane reflection gratings are made by carefully ruling, with a diamond point and an accurate dividing engine, equidistant parallel lines on a polished plane surface of speculum metal. The gratings used for laboratory instruction purposes are invariably replicas of a good grating made by taking a celluloid cast. It is possible to con-

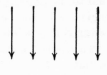

vert these into reflection gratings by coating them with a thin layer of metal. Good reflection gratings can also be made by depositing a reflecting layer of aluminum on glass with regular rulings.

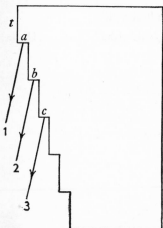

Fig. 11.24. The echelon grating. Light is diffracted at openings such as 1, 2, etc., formed by placing glass slabs of equal thickness t in a step-like arrangement.

11.20. Echelon, Echelette and Echelle Gratings. In section 11.17 it has been shown that the resolving power of a transmission grating is equal to the product of N, the total number of rulings on the grating, times n, the diffraction order.* To obtain the high resolving powers necessary for the examination of the Zeeman effect (section 17.7) or the hyperfine structure of spectral lines (section 19.12), one method is to use gratings ruled with a large number of lines, 100,000 or more, for example, and low values of n. A good example of another method is provided by the *echelon*, an instrument first suggested by Michelson, in which N has a low value, 40 being about the highest ever used, but n has an extremely high value. In our discussion of the transmission grating n has been used to designate a particular diffraction order. More generally, since $n\lambda$ is the path difference between corresponding rays from two successive grating elements, n is called the order of interference.

In the transmission echelon, a number of glass plates of thickness t are ar-

* Alternately, it is sometimes useful to note that the R.P. depends on the total width W of the ruled space and the angles of incidence and diffraction. This is easily proved by substituting in the relation R.P. $= nN$, the value of n in relations 11.10 and 11.11, from which

$$n = \frac{a + b}{\lambda} (\sin i \pm \sin \theta).$$

The expression for the R.P. then becomes

$$\text{R.P.} = \frac{N(a + b)}{\lambda} \cdot (\sin i \pm \sin \theta)$$

$$= \frac{W}{\lambda} (\sin i \pm \sin \theta).$$

ranged, as shown in Fig. 11.24, to form a series of steps (hence, the name *echelon*). When a beam of parallel rays falls on the echelon, the light is diffracted at the openings a, b, c, . . . , all of equal width, and the N parallel beams in any given direction are superimposed in the focal plane of a lens. Since the width of the openings is of the order of 1 mm, the total angular spreading of the diffracted beams is very small. (Recall section 11.2.) In such an arrangement the path difference between corresponding rays, such as 1 and 2 is *approximately* $(\mu - 1) \cdot t$, since one ray travels a thickness of t cm of glass more than the other. If $t = 1$ cm and μ (the index of refraction of the glass) $= 1 \cdot 524$, simple arithmetic shows that for a wavelength of 5240 A, the value of n, the order of interference, is about 10,000. Even with N no larger than 40, therefore, high resolving powers* are obtained.

In the reflection echelon, in which the construction is altered so that reflected rather than transmitted light is used, similar high values of resolving power are obtained.

Echelette Grating. The relative *intensities* of the light in the various orders of an ordinary reflection grating depend on the nature of the grooves ruled on the metal surface. Many years ago R. W. Wood (United States), after an examination of this problem, made gratings of some 1000 to 2000 lines per inch with each groove of such a shape that in the infrared region of the spectrum the energy was thrown into one or two diffracted orders. Gratings of this sort, comparatively coarse in structure and with a broad groove, Wood called *echelette*. They have proved of great value in infrared investigations.

Echelle Grating. It has been pointed out recently by G. R. Harrison (United States), a world authority on gratings, that, since the resolving power of a grating depends fundamentally on the total ruled width W and the angles of incidence and diffraction, high resolving powers can be obtained by using a grating, coarser than the echelette, with 100 grooves or so per inch, and with a much finer groove. Harrison points out that, if the groove of such a grating is chosen to reflect light of all orders in a narrow bundle, a compact instrument can be constructed with a resolving power equal to that of a 30,000-line grating and with other advantages.

11.21. Concave Grating. By far the most important grating is one whose surface, $AMNC$, Fig. 11.25, is spherical and ruled with lines which are the projection of equidistant parallel lines along the plane surface represented by AC. Such a grating may be used to give extremely sharp spectral lines without the use of any lenses, provided certain conditions are fulfilled. Suppose R is the center of curvature of the sphere of which the grating surface is a part and that S and P are two points lying on a circle having r the radius of curvature of the grating as diameter. Then, mathematical analysis shows that the difference in

---

* The exact expression for the resolving power of an echelon is not nN, but a knowledge of the correct value is not necessary to understand the point which is being emphasized.

the paths S to P between corresponding rays from two successive elements at M, is the same for a pair of elements at any other region N, for example. Thus, if this path difference is $n\lambda$ for any pair of corresponding rays, it is so for all, and in that case P is a bright order, or a spectral image of this wavelength. If a curved screen were placed so as to coincide with a portion of the circle in the neighborhood of P, on it would be observed the various orders of diffracted spectra all sharply focused. As gratings with radii of curvature as large as 20 ft or more are often used, while the actual surface of the grating itself is only a very few inches, it will be evident that in the figure, the width of the grating is enlarged out of all proportion in comparison with the other dimensions.

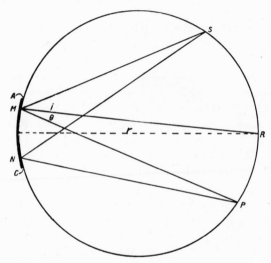

Fig. 11.25. In the concave grating AC, diffracted images of a narrow source S are obtained at points such as P when S, P, and the center of the grating lie on the circumference of a circle whose diameter is equal to the radius of curvature of the grating.

The first use of a concave grating was made in 1881, by Rowland (United States), who arranged his apparatus to fulfill the foregoing condition after a method now described by his name. In the Rowland arrangement, the grating G, Fig. 11.26, and the screen P (or eyepiece or photographic plate) are at opposite ends of a rigid arm whose length PG is equal to the radius of curvature of the grating. P and G are on carriages which can run along two rails on the rigid arms GS and PS set at right angles to each other. With this device P, S, and G always lie on the circle whose diameter is PG, and hence, if light emerging from a narrow slit at S falls on the grating and is diffracted, sharply focused images will be formed in the neighborhood of P. Moreover, since, for the central image, θ (the angle between the diffracted beam and the normal to the grating) is equal to zero, we may write for this image,

$$n\lambda = (a + b) \sin i$$

$$= (a + b) \frac{SP}{PG}. \qquad (11.13)$$

It follows that distances along SP are directly proportional to the wavelength in any given order.

To sum up, the importance of the concave grating lies in the fact that by means of it extremely sharp focused images may be obtained *without the use of lenses.* In the vast work of measuring accurately the multitude of wavelengths for all elements in various luminous sources it has played a very important part. In modern research it is particularly useful in the measurement of wavelengths

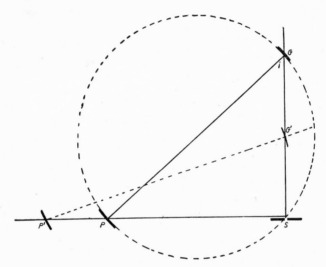

Fig. 11.26.   Rowland mounting of a concave grating.

in the extreme ultraviolet region not accessible with ordinary instruments because of the absorption of quartz, of fluorite, and of air itself. For this purpose, gratings with radii of curvature of the order of a meter or two are used, enclosed in a chamber from which the air is exhausted.

11.22. Scattering by Small Particles.   A beam of light traversing dust-free air under ordinary circumstances cannot be seen even in a darkened room.   If, however, dust is placed in its path, light is reflected from the particles of dust, and the beam becomes visible.   Suppose, now, that a beam of white light traverses a tank of water in which are suspended particles whose diameters are smaller than the mean wavelength of visible light.   Such a suspension may conveniently be made by adding to clean water a few drops of milk or a drop or two of an alcoholic solution of gum mastic.   It is now observed that the light seen in a direction at right angles to the path of the beam has a distinctly bluish cast. An interesting variation of this simple experiment may be made by using, instead of the gum mastic suspension, a weak solution of sodium thiosulphate to which a few cubic centimeters of hydrochloric acid are added. By this means a precipitate of sulphur particles is obtained, whose number and size are for a short time* suitable for studying the light at right angles (and in other directions) to a beam traversing it, as well as the light transmitted and allowed to fall on a screen. At a certain stage the bluish side light is very marked and the transmitted light has an orange-reddish shade. Evidently an excess of shorter wavelengths is emitted in a direction at right angles to the beam, while the transmitted beam has a corresponding excess of the less refrangible red and yellow wavelengths.

This phenomenon is known as *scattering* and occurs when a train of waves encounters particles whose dimensions are comparable with the lengths of the waves. Because of their size, such particles act as independent centers from which disturbances spread out in all directions. For particles considerably smaller than one wavelength the intensity of the scattered light can be shown both experimentally and theoretically to vary inversely as the fourth power of the wavelength. Hence, the scattered light must contain an excess of blue and violet; the transmitted, an excess of the less refrangible rays. Scattering is responsible for certain color phenomena seen in nature, for example, the blue of the sky, the reddish color of a setting sun, and the color of many minerals. Rising smoke seen against a dark background is bluish because there is little or no transmitted light, whereas the scattered light received by the eye is relatively intense. On the other hand, against a clear sky or a bright cloud the smoke through which light is passing (from the bright background) may appear brown or reddish.

When scattering by particles over a range of sizes is examined it is found that the color observed both when looking sideways and by transmitted light is a marked function of the particle size. For this reason, as a result of work done by such men as Kerker, La Mer and Sinclair (all United States), scattering of light has provided an important analytic tool for measuring the size of particles in aerosols (fogs) and hydrosols (liquid suspensions). One or two examples will illustrate practical uses.

When a beam of white light traverses a uniform suspension of particles, each of whose radius is of the order of a wavelength, and the beam is viewed sideways at angles ranging from 0° to 180°, it is found that the scattered light is alternately red and green. Moreover, the radius of a scattering particle expressed in microns is equal to one-tenth of the total number of red bands observed in the 180° interval.

The transmitted light also gives valuable information about particle size.

---

* By using sufficiently dilute solutions the increase in size takes place very slowly and the changes in the light phenomena as the particle size increases can be studied over a period of a few hours.

The orange-reddish light noted above applies only to particles whose radii are smaller than a wavelength.   With larger particles, such as droplets of radius 0.5 micron, the transmitted light is azure, but it becomes a pure green if the size is increased to 0.6 micron.   This work is of importance in studying smoke screens for military uses.   When the sun is viewed through a smoke screen and the transmitted light is yellow or red, the particles are too small; if blue or green, too large; but if magenta, just right for the most effective screen.

11.23. The Blue of the Sky.   In considering this phenomenon it is natural to ask one or two questions.   In the first place, why is the sky blue and not violet? To answer this question it is necessary to realize that, when an observer at A, Fig. 11.27, is receiving scattered light from a portion of the blue sky B remote

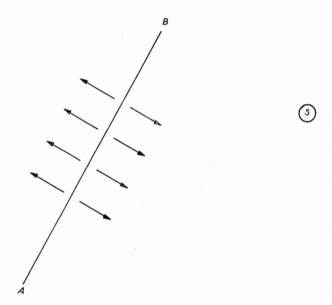

Fig. 11.27.   Light from the sun, scattered at B, is rescattered in its passage to an observer on the earth at A, giving rise to characteristic blue of the sky.

from the sun S, this scattered light must itself traverse a stretch of the atmosphere represented by BA.   From this light, therefore, which originally contained an excess of green, blue, and violet, the latter being most intense, there is rescattering in the direction of the arrows, an excess of the shortest wavelengths being removed in this way.   The resultant light which finally reaches the eye has a maximum intensity in the blue region.

Again, it may be asked, what are the scattering particles?   While extremely fine particles of dust are undoubtedly present in the low layers of the atmosphere, the brilliant blue of the sky, seen over sea as well as land, cannot be ascribed entirely to that cause. Can it be, then, that the cause is found in the scattering of molecules of gases or of water vapor? For some time the answer to that question was a debatable matter, but finally was given by the research work of such men as Lord Rayleigh, who showed by direct experiment that it is possible to observe scattering from molecules of a gas. There can be little doubt, then, that scattering from molecules is largely responsible for the blue of the sky.

In regard to the red color of a setting sun, fine particles in suspension no doubt play a more important part, for, in this case, the light travels approximately horizontally through a long layer of air near the surface of the earth. In such a layer fine particles of foreign matter are to be expected.

PROBLEMS

1. Find, with respect to a point 60 cm distant, for wavelength 5.56×10^{-5} cm, how many half-period elements are contained in a circular hole of radius (a) 1 mm; (b) 1 cm.

2. P is a point on a screen at a distance of several centimeters from an aperture illuminated by parallel rays of monochromatic light. Prove that the decrease in amplitude at P because of increasing distance of a half-period element from P is exactly counterbalanced by the increase due to the slight increase in area of the element.

3. A parallel beam of monochromatic light of wavelength 6.67×10^{-5} cm falls perpendicularly on an opaque screen which has cut in it a circular hole of radius 1.414 mm. The emergent light is received on a screen at a distance of 100 cm from the opaque screen. Prove that the intensity of the light at the center of the diffraction pattern on the second screen is approximately 4 times greater than the intensity at the same point if the original opaque screen is removed altogether.

4. A circular opening of radius 0.8 mm in an opaque screen is illuminated by plane waves of monochromatic light and the emergent light allowed to fall on a movable screen. As the movable screen is gradually brought from a distance toward the aperture, it is found that a succession of alternately light and dark spots appear at the center of the diffraction patterns. (a) If a dark spot appears for the *second* time when the distance between the screens is 36.2 cm, find the wavelength of the light. (b) Find at what distance a dark spot appeared for the first time.

5. Plane waves of monochromatic light fall normally on an opaque screen containing a small circular aperture. When an eyepiece is moved along the axis of the aperture from some distance in a direction toward the aperture, two successive maxima are observed, at distances of 60 cm and 36 cm, at the center of the diffraction pattern. If the radius of the aperture is 0.98 mm, find the wavelength of the light.

6. Find the radius of the smallest pin-hole in a large opaque sheet such that when it is illuminated with plane waves of monochromatic light of wavelength 5.46×10^{-5} mm, and the emergent light is received on a screen 88 cm away, the intensity at the center of the diffraction pattern is the same as at the same point when the opaque sheet is removed. (Apply section 10.7 and Fig. 10.16.)

7. Plane waves of monochromatic light fall on a small circular aperture and the emergent light is observed at a point P on the axis of the aperture at a certain distance from the aperture. If this distance is such that the path difference between a ray from the edge of the aperture to P and a ray from the center is one-quarter of a wavelength, prove that the intensity at P is twice as great as when the aperture is removed altogether. (Apply method of section 10.7 and Fig. 10.16.)

8. In an arrangement such as described in problem **7**, the area of the aperture (with respect to a point P on the axis) is reduced from exactly one half-period element to one-third of an element. Find by how much the intensity at the point P has been reduced.

9. Monochromatic light from a distant point source falls on a small circular aperture and the intensity of the diffracted light is observed at P, a point at the center of the diffraction pattern on a screen placed beyond the aperture. (a) Prove that the intensity at P is the same when the aperture contains exactly $\frac{1}{2}$ of a half-period element as when it contains 3/2 of an element. (b) Find, for either case, the ratio of the intensity at P to the intensity at the same point when the hole contains exactly one half-period element.

10. A linear aperture whose width is 0.064 mm is placed immediately in front of a lens of focal length 50 cm. If this aperture be illuminated with a beam of parallel rays whose angle of incidence is zero, and whose wavelength is 6.24×10^{-5} cm, find the distance between the center and the first dark band of the diffraction pattern on a screen placed 50 cm from the lens.

11. A rectangular aperture of width 0.67 mm is set up in front of an objective lens of focal length 60 cm as in problem 10. If light of wavelength 5.36×10^{-5} cm is used, find the difference in phase between the rays from the two edges of the aperture arriving at a point P which is in the focal plane of the lens, but 0.1 mm to one side of the principal focus.

12. Light of wavelength 6.2×10^{-4} mm, on emerging from a very narrow slit, falls on a collimating lens placed so that parallel rays emerge. The beam of parallel rays falls on an objective lens of focal length 1000 mm, and the diffraction pattern, when a rectangular aperture of width 0.62 mm is placed in front of this lens, is photographed in its focal plane. Find the ratio of the intensity of the light at a point in the center of this pattern to the intensity at a point 0.5 mm from the center (both points in the focal plane of the objective). (Apply method of section 11.1.)

13. Plane waves of monochromatic light of wavelength 4.8×10^{-5} cm fall normally on a rectangular aperture of width 0.4 mm placed in front of the objective (of a telescope) whose focal length is 60 cm. (a) Find at what distance from the principal focus of the objective a point P is situated, in the focal plane, if the difference of phase between the rays superimposed at P from the two edges of the aperture is (i) 90°; (ii) 60°. (b) Find in each case the ratio of the resultant *amplitude* at this point due to all rays from the aperture, to the amplitude at the principal focus.

14. The Yerkes Observatory telescope has an objective lens of diameter 40 in. Assuming a mean wavelength of 5.5×10^{-5} cm, estimate the smallest angular separation of two stars which can be resolved by it.

15. Discuss the importance of the aperture of the objective of a telescope (assumed free of common defects) on: (a) the brightness of the image of a small distant source; (b) the diameter of the eye ring; (c) the resolving power.

16. The slit of a spectrometer is replaced by two narrow slits whose centers are 0.03 cm apart, and the spectrometer is adjusted in the usual way. The focal length of the collimator is 20 cm. If an adjustable rectangular aperture is placed in front of the objective and gradually narrowed, find for what width of this aperture it is first no longer possible to detect two images, when yellow sodium light is used.

17. The slit of a spectrometer is replaced by a wire mesh placed, with one set of wires vertical, at the focal distance from the collimating lens of focal length 18 cm. The gauze is illuminated by green light of wavelength 5461 A. If an adjustable rectangular aperture, placed in front of the objective of the telescope, is gradually narrowed, find for what width the vertical wires of the mesh just cease to be visible.   There are 10 wires per cm in the mesh.

18. A brass plate has two vertical narrow openings cut in it, with centers 1.6 mm apart. A sodium flame is placed directly behind these slits, and a telescope 5 meters away is focused on the slits.   A rectangular aperture is then placed immediately in front of the objective of the telescope, and its width is gradually lessened until it is no longer possible to see two images.   What is the width of the aperture when this occurs?

19. A narrow vertical filament of an incandescent lamp, covered with red glass which transmits light of wavelength 6.2×10^{-5} cm, is viewed by the naked eye through a narrow vertical rectangular aperture of width 0.4 mm.   If the distance from the eye to the filament is 5.00 meters, find approximately the linear distance between the first dark bands on either side of the center of the diffraction pattern observed in the plane of the filament.

20. If a normal eye cannot separate two objects (or images) subtending an angle of less than 1.5 minutes, find approximately the magnifying power that is necessary to make use (visually) of the full resolving power of a telescope whose objective has a diameter of 40 in.   (Assume a mean wavelength of 5.5×10^{-5} cm.)

21. A small object has a fine structure of 12,000 lines to the inch.   Find: (a) the smallest N.A. the objective of a microscope can have in order to resolve this structure; and (b) the minimum M.P. necessary to see the resolved structure.

Take $\lambda = 5.46 \times 10^{-5}$ cm, and assume that the smallest angular separation observable by the eye is 1.5 minutes.

22. Find how many lines to the inch can be resolved by a microscope whose objective has a N.A. of 0.5, for light of wavelength 5500 A, and also for wavelength 4000 A.

23. The opaque region between the two narrow openings of a double slit is twice as wide as the width of each slit.   Prove that with such a double slit every third bright interference fringe is absent.   (N.B.   Show that the places of zero intensity for each slit separately coincide with the positions of every third fringe.)

24. When a fairly coarse diffraction grating is placed on the table of a spectrometer adjusted in the usual way, and the slit is illuminated with sodium light ($\lambda = 5.89 \times 10^{-5}$ cm), a large number of diffraction orders are observed.   If the angular separation between the central and the 20th order is 15° 10′, find the number of grating elements in 1 cm.

25. When a narrow vertical slit, illuminated with monochromatic light, is viewed through a grating having 14,500 lines per inch, two bright first-order images are observed on either side of the slit.   The position of each of these images is located and they are found to be 372 cm apart.   If the distance from source slit to the eye is 5.20 meters, find the wavelength of the light.   (N.B.   This is a simple method of measuring wavelength to about 1 per cent.)

26. A grating is made of six equally spaced narrow openings, of equal width, with distance between the centers of each successive two equal to 0.306 cm.   The grating is placed on the table of a spectrometer adjusted so that the parallel rays leaving the collimator strike the plane of the grating perpendicularly and the emergent light is observed in the focal plane of a converging lens of focal length 100 cm.   Light of wavelength 6.24×10^{-5} cm is used.   Find the linear separation between the two first-order images observed on either side of the central image.

27. An observer looks through a piece of fine wire gauze, with one set of wires vertical, at a vertical slit illuminated by light of wavelength 5.46×10^{-5} cm. He finds that the distance apart of the first two diffracted images on either side of the vertical slit is 3.14 cm. Find approximately the distance apart of the vertical wires in the gauze. The distance from the slit to the eye is 6.0 meters.

28. A third-order image (of wavelength 4340 A) in the spectrum produced by a diffraction grating occurs at a certain place in the spectrum. Find what wavelength in the visible region, and what order of this wavelength occurs at the same place.

29. The images of two wavelengths λ_1 and λ_2, which differ by a small amount, are observed in the first-order spectrum produced by a grating. If θ is the mean deflection and $\Delta\theta$ the angular separation of the two beams, prove that $\Delta\theta = \dfrac{\lambda_2 - \lambda_1}{s \cos\theta}$ where $s =$ grating element. *Note:* Expand sin $(\theta + \Delta\theta)$ or differentiate.

30. Plane waves of monochromatic light of wavelength 6.24×10^{-5} cm fall normally on a grating consisting of a number of very narrow slits, each of width 0.012 mm separated by opaque regions of width 0.298 mm. The emergent light is observed in a telescope focused for infinity. (a) Find the angular width of the central unbroken band of light *due to a single opening*. (b) Find how many spectral orders of appreciable intensity, due to the whole grating, will be observed.

31. In what two general ways is the term *resolving power* used?

32. What resolving power is necessary to separate the two components of a spectral line, of mean wavelength 6000 A, if the two differ in wavelength by $1/10$ of an angstrom?

33. A transmission diffraction grating has 15,000 lines per inch, with a total width of 3 cm, and is set on the platform of a spectrometer. Find: (a) for $\lambda = 5000$ A the dispersion in the second order; (b) the resolving power, in the second order, when a rectangular aperture 1 cm wide is placed in front of the objective of the telescope perpendicular to the second-order beam; (3) the *maximum* resolving power which could be obtained with this grating, in the first order.

34. The slit of a spectrometer is illuminated with sodium light and the telescope set with its crosshair line midway between the second-order images of the D_1 and D_2 lines, obtained when a transmission grating, with 14,000 lines to the inch, is on the table of the instrument, its face being perpendicular to the parallel rays leaving the collimator. An adjustable rectangular aperture is then placed in front of the objective of the telescope (and perpendicular to the diffracted beam) and narrowed until the two images just begin to fuse into each other. Find the width of the aperture for which this occurs. (Take wavelengths 5896 A and 5890 A.)

35. The telescope of a spectrometer is replaced by a camera whose lens has a focal length of 50.0 cm. A plane transmission grating with 15,000 lines per inch is set on the table of the instrument as in problem 34, and the first-order spectrum is photographed. Find the dispersion, in *angstroms per mm*, on the photographic plate, in the neighborhood of 6000 A.

36. In a transmission grating the width of the opaque region between two successive openings is equal to the width of an opening. Prove that every second order is missing when such a grating is used in the usual way on the table of a spectrometer.

37. A source emitting two wavelengths in the neighborhood of 5461 A illuminates the narrow slit of a spectrometer. When the light emerging from a prism on the spectrometer table is observed in a telescope with micrometer eyepiece, it is found that the centers of the images of the two spectral lines are 0.4 mm apart. When a narrow rectangular slit is placed in front of the objective, the two spectral lines fuse into each other for a width of 0.5 mm. Find the focal length of the objective.

38. A large number n of S.H.M. of the same period, in the same straight line, each successive two of which differ in phase by π radians, are superimposed. If the amplitudes d_1, d_2, . . . d_n decrease in arithmetical progression and n is even, prove by a graphical method that the resultant amplitude, with small error, $= \dfrac{d_1 - d_n}{2}$.

XII

Double Refraction

12.1. In the chapters on Interference and Diffraction phenomena have been described, the explanation of which is possible only in terms of some form of wave theory. We have seen how such phenomena provide us with means of measuring wavelengths of light, but, thus far, nothing has been said regarding the nature of the vibrations. Are they transverse or longitudinal, or a combination of both? In sound we know that we have to do with longitudinal vibrations; what about light? The answer to that question will be found by study of the work of the next few chapters, in which for the first time we consider the propagation of light through transparent crystalline substances. Hitherto we have considered only isotropic substances, those for which physical properties are independent of the direction. But if one takes a piece of a substance like crystalline quartz, it is not difficult to show that heat, for example, travels at unequal rates in different directions. In general, for crystals, physical properties do vary with the direction. It is not surprising, therefore, to find that the passage of light through transparent crystals is subject to laws which, in some important respects, differ from those applicable to isotropic substances.

12.2. The Fact of Double Refraction. To obtain our introductory ideas we shall make use of *Iceland spar* (calcium carbonate), a substance whose fundamental crystal form is the rhombohedron. In this crystal form, represented by Fig. 12.1, it is to be noted that, at certain corners such as A, the edges form both obtuse and acute angles, of magnitude 101° 55′ and 78° 5′, while at the corners B and D the three edges form obtuse angles only. A line drawn through B making equal angles with each of the three edges, *or any line parallel to this*, defines the *optic axis* (O.A.) of this crystal. Note, then, that the optic axis is a *direction*, and, moreover, it is not defined by the line joining B and D except for one particular length of the crystal.

In the latter half of the seventeenth century it was shown by Bartholinus of Denmark that Iceland spar had the property of refracting a beam of light in two different directions. The phenomenon may be shown by the following simple experiment. If a narrow beam of light, such as LM, Fig. 12.2, falls *normally* on one of the faces of such a crystal, *two* spots of light, O and E, are observed on a screen placed in the path of the emerging light. Moreover, if the crystal is

247

rotated about an axis parallel to the beam, the spot O remains stationary, while the spot E rotates about it. A single beam, therefore, has been *doubly* refracted, that is, has given rise to two beams, one of which, at least in this simple experiment, corresponds to the single beam which would have been transmitted had a substance like glass been used. This beam is called the ordinary (O) beam; the other, the extraordinary (E).

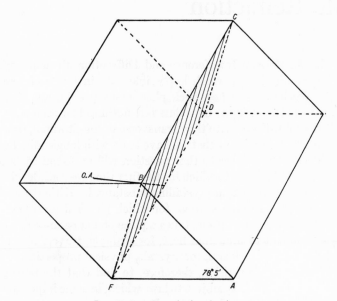

Fig. 12.1.   Crystal of Iceland spar.

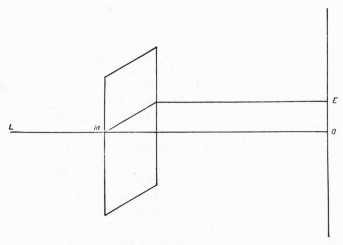

Fig. 12.2.   A single incident ray LM gives rise to the two emergent rays O and E from a doubly refracting crystal.

If the beam of light is incident in a direction other than normal, and measurements are made of angles of incidence and of refraction, it is found that the sine law holds for the O beam, whereas for the E beam, the value of $\sin i/\sin r$ varies with the angle of incidence. Now it will be recalled that in section 3.4 it was proved that, for ordinary media, the sine law holds because $\sin i/\sin r$ is equal to the ratio of the velocity of light in air to that in the denser medium. Its constancy, therefore, regardless of the direction of the incident light, is a proof that the velocity of light is the same in all directions. Conversely, the lack of constancy of this ratio when we have to do with the E beam is a proof that the velocity of this component in a crystal is different in different directions.

If the position of the crystal with reference to the incident beam is varied, in general two beams are always obtained. When, however, a crystal is used which has been cut so that the beam can be sent in a direction parallel to the optic axis, only one spot is obtained. We may conclude, then, that in this direction the velocities of the two beams are equal. (See also end of section 12.4.)

12.3. Uniaxial and Biaxial Crystals. Double refraction can be observed in many crystalline substances, such as Iceland spar, quartz, ice, tourmaline, apatite, nitrate of soda, borax, mica, selenite, topaz, and aragonite. An examination of such substances shows that they may be divided into two groups. In the first, called *biaxial*, there are two directions along which the two disturbances travel with the same velocity; in the second, called *uniaxial*, there is only one such direction. Of those given above, the last five are biaxial, the remainder uniaxial. While the general explanation of the phenomenon of double refraction shows that the latter is just a special case of the former, in the work of this text we shall confine our attention to uniaxial crystals, of which Iceland spar and quartz will chiefly interest us.

12.4. Huygens' Explanation of Double Refraction. In considering the explanation of the phenomenon for uniaxial crystals, enunciated first by Huygens and subsequently verified by experiment, it is well for the student to note again the simple facts.

(*a*) There are actually two beams traversing the crystal; therefore, two wavelets must spread out from a particle which has been disturbed.

(*b*) The velocity of the O beam is the same in all directions; therefore, the corresponding wavelet must be spherical.

(*c*) The velocity of the E beam varies with the direction, but, as already noted, may reasonably be assumed to be the same as that of the O beam along the optic axis. Now Huygens assumed that the E wavelet was spheroidal, or an ellipsoid of revolution, the O and the E wavelets touching at the places where they were intersected by the optic axis. The E wavelet, therefore, is formed by the revolution of an ellipse about a diameter coinciding with the optic axis. A cross-section of the two wavelets is then represented by such diagrams as (*a*) and (b), Fig. 12.3.   In (a) it will be observed that the O wavelet is represented as entirely outside the E, whereas in (b) the converse is the case.   That both conditions are possible, we shall see presently.

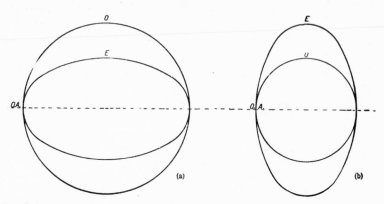

Fig. 12.3.   Cross-section of O and E wavelets: (a) for a positive crystal; (b) for a negative.   The dotted line represents the optic axis.

The importance, as well as the use of Huygens' construction, will be evident from a consideration of the following illustrations, in all of which cross-sectional diagrams alone are used.

(a) *Plane waves are incident obliquely on a piece of doubly refracting crystal so placed that the O.A. is in the plane of incidence, but subject to no other restriction.*

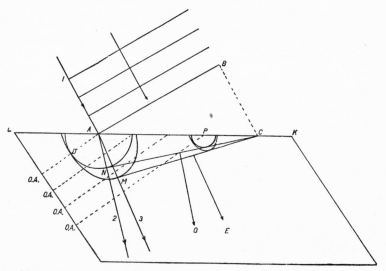

Fig. 12.4.   Huygens' construction for showing the existence of O and E wave-fronts when plane waves are incident obliquely on the surface of a doubly refracting crystal.

Use Huygens' construction to show the existence of O and E plane waves traversing the crystal.

In Fig. 12.4, let AB be a plane wave-front incident on the plane face LK of a crystal whose optic axis is represented by the dotted lines marked O.A. To obtain the refracted wave-fronts we use exactly the same method as was employed in section 3 4 when ordinary refraction was under consideration. Thus, by the time the edge B of the incident wave-front has reached the point C on the surface of the crystal, the O wavelet, originating at A, has reached the position DN, while the E wavelet, originating at the same point, has reached DM. By drawing the position of a number of other wavelets originating from points such as P between A and C, we finally obtain: (1) a plane wave-front CN tangent to all the O wavelets, (2) a plane wave-front CM tangent to all the E wavelets.

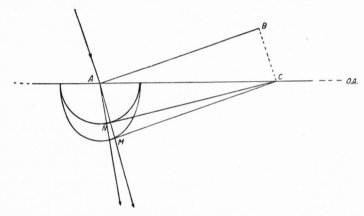

Fig. 12.5. Simplified Huygens' construction when the optic axis lies in the plane of incidence and is parallel to the surface of the crystal.

There are, therefore, two sets of refracted wave-fronts traveling in different directions. It is to be noted further that, if we consider a ray such as 1, incident at A, the corresponding O ray 2 is, as in the case of an isotropic substance, perpendicular to the wave-front NC, whereas *the refracted E ray is, in general, not perpendicular to the wave-front MC.*

(b) *When conditions are similar to case (a), except that the optic axis is not only in the plane of incidence but also parallel to the surface of the crystal.*

No detailed explanation should be necessary for the cross-sectional diagram of this case shown in Fig. 12.5.

(c) *Fig. 12.6 is the diagram for the case when the O.A. is perpendicular to the plane of incidence and parallel to the surface of the crystal.* The student should note this case particularly, for, the O.A. now being perpendicular to the plane of the paper, the sections for both O and E wavelets are circular. Moreover, they are circles regardless of the inclination of the original wave-front. It follows, there-

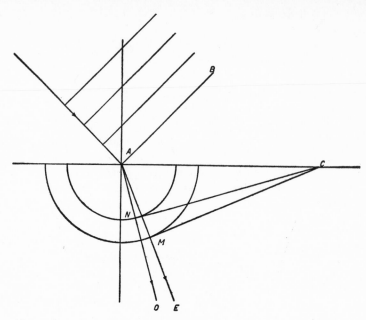

Fig. 12.6. Huygens' construction when the optic axis is perpendicular to the plane of incidence and parallel to the surface. Note that, in this case, the cross-sections of both the O and the E wavelets are circular.

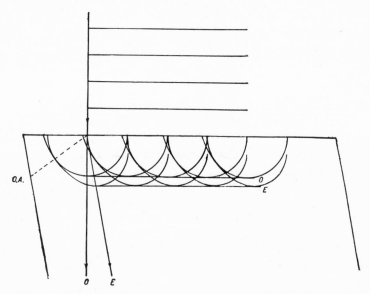

Fig. 12.7. Huygens' construction when plane waves strike the surface of the crystal normally.

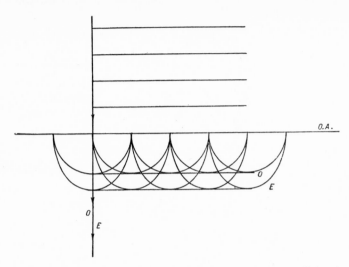

Fig. 12.8.   Another case of normal incidence, in which the optic axis is parallel to the surface and in the plane of the diagram.   Note that the O and E rays emerge in the same direction but with different velocities.

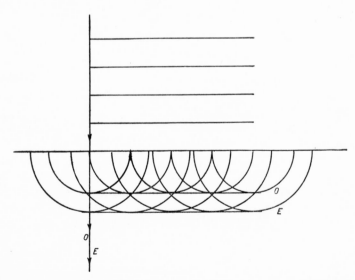

Fig. 12.9.   Another case of normal incidence, in which the optic axis is parallel to the surface but perpendicular to the plane of the diagram.   The O and the E beams emerge in the same direction but with different velocities.

fore, that, *provided one works in this plane*, the velocity of the E disturbance is the same in all directions, and that the sine law holds for both O and E beams— again, however, *only in this plane*. That being the case, we may now agree on the following definition of the extraordinary index of refraction, which we shall represent by n_E.

$$n_E = \frac{\text{velocity of light in air}}{\text{velocity of the } E \text{ beam in a plane perpendicular to the optic axis}}.$$

Cases when plane waves fall normally on the face of a crystal are shown in Fig. 12.7, where the O.A. is in the plane in which the cross-section of the wavelets is taken but not otherwise restricted; Fig. 12.8, where the O.A. is in this plane and parallel to the surface of the crystal; Fig. 12.9, where the O.A. is perpendicu-

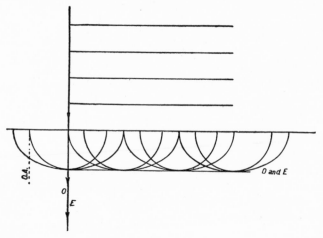

Fig. 12.10. Another case of normal incidence, in which the optic axis is perpendicular to the surface of the crystal. The O and E beams emerge in the same direction and with the same velocity.

lar to this plane but parallel to the surface; and Fig. 12.10, where the O.A. is perpendicular to the surface of the crystal. Figures 12.8 and 12.9, which should be compared with Fig. 12.10, show that, when plane waves fall normally on crystals cut so that the beam travels *at right angles* to the O.A. there is no separation into two beams, although the two travel at different rates. (Note again end of section 12.2.)

12.5. Determination of Refractive Indices. If a piece of Iceland spar is cut in the form of a prism and placed on the table of a spectrometer, two images are observed, and the angle of minimum deviation can be measured for each. Moreover, if the crystal is so cut that the O.A. is parallel to the refracting edge of the prism, the plane of incidence is perpendicular to the optic axis, and hence the usual calculation by the use of relation (6.03) gives both n_O and n_E.

In Table IX, values of indices obtained in this or in other ways are given for a few uniaxial crystals. An examination of these values will show that, for some substances, the E index is greater than the O; for others, less. Now, for the first class, it follows that the velocity of the E disturbance in a plane perpendicular to the O.A. must be *less* than that of the O disturbance. This means that, for these crystals, the O wavelet is entirely outside the E. Such crystals are called *positive*. For the other class, *negative*, the converse is true, that is, the E wave surface is entirely outside the O. Thus, Fig. 12.3(a), corresponds to a positive crystal; Fig. 12.3(b), to a negative. The student will observe that Iceland spar is a negative crystal, whereas quartz is a positive.

Table IX.

Substance	n_E	n_O
Iceland spar.................	1.486	1.658
tourmaline..................	1.62	1.64
nitrate of soda..............	1.337	1.585
quartz.....................	1.553	1.544
ice........................	1.307	1.306
sulphate of potash...........	1.502	1.493

12.6. The Nicol Prism. For reasons which will appear in the next chapter, it is frequently desirable to get rid of one of the doubly refracting beams. This can readily be done by the use of a Nicol prism, a device in which the O beam is removed by total reflection. Its construction should be clear by a consideration of Figs. 12.11 and 12.12. To begin with, a crystal of Iceland spar, about three

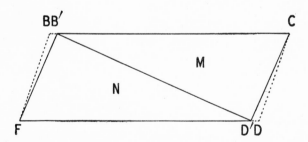

Fig. 12.11.   Diagram showing alteration of a crystal of Iceland Spar when a Nicol prism is made.

times as long as it is broad, is taken, and small pieces are cut off each end somewhat as indicated in Fig. 12.11. In this figure $BCDF$ represents the section of the crystal marked with the same letters as in Fig. 12.1. After end pieces represented by FBB' and $D'CD$ are removed, the angle $B'CD'$ is about 68° instead of the original 71° 5' of the angle BCD. The crystal is next cut into two pieces M and N along a plane represented by $B'D'$, that is, by a cut which passes through B' and D' (see again Fig. 12.1) and is at right angles to the section $B'CD'F$. These two pieces are subsequently cemented together by Canada Balsam, after which, to all appearances, the crystal is as transparent as before the cut. There is a very important difference, however, which arises from the fact that the index for Canada Balsam, 1.55, is intermediate in value between n_E and n_O for Iceland spar. This means that Canada Balsam is optically always less dense than the prism as far as the O beam is concerned, and optically more dense for the E beam (provided the latter does not travel in a direction too near that of the optic axis). It follows, therefore, that when the E beam is incident on the layer of cement, it is transmitted, since total reflection does not occur, whereas the O beam is totally reflected if the angle of incidence is greater than the critical angle. With the arrangement we have just described, this is ordinarily the case, and consequently, as shown in Fig. 12.12, the O beam is reflected to one side and the E beam transmitted.

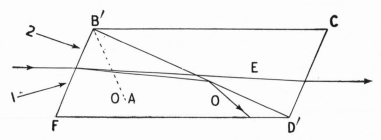

Fig. 12.12. Cross-section of a Nicol prism. Note the total reflection of the O beam at the interface $B'D'$.

The student should note, however, that at one edge of the field of view it is *possible* to have the O beam transmitted, and at the other edge, to have the E beam totally reflected. The transmission of the O beam occurs if light is incident on the prism along a direction somewhat as indicated by the arrow marked 1, in Fig. 12.12, so that inside the prism the O beam strikes $B'D'$ near B' at an angle of incidence less than the critical angle. To understand why a beam, incident somewhat as indicated by the arrow marked 2, can give rise to an E beam which is totally reflected, the student must recall that n_E, *the* index of refraction refers only to the light traveling in a direction *perpendicular* to the optic axis. But if an E beam travels in a direction *parallel* to the optic axis, its velocity is the same as that of the O beam (see again Fig. 12.3). Consequently the E beam has a whole range of velocities between these two extremes and, therefore, corresponding values of indices ranging from that usually called n_E to a value equal to n_O. When the E beam, therefore, travels more nearly parallel than perpendicular to the optic axis, its index may be less than that of the balsam and so even the E beam may be totally reflected. For light incident as in 2, then, we may have total reflection of the E beam incident on $B'L'$ (near D').

When approximately parallel light is transmitted through the Nicol (and this is usually the case) such edge effects have no practical importance.

12.7. Principal Plane. A plane perpendicular to the face of a crystal on which light is incident and containing the optic axis is called a *principal plane*. If one looks at the end of a Nicol prism, a principal plane may conveniently be represented in a sectional diagram such as Fig. 12.13, by the line AB, joining the corners of the two obtuse angles. Since the optic axis is a direction, it must be realized that there are an infinite number of principal planes.

12.8. Foucault Prism. In this type of prism, the O beam is removed by total reflection, as in the Nicol, but the thin layer separating the two pieces in which the original crystal is cut is air, not Canada Balsam.

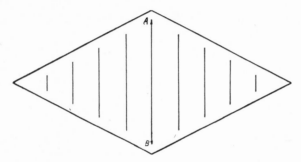

Fig. 12.13.   When looking at the end of a Nicol prism, principal planes may be represented by lines parallel to $A\,B$.

Since air is optically less dense than the crystal for both the O and the E beams, obviously total reflection is possible for both. But the critical angles are not the same, having, in fact, the values 42° 16′ for the E beam and 37° 6′ for the O, if we use the indices for Iceland spar given in Table IX. If, then, the prism is so designed that the angles of incidence of the light striking the film are intermediate between these values, it follows that the E beam will be transmitted and the O beam totally reflected. This condition is ensured by using a crystal in which the ratio of length to width is considerably less than in the Nicol prism, thus giving an advantage which is largely commercial.

A disadvantage of the Foucault prism, which is not in general use like the Nicol, is the fact that, although the E beam is transmitted, even for it a fair amount of intensity is lost by reflection.

12.9. Polaroid, a Substitute for a Nicol Prism. Certain doubly refracting crystals exhibit to a marked degree *dichroism*, that is, a property measured by the difference in the absorption of the O and the E beams. For example, a piece of tourmaline, 1 millimeter or so in thickness, transmits only the E beam because of the complete absorption of the O beam. As a practical means of getting rid of one of the doubly refracting beams, however, tourmaline is of little use because the absorption of the E beam is a marked function of the wavelength and the emergent light is strongly colored.

Since 1932 an excellent substitute for a Nicol prism has been available in the substance which bears the trade name *Polaroid*. Essentially this is an extremely thin layer of a crystalline substance called *herapathite* whose dichroism is so pronounced that a thickness of only $\frac{1}{200}$ inch absorbs one of the doubly refracted beams, but transmits the other to a marked degree for all wavelengths in the visible spectrum. Herapathite is a compound of iodine and quinine sulphate which was given this name because it was discovered by W. B. Herapath as long ago as 1851. Although its dichroic properties had been known for many years, it was not until 1932 that E. H. Land (United States) invented the process which is the basis of Polaroid. Land succeeded in making a thin sheet of a matrix, nitrocellulose, in which ultra-microscopic crystals of herapathite were imbedded *with their optic axes all parallel*. His general method is utilized by the Polaroid Corporation for the manufacture on a commercial scale of this substitute for Nicol prisms. A thin layer of Polaroid is placed between protecting plates or films, and pieces with surface areas many times greater than those of the largest Nicols may readily be obtained at a comparatively low cost. To quote from recent literature of the Polaroid Corporation, "today the commercial grades of the basic Polaroid sheeting come from almost completely automatic machines, in pieces 30 inches wide and indefinitely long."

Herapathite is not the only material for making Polaroid sheets. As a result of investigations in the laboratories of the Polaroid Corporation, polarizing sheets can be made without using preformed crystals at all. According to E. H. Land, director of these investigations, the sheets are made by creating "a brush-like structure inside of a plastic sheet . . . ," which "is stretched in one direction so that the long, tangled molecules straighten out, all parallel to the direction of stretch." After further chemical treatment, the final result is a first-class light polarizer.

Before giving further information about Polaroid it is necessary to explain in detail the peculiar property of the light which emerges from either a Nicol prism or a piece of Polaroid. This is the subject of the next chapter, where, it should be noted, Nicol prisms may be replaced by Polaroid.

XIII

Plane Polarized Light

13.1. The Meaning of Polarization of Light. If one views an ordinary source of light through a Nicol prism, nothing peculiar is observed, no matter what the position of the Nicol. If, however, the light is viewed through two Nicol prisms, the one nearest the light being stationary, while the other is rotated, marked changes in the intensity are observed. Thus, when the principal planes of the two Nicols are at right angles, no light at all is transmitted through the second. As it is rotated, light is transmitted with greater and greater intensity until a maximum is reached when the principal planes are parallel, that is, after a rotation of 90° from the first position. As rotation is continued, the light again becomes dimmer, a second time falling to zero intensity after another 90°. Exactly the same phenomenon may be observed by leaving the Nicol next the eye fixed and rotating the other one.

One may conclude, therefore, that light which has emerged from a Nicol prism differs from ordinary light. Moreover, since the intensity of the emergent light depends on the position of the principal plane of the rotating Nicol with respect to any fixed plane of reference in space, the difference, whatever it is, must be due to a property of the beam of light which depends on its orientation with respect to such a plane of reference. What, then, can such a property be?

Before answering that question, it is well to consider a medium such as the string of a violin which can vibrate either longitudinally or transversely. If such a string is stroked longitudinally, the vibrations of all particles along its length bear the same relation to a vertical or to a horizontal, or to any other plane passing through the string. If, however, the string is stroked or plucked sideways and thus made to vibrate transversely, then the relation of the vibration of any particle to a plane of reference through the string depends very decidedly on what that plane is. For example, if the string is vibrating in a plane perpendicular to the chosen plane of reference, no component of the vibration of the particle takes place in that plane, whereas, if the plane of reference is parallel to the vibrating plane, the whole of the vibration of each particle takes place in it. If, therefore, transverse vibrations are confined to a definite plane, the component of the vibration of any particle in any arbitrary plane of reference depends on the angle which this plane makes with the vibration plane. With longitudinal vibrations, however, no such relation exists.

It is concluded, then, from the results obtained by looking through two Nicol prisms, (1) that light waves must be transverse; (2) that as a result of the passage of light through a Nicol prism, the vibrations are all in one definite plane. Light for which condition (2) is the case is said to be plane polarized. In ordinary light, on the other hand, while the vibrations are transverse, the direction in which each particle is vibrating is continually and rapidly changing. *On the average*, then, the magnitude of the component of a vibration in one plane is the same as for any other. In the case of a Nicol prism, polarization results because the crystalline structure forces, as it were, the vibrations all to take place in one plane. When, therefore, two Nicols are symmetrically placed (that is, with principal planes. parallel), the vibrations of the light emerging from the first and incident on the second are parallel to the plane in which alone it transmits vibrations and the transmitted intensity is a maximum. Again, when the two are placed with their principal planes at right angles, there is no component of the incident light in the plane in which the second transmits vibrations, and no light emerges.

It is natural now to ask, what *is* this vibration plane, that is, how is it related to the principal plane? Anything which has been said so far is true regardless of what angle the vibration plane may make with the principal plane. Can we find what this angle is? The answer to that question can be found by a consideration of another method of obtaining plane polarized light.

13.2. Polarization by Scattering.   In section 11.22 attention was directed to the phenomenon of scattering by small particles. Suppose now that light scat-

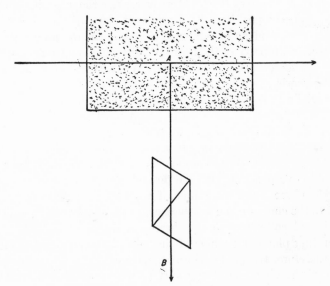

Fig. 13.1.   When an observer looks through a Nicol prism (or Polaroid film) at right angles to a beam of ordinary light traversing a tank containing scattering particles in suspension, the scattered light is found to be plane polarized.

tered in a direction, AB, Fig. 13.1, that is, along lines perpendicular to the path of the original beam, is observed *through a Nicol prism*. It is found that, as the Nicol is rotated, the intensity changes from a maximum to a minimum every 90°. The scattered light is, therefore, plane polarized. Moreover, if the original beam

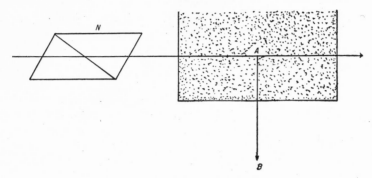

Fig. 13.2. When polarized light leaving a Nicol prism (or Polaroid film) traverses a tank with scattering particles in suspension, the intensity of the scattered light as viewed along AB by a naked eye goes through maxima and minima values as the Nicol is rotated.

is horizontal, and if light waves are transverse, it follows that the vibration plane for light scattered in the direction AB must be a vertical one. Now if the position of the Nicol prism is noted when a maximum amount of light is transmitted, it is found that the principal plane is also vertical. We conclude, therefore, that *the plane in which a Nicol prism transmits vibrations must be a principal plane.*

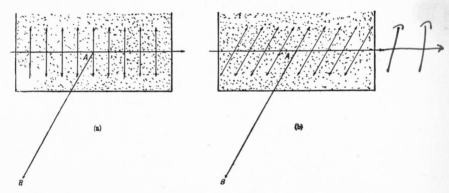

Fig. 13.3. In (a) the intensity of the light scattered along AB is a maximum; in (b), a minimum.

In the same way the vibration plane of the light transmitted by a piece of Polaroid may be located. (Alternately, the Polaroid may be used in conjunction with a Nicol prism.)

A variation of the preceding experiment leads to the same conclusion. Suppose the *original* beam is plane polarized as a result of passage through a Nicol prism placed as N, Fig. 13.2. We now find, if we look in the direction AB *with the unaided eye* that, as the Nicol is rotated, the intensity of the scattered light changes from a maximum to a minimum every 90°. Moreover, when the intensity is a maximum, the principal plane of the Nicol is vertical, whereas, when it is a minimum, the principal plane is horizontal. The explanation of these results is at once forthcoming, if the vibration plane of light transmitted by a Nicol is a principal plane. For when the principal plane is vertical, the plane polarized beam which encounters the scattering particles causes vibrations at all places in a vertical direction, that is, along lines at right angles to the line of sight (Fig. 13.3(a)), and such vibrations are transmitted. On the other hand, when the principal plane is horizontal, the plane polarized beam gives rise to vibrations at all places in a direction parallel to AB and, therefore, with no component perpendicular to the line of sight. (Fig. 13.3(b).) Because of the transverse nature of light vibrations, therefore, no disturbance is sent in the direction AB. If that were the case, we should have longitudinal vibrations giving rise to light. Once more we conclude that the vibration plane of light transmitted by a Nicol prism is a principal plane.

Before leaving the subject of polarization by scattering, it is not amiss to point out that it follows from the foregoing considerations that the blue light from the sky should be polarized. This can readily be verified by the simple use of a Nicol or a piece of Polaroid.

13.3. O and E Beams Each Polarized. It should now be abundantly clear to the student that, if we wish to test a beam of light for polarization, all that is necessary is to examine the light by a rotating Nicol. For example, if the O and E beams emerging from a piece of Iceland spar are examined in this way, it is found not only that each beam is plane polarized but that the vibration planes are at right angles. For, when the intensity of the E beam is a maximum, the O beam is absent, and on rotating the Nicol through 90° from this position, the E beam disappears, the O beam being of maximum intensity. Now, since in a Nicol prism it is the E beam which is transmitted, it follows that the vibration plane for O light is perpendicular to the principal plane, while for the E beam, it is in a principal plane. In the general mathematical treatment dealing with the propagation of plane waves through a crystalline medium, it is shown that, in a given direction, only waves with vibrations either in, or perpendicular to, a principal plane can be transmitted.

13.4. Double-Image Prism. Suppose a beam of light is incident normally on the face MA, Fig. 13.4, of a rectangular block made of two wedge-shaped pieces of a doubly refracting medium such as quartz. Suppose, further, that the piece MNA has been cut so that the optic axis is parallel to the surface MA and in the plane of the paper, whereas, for the piece NAB, the optic axis is parallel to the surface NB but perpendicular to the plane of the paper. For the first prism, then, the optic axis is perpendicular to the refracting edge (through A); for the second, it is parallel to its refracting edge (through N).

Consider, now, ray 1 incident normally on the face MA. In the prism it gives rise to O and E disturbances, which, although not separated, travel at unequal rates and with vibration planes at right angles. On entering the second prism, since the optic axis of this is at right angles to that of the first, the original E beam proceeds as an O beam; the O beam as an E beam. The velocity of one, therefore, is increased; of the other, decreased. Hence, at the oblique surface NA, the beams are refracted in opposite directions, and, on emergence from the face NB, two widely separated beams are obtained.

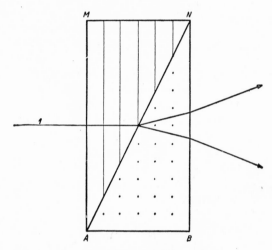

Fig. 13.4. A double-image prism.

Such an arrangement constitutes a Wollaston double-image prism. A prism of this sort is sometimes attached to an eyepiece when one is examining phenomena which exhibit polarization. For example, when the transverse normal Zeeman effect is being observed through a telescope equipped with a (properly oriented) double-image eyepiece, one of the two images seen shows the two outer components of the normal triplet; the other, the central component. (See also section 17.10.)

13.5. Polarization by Reflection. A third important method of obtaining polarized light was discovered by Malus (France, 1775–1812) early in the nineteenth century. The method may be demonstrated by allowing a beam of ordinary light to be reflected from a pile of thin glass plates, as in Fig. 13.5, at an angle a little less than 60°. By examining the reflected beam with a rotating Nicol prism, it is easy to show that this light is plane polarized, with the vibration plane perpendicular to the plane of incidence. If, at the same time, the beam transmitted by the plates is tested, it too will be found to be polarized, but with the vibration plane* in the plane of incidence. Instead of glass, other transparent media may be used.

By varying the angle of incidence, in the case of a beam incident on glass, it is found that there is one angle for which polarization is practically complete. For other angles, while the rotating Nicol shows changes in intensity, at minima the light is not completely cut off. In such cases the reflected beam consists of a mixture of plane polarized and ordinary light, or is said to be partially polarized. For substances other than glass, while there is always an angle of maximum polarization, even at this angle polarization is not always complete. Sir David

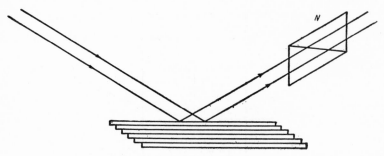

Fig. 13.5. Light reflected obliquely from a pile of glass plates is polarized to an extent which depends on the angle of incidence.

Brewster (Great Britain, 1781–1868), who made measurements on the angle of maximum polarization, showed that, for any substance, its value could be found from the relation

$$\tan i = n, \tag{13.01}$$

where i is the required angle of incidence and n is the index of refraction.

If a single plate of glass is used, the reflected beam is of feeble intensity and a large portion of the transmitted light is unpolarized. When two plates are used, a second reflected beam is added to the first, thus making the reflected beam more intense, while at the same time the percentage of polarized light in the transmitted beam is increased. By using a number of plates, a strong reflected beam of polarized light is obtained, and with a sufficient number, the transmitted light becomes polarized to a high degree.

Pile of Plates as Analyzer. In the case of a Nicol prism we have seen that it may be used either to produce plane polarized light, thus constituting a

---

* The student must not confuse vibration plane with plane of polarization. The latter term, now seldom used, was defined originally as that plane of incidence in which *polarized* light is most completely reflected. By examining polarized light using the arrangement shown in Fig. 13.6, it is easy to show that the vibration plane is perpendicular to the plane of polarization, as thus defined. It is not at all necessary, however, to make any use of the term "plane of polarization,"

polarizer, or, as a means of examining a beam for the presence of polarization, in which case it is called an *analyzer*. The same is equally true of a pile of glass plates. It may be used either to produce plane polarized light or to analyze it. Thus, if the polarized light leaving a pile of plates P_1, Fig. 13.6, is allowed to fall on a second similar pile P_2 at the polarizing angle, a rotation of P_2 about an axis such that the beam is always incident at the same angle, shows marked changes in the intensity of the reflected beam B. When the planes of incidence of the two piles are parallel, the intensity of this beam is a maximum, whereas, when the planes of incidence are at right angles, the intensity is a minimum. Thus, like a Nicol, a rotating pile of plates shows the presence of polarized light

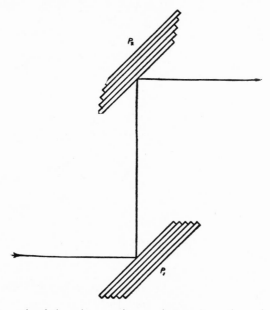

Fig. 13.6. P_1 is a pile of glass plates used as a polarizer; P_2, a pile used as an analyzer.

in a beam incident on it. A combination of a polarizer and an analyzer, such as two Nicol prisms, or a pile of plates and one Nicol, or two piles of plates, or two Polaroids constitutes the essential parts of a *polariscope*.

13.6. Law of Malus. When a beam of plane polarized light is analyzed by either a Nicol prism or a pile of glass plates, we have seen that the intensity changes from a maximum to a minimum when the analyzer is rotated through 90°. This intensity change must take place subject to some law. Such a law, first suggested by Malus, after whom it is called, and amply confirmed by experiment, for perfectly polarized light is given by the relation

$$I_\theta = I_0 \cos^2 \theta, \qquad (13.02)$$

where I_θ is the intensity of the beam when the analyzer has been rotated through an angle θ from the position of maximum intensity (I_0). As a simple example, it is readily seen that, if a Nicol is turned $30°$ from the position of maximum intensity, the intensity has dropped to $\left(\dfrac{\sqrt{3}}{2}\right)^2$ or $\frac{3}{4}$ of the maximum.

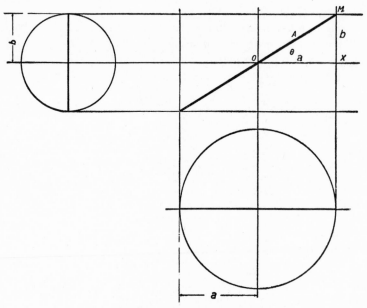

Fig. 13.7. OM is the amplitude of the resultant linear S.H.M. when two S.H.M. of amplitudes OX and XM, along lines at right angles and with zero phase difference, are combined.

Since at any given place in the path of a beam of light, the intensity is proportional to the square of the amplitude, the Law of Malus may be written

$$A_\theta = A_0 \cos \theta, \qquad\qquad (13.03)$$

where A_θ is a measure of the amplitude when an analyzer has been turned through an angle θ from the position of maximum intensity, and where A_0 is a measure of the maximum amplitude. Now it is frequently more convenient to work with amplitudes than with intensities because of the convenient way in which amplitudes may be either combined or resolved. In section 7.13, for example, it was shown how readily a resultant amplitude could be found when a particle is acted on by two S.H.M. of the same period, along lines at right angles. In particular, when the phase difference is zero, the solution illustrated by Fig. 13.7 (and Fig. 7.14) shows that the resultant in such a case is a linear S.H.M. of amplitude OM, in a direction making an angle θ with the direction of the disturbance of amplitude OX along the x-axis. Now,

$$\tan \theta = \frac{MX}{OX} = \frac{b}{a},$$

where b and a are the amplitudes of the individual y and x motions.

We see then, that *in the special case* of two S.H.M. at right angles, of equal periods, with zero phase difference, the resultant amplitude A is represented by the hypotenuse of a right-angled triangle, the other two sides being a and b. A may quickly be found, therefore, by the simple diagram shown in Fig. 13.8. The converse is equally true, that is, *a linear S.H.M. of amplitude A may be resolved into, or is dynamically equivalent to, two linear S.H.M. along lines at right angles, one of amplitude $a = A \cos \theta$, and other of amplitude $b = A \sin \theta$.* In dealing with simple quantitative questions having to do with plane polarized light, this idea is extremely useful, as the solution of the following question will show.

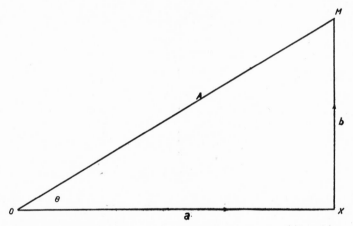

Fig. 13.8.   A linear S.H.M. of amplitude OM can be replaced by two S.H.M. along lines at right angles: one of amplitude OX, and the other of amplitude XM.

PROBLEM.   *A beam of plane polarized light falls on a piece of Iceland spar thick enough to separate the O and the E components.   If the vibration plane of the incident light makes an angle of 20° with the principal plane of the crystal, find the ratio of the intensity of the E beam to that of the O beam.*

If the intensity of the original beam is proportional to a^2 or $= K^2 a^2$, where K^2 is a constant, then the amplitude of the original beam $= Ka$.

Since the crystal transmits vibrations only in the principal plane (the E beam), or perpendicular to it (the O beam), it is natural to resolve the incident disturbance of amplitude $a = OA$, Fig. 13.9, into one component, $OM = Ka$ $\cos 20°$ in the principal plane, and the other, of amplitude $AM = Ka \sin 20°$ perpendicular to the principal plane.   The first component will then be transmitted as the E beam, the second as the O beam, so that we have

$$\frac{\text{amplitude of } E \text{ beam}}{\text{amplitude of } O \text{ beam}} = \frac{Ka \cos 20°}{Ka \sin 20°} = 2.75$$

and, therefore,

$$\frac{\text{intensity of } E \text{ beam}}{\text{intensity of } O \text{ beam}} = (2.75)^2 = 7.5.$$

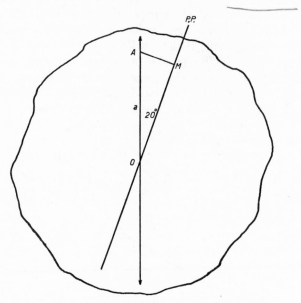

Fig. 13.9.   Diagram used in solving the problem in section 13.7.

13.7. Advantages and Disadvantages of Polaroid.   The chief advantage of Polaroid lies in the fact that it provides us with a means of obtaining wide beams of plane polarized light at comparatively small cost.   For that reason Land's invention has given popular emphasis to certain practical uses of polarizing devices.   Of these we note the following.

(1) A certain portion of the light incident on many semi-smooth surfaces, such as blackboards, cover glasses of paintings, polished tables, pavements, and glazed pottery gives rise to unwanted and sometimes annoying reflected beams which are polarized to a considerable extent.   For either visual or photographic purposes, these reflections may be removed by viewing the surface through a piece of Polaroid placed so that its vibration plane is perpendicular to that of the reflected light.   In some cases it is convenient to use Polaroid spectacles.

(2) The problem of glare in motor-car night driving can be solved, provided all cars are equipped with Polaroid over the headlights and a Polaroid plate through which the driver views the oncoming traffic.   If the vibration plane of the viewing plate is perpendicular to that of the plates over the headlights of an approaching car, these lights are almost invisible and the cause of glare is re-

moved. At the same time objects illuminated by the driver's car are clearly seen. When the road surface is fairly horizontal, a suitable arrangement is to place all the pieces of Polaroid on any one car with vibration planes at an angle of 45° with the vertical. On a high-crowned road, where a car near the ditch may be off horizontal, the vibration plane of the light from such a car would not be at right angles to the plane of the light transmitted through the viewing plate of an approaching car in the middle of the road, and this arrangement would not be entirely satisfactory. The difficulty arising in such a situation can be overcome by the use of circularly polarized light. This is explained in section 14.7. It is significant that, to quote from the *Journal of the Optical Society of America*, "the New York State Legislature has before it for consideration a bill to make mandatory by 1954 the use of a polarizing viewer and polarizing driving lamps as well as nonpolarizing lamps on all motor vehicles."

(3) Stereoscopic moving pictures are possible with the aid of Polaroid. Two views of the same scene are made simultaneously, one corresponding to the view seen by the right eye, the other by the left. The two pictures are projected on a screen, one through one piece of Polaroid, the second through a piece with vibration plane at right angles to the first. If an observer views the superimposed pictures through Polaroid spectacles, with the vibration plane of the piece over the right eye parallel to the vibration plane of the corresponding projected beam, and with the left spectacle similarly placed with respect to the other beam, then the effect of binocular vision is obtained and the scene appears to be in three dimensions. The material of the screen used must be of such a nature that the light is not depolarized by reflection.

The Polaroid Corporation has invented a device called the Vectograph by means of which the foregoing principle is extended for widespread use. Essentially the Vectograph consists of two stereoscopic images, with vibration planes at right angles, superimposed one over the other on either a print or a transparency. By viewing the prints, or, in the case of a film, the projected image, through stereoscopic Polaroid spectacles or cards, three-dimensional vision results.

(4) A desk lamp, fitted with a Polaroid screen with vibration plane suitably oriented, removes the annoying glare reflections from both the desk top and the paper itself.

Although in most experiments, a piece of Polaroid can be used instead of a Nicol prism, it is a good substitute only over a limited range of the spectrum. This may readily be shown by the following simple experiment. Take two Polaroid plates and set them in the "crossed" position, that is, with their vibration planes at right angles, and then view through them a tungsten filament lamp of clear glass. It will be found that, although the general background is dark, the incandescent filament is seen in a purple color. This is proof that there is transmission of light at both the red and the violet ends of the spectrum. Careful tests made with a pair of crossed plates and with monochromatic light show that the amount of light transmitted by the pair for any wavelength in the visible part of the spectrum never exceeds 5 per cent of the incident light, and in that part of the spectrum to which the eye is most sensitive the percentage is considerably less. At the extreme red end, however, the transmission begins to increase rapidly. In the near infrared region the amount transmitted through crossed plates or films is just about the same as when the two pieces are parallel. A pair of crossed plates of Polaroid, therefore, may be used as an infrared filter, that is, a device which eliminates the visible but transmits the infrared. To test this the writer photographed on infrared plates an incandescent lamp with a pair of crossed Polaroid plates in front of the camera. The resulting picture showed the lamp in full detail. In this connection it is worth while noting that crossed Nicol prisms give almost complete extinction over the entire spectrum as far as 200,000 angstroms or 2μ.

XIV

Interference of Polarized Light

14.1. We have seen that when a beam of light is incident on a doubly refracting crystal it is in general broken into two plane polarized beams, with vibration planes at right angles, which travel at unequal rates in any specified direction. In the case of a very thin crystal, or of one cut so that light is traveling perpendicular to the optic axis (see again Figs. 12.8 and 12.9), there is no separation into two distinct beams. Because of the unequal velocities, however, on emergence from the crystal there is a difference in phase between the two disturbances. The value of this difference in phase, for any given kind of light, depends on two things, (1) the ratio of the velocities, (2) the length of the path through the crystal. If, therefore, a thin piece of variable thickness is used, the difference in phase is different for each part of the surface from which the light is emerging. Interference phenomena may then be expected. Do such phenomena exist? Before answering this question, an examination of the following quantitative example is advisable.

PROBLEM. *A beam of plane polarized light, for which* $\lambda = 6 \times 10^{-5}$ *cm, falls normally on a thin piece of quartz cut so that the optic axis lies in the surface. If* $n_E = 1.553$ *and* $n_O = 1.544$, *find for what thickness of the crystal the difference in phase between the E and the O beams, on emergence, is* π *radians.*

Let $\qquad\qquad\qquad$ $t =$ the required thickness.

Then, as far as O light is concerned, we have t cm of crystal $= 1.544t$ cm of air. As far as the E beam is concerned, it is to be noted that the light is traveling perpendicular to the optic axis, and therefore the velocity is given by the value of the extraordinary index (see again section 12.4). Hence,

$\qquad\qquad$ t cm of crystal $= 1.553t$ cm of air, for E beam.

Therefore, the path *difference* for the two beams

$\qquad\qquad$ $= (1.553 - 1.544)t$ cm of air, that is $(n_E - n_O)t$.

But the phase difference

$$= \frac{2\pi}{\lambda} \cdot \text{path difference}$$

$$\therefore \qquad = \frac{2\pi}{\lambda} \cdot (1.553 - 1.544)t.$$

The phase difference, however, equals π;

$$\therefore \qquad \frac{2\pi}{\lambda}(1.553 - 1.544)t = \pi$$

or

$$t = \frac{6 \times 10^{-5}}{2 \times .009} = 0.033 \text{ mm}.$$

A Second Solution

Since λ_O, the O wavelength in the crystal $= \dfrac{6 \times 10^{-5}}{1.544}$,

and $\qquad$ λ_E, the E wavelength in the crystal $= \dfrac{6 \times 10^{-5}}{1.553}$,

$$\therefore \qquad \text{the number of } O \text{ waves in } t \text{ cm} = \frac{1.544t}{6 \times 10^{-5}}$$

and $\qquad$ the number of E waves in t cm $= \dfrac{1.553t}{6 \times 10^{-5}}$,

or the difference in the number of E and of O waves

$$= \frac{t}{6 \times 10^{-5}}(1.553 - 1.544).$$

But, since the phase difference is π, the difference in the number of O and of E waves must be $\frac{1}{2}$ or any odd multiple of $\frac{1}{2}$.

$$\therefore \qquad \frac{t}{6 \times 10^{-5}}(1.553 - 1.544) = K \cdot \tfrac{1}{2}, \text{ where } K \text{ is any odd integral member.}$$

Hence, just as before,

$$t = 0.033 \text{ mm when } K = 1.$$

14.2. Supposing now that we had a crystal of this thickness, would the resultant of the two beams, differing in phase by π, give rise to darkness? That this cannot be the case should be at once evident if the student recalls that the vibrations of the two disturbances are at right angles. For two S.H.M. acting on a single particle along lines at right angles could never bring that particle to rest, no matter what the phase difference. As the work of section 7.13 shows, in such cases we have resultant paths which may be along straight lines, or in ellipses, or occasionally in circles—never zero disturbance. We see, then, that we cannot expect to have interference phenomena with such an arrangement.

If, however, the light emerging from the crystal passes through a Nicol prism (or any analyzer), then a portion of each disturbance is transmitted with vibrations in the principal plane of the Nicol, and we then have the necessary conditions for interference. The exact arrangement necessary for the observation of interference effects with polarized light, as well as for the explanation of what is observed, will perhaps be clear with the aid of Fig. 14.1 and Fig. 14.2. In Fig. 14.1, P and A represent a polarizer and an analyzer between which a thin piece of doubly refracting crystal C is placed; the line MM' represents the vibration plane of the plane polarized light leaving P, NN', that of the light transmitted by A. In the diagram these two vibration planes are at right angles, in which case the analyzer and the polarizer are said to be in the *crossed* position. In the absence of the crystal, obviously no light at all is transmitted when the analyzer and polarizer are crossed.

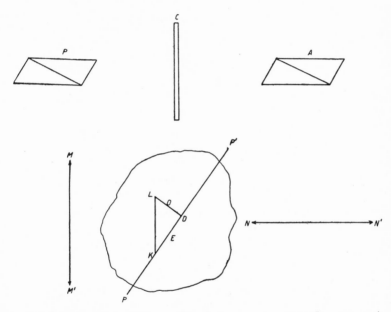

Fig. 14.1. P and A are a polarizer and an analyzer in the crossed position, the corresponding vibration planes being represented by MM' and NN'. C is a thin section of a doubly refracting crystal seen face on in the lower diagram.   A vibration of amplitude LK incident on C gives rise to an E component of amplitude KD, an O component of amplitude LD.

The diagram immediately below C represents the face of the crystal whose principal plane passes through PP'. If, then, LK represents the amplitude of the incident light, it will be broken into an E component of amplitude KD with vibrations in the principal plane, and an O component of amplitude LD with vibrations perpendicular to the principal plane. On emerging from the thin crystal there will be a difference in phase between the two components, whose magnitude, once again, for a given wavelength, and a given direction, depends upon the thickness of the crystal.   On striking the analyzer, a portion of each will be transmitted with amplitudes as represented in Fig. 14.2. Thus, since the E disturbance of amplitude KD is equivalent to one of amplitude DX with vibrations parallel to NN' together with another of amplitude XK with vibrations perpendicular to NN', the first of these only will be transmitted (with amplitude DX). Similarly, since the O disturbance of amplitude LD is equivalent to one of amplitude HD, parallel to NN', and LH perpendicular to NN', HD alone will be transmitted by the analyzer. We have then, finally, two disturbances, one of amplitude HD, the other of amplitude DX, emerging from the analyzer with a phase difference depending on the thickness of the crystal. Interference is now possible.

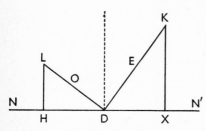

Fig. 14.2. On striking the analyzer, a portion of the E component of Fig. 14.1. is transmitted with amplitude DX, as well as a portion of the O component, with amplitude DH.

If the light is monochromatic and the crystal is of variable thickness, we see on a screen on which the emergent light falls some places bright, others dark. For example, if a piece of quartz in the form of a wedge is used, there are alternately bright and dark regions parallel to the thin end of the wedge. An actual photograph of such fringes is reproduced in Fig. 5, Plate IV, facing p. 153.

If white light is used, the pattern on the screen is generally brilliantly colored. The reason for this is the same as that given in section 9.1, when the question of inteference colors observed with soap films was under discussion. Destructive interference (that is, zero intensity) in general can be obtained for only one wavelength at a time, for, if the phase difference is π for λ_1, it will not be so for most wavelengths differing from λ_1. In the light pattern, therefore, corresponding to a particular thickness, while there may be a place of zero intensity for λ_1 (and possibly other wavelengths), for most wavelengths the intensity will not be a minimum. This place on the screen will accordingly be colored, for it will represent white light minus a certain percentage of the constituent wavelengths.

PROBLEM. *Prove that the amplitudes HD and DX, Fig. 14.2, are equal for all values (except $0°$ and $90°$) of the angle LKD, in Fig. 14.1.*

Complementary Colors. An interesting variation of the above arrangement is obtained when a piece of ordinary Iceland spar (or a double-image prism) is substituted for the analyzing Nicol. If the piece is so chosen that the O and E beams, while separated, overlap to some extent, in the overlapping portion there must always be white light, for it represents the *total* energy of the beam incident on the analyzer. Accordingly, if the thin crystal is chosen of uniform thickness so that a uniform patch of colored light is obtained with an ordinary analyzer, the change to the piece giving two emergent beams will show complementary colors, with white in the overlapping portion.

To obtain such interference phenomena the analyzer and polarizer need not be necessarily in the crossed position. Indeed, if the analyzer is rotated, while the color pattern changes, it is always present, *except for four critical positions* in each revolution. That there should be such critical positions it is easy to see with reference to Fig. 14.1. For when the analyzer is being rotated and the vibration plane NN' becomes parallel to KD, the E beam is transmitted with undiminished intensity, while the O beam of amplitude LD is completely cut off. Only one beam being then transmitted, interference is impossible. Similarly, when NN' becomes parallel to LD, the E beam is completely cut off, the O alone being transmitted, and again interference is out of the question.

If the analyzer and polarizer are left in fixed positions, and the crystal is rotated about an axis parallel to the beam of light, the same result is obtained, although for a slightly different reason. Thus, on rotating the crystal, when PP' becomes parallel to MM' the whole of the beam of amplitude LK is transmitted as an E beam, the O beam being absent. Again, when PP' is perpendicular to MM', there is no component of LK in the principal plane; hence the E beam is absent, the disturbance being transmitted with amplitude LK as an O beam. In both these cases, there being only one beam leaving the thin crystal, interference is impossible.

14.3. Interference Phenomena with Scattering Medium as Analyzer. An interesting variation of the foregoing arrangement may be had by using as analyzer a tank of water with a suspension of scattering particles (see section 13.2). In the following experiments, in which thin pieces of doubly refracting material of uniform thickness are needed, cellophane is satisfactory.

(1) A horizontal, approximately parallel, beam of unpolarized light falls on an opaque screen containing two or three windows of Polaroid mounted with vibration planes horizontal. Immediately beyond the Polaroid is a second opaque screen with corresponding windows of different thicknesses of cellophane. For the best results the cellophane should be cut so that the principal plane makes an angle of 45° with the vertical. The resulting beams traversing the tank placed in the path of the light are beautifully colored when viewed from a direction at right angles to the beam. The particular shade of each beam of course depends on the thickness of the corresponding window of cellophane.

(2) If the polarizing screen is replaced by a single fair-sized piece of Polaroid, such as the standard 4-in. square, and if this is rotated through 90°, the colors of the beams change to their complements. During the rotation a critical position for which each beam loses its color can be observed.

(3) If a single window of cellophane is used, complementary colors may be observed simultaneously by mounting a plane mirror above the tank. If the mirror is suitably inclined the observer can view the beam both horizontally, by direct light, and vertically, by light reflected from the mirror. The two beams thus seen are always complementary in color.

(4) Adjacent beams of complementary colors may be obtained by using as polarizer two pieces of Polaroid placed one above the other, with their line of

separation horizontal, but with the vibration plane of one vertical, the other horizontal. When some of the light emerging from each piece traverses a cellophane window (preferably made of several layers), the colors in the upper and lower halves of the beam in the tank are complementary.

14.4. The whole question may conveniently be discussed analytically and somewhat more generally. In Fig. 14.3, OP represents the vibration plane of light transmitted by the polarizer, while OP'' represents the principal plane of the crystal, with OR a plane at right angles to the latter.

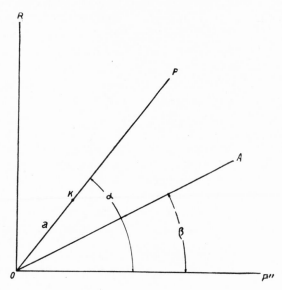

Fig. 14.3. Diagram used for an analytic treatment of the interference of polarized light discussed in section 14.2.

Let $POP'' = \alpha$; $AOP'' = \beta$, and let $OK = a$, represent the amplitude of the light incident on the thin crystal. OK is then the equivalent of LK of Fig. 14.1.

We have then, leaving the crystal, an E beam of amplitude $a \cos \alpha$, with vibrations parallel to OP'', and an O beam of amplitude $a \sin \alpha$, with vibrations perpendicular to OP'' or parallel to OR.

When these two components strike the analyzer, they give rise to

$a \cos \alpha \cos \beta$, vibrations parallel to OA,
$a \cos \alpha \sin \beta$, vibrations perpendicular to OA,
$a \sin \alpha \sin \beta$, vibrations parallel to OA,
$a \sin \alpha \cos \beta$, vibrations perpendicular to OA.

Thus we have *transmitted* by the analyzer two components of amplitudes $a \cos \alpha \cos \beta$ and $a \sin \alpha \sin \beta$, between which there is the difference in phase resulting from the unequal velocities of the E and the O beams in the thin crystal. If this phase difference $= \delta$, the final resultant amplitude A of the light transmitted is then found just as has been indicated in section 8.1. Thus

$$A^2 = a^2 \cos^2 \alpha \cos^2 \beta + a^2 \sin^2 \alpha \sin^2 \beta + 2 \, a^2 \cos \alpha \cos \beta \sin \alpha \sin \beta \cos \delta$$

$$= a^2 \left[\cos^2 \alpha \cos^2 \beta + \sin^2 \alpha \sin^2 \beta + 2 \cos \alpha \cos \beta \sin \alpha \sin \beta \right.$$
$$\left. - 4 \cos \alpha \cos \beta \sin \alpha \sin \beta \sin^2 \frac{\delta}{2} \right]$$

$$= a^2 \left[(\cos \alpha \cos \beta + \sin \alpha \sin \beta)^2 - 4 \cos \alpha \cos \beta \sin \alpha \sin \beta \sin^2 \frac{\delta}{2} \right]$$

$$= a^2 \left[\cos^2 (\alpha - \beta) - \sin 2\alpha \sin 2\beta \sin^2 \frac{\delta}{2} \right]. \tag{14.01}$$

Since the intensity is proportional to the square of the amplitude, this expression enables us to find how the intensity varies due to changes in δ, as well as in α and β. We note the following cases:

(1) When the analyzer and polarizer are in fixed positions, that is, when α and β remain constant. The intensity then varies with the value of $\sin^2 (\delta/2)$, and δ, as we have already seen, varies with the thickness of the crystal and the wavelength. The general results already discussed at once follow.

(2) When the analyzer and polarizer are crossed. In this case $\alpha - \beta = 90°$, and we have

$$A^2 = a^2 \left[o - \sin 2\alpha \sin (2\alpha - 180°) \sin^2 \frac{\delta}{2} \right]$$

$$= a^2 \sin^2 2\alpha \sin^2 \frac{\delta}{2}. \tag{14.02}$$

(3) When the analyzer and polarizer are parallel. In this case $\alpha = \beta$, and we have

$$A^2 = a^2 \left[1 - \sin^2 2\alpha \sin^2 \frac{\delta}{2} \right]. \tag{14.03}$$

It will be noticed that the sum of the two expressions (14.02) and (14.03) is always a^2, regardless of the value of δ or of α. This is just what should be expected, for the sum of these two beams must represent the total intensity, provided there is no actual absorption by the analyzer. In the case where an ordinary doubly refracting crystal replaces the analyzer, and complementary colors are obtained, the overlapping portion represents this sum, and, as we have seen, is white.

14.5. Elliptically and Circularly Polarized Light. We return now to a consideration of the nature of the light emerging from a thin crystal such as we have been discussing. Since we are dealing with cases where the O and the E beams are not separated, although vibrating in planes at right angles, we have to do with an application of the work discussed when considering the composition of two S.H.M. at right angles.

Diagrams such as those shown in Figs. 7.14, 7.15, 7.16, 7.17 and 7.18 tell us that the resultant in such cases may be a linear motion or a motion in an elliptical or in a circular path. The first of these results when the phase difference between the two components is any multiple of π. To obtain circular vibrations, two conditions must be fulfilled: (1) the phase difference must be $\pi/2$; (2) the amplitudes of the individual beams must be equal. Such conditions obtain (1) if a piece of thin crystal is chosen of such a thickness t that the required phase difference results, that is, such that

$$\frac{2\pi}{\lambda} \cdot (n_E - n_O)t = \frac{\pi}{2}, \qquad \text{(see section 14.1)}$$

or
$$t = \frac{\lambda}{4(n_E - n_O)};$$

and (2) if this crystal is so placed in the path of the plane polarized beam that its principal plane makes an angle of 45° with the vibration plane of the incident light.

A crystal of such a thickness is called a *quarter-wave plate.*

Elliptical vibrations represent the general case when the two beams with vibrations at right angles have any phase difference other than a multiple of π— except the special case giving rise to circular vibrations.

14.6. We see then that in the beam of light leaving a thin crystal on which plane polarized light is incident, we may have resultant vibrations confined to a definite plane, or taking place in elliptical paths or in circular. In other words, we may have either plane polarized light or elliptically polarized light or circularly polarized. The question then arises, can one analyze a beam of light and detect the presence not only of plane polarization but also of the other kinds? The answer to that we shall briefly discuss, considering the following four cases.

(1) As we have seen several times, if light is completely plane polarized, a rotating Nicol will show regions of maximum intensity alternating with minima *where complete extinction occurs.*

(2) If the beam consists of a mixture of plane polarized and ordinary light, the rotating Nicol again shows places of maxima and minima intensities, but at the latter the intensity does not drop to zero. Only the polarized part of the beam can be completely cut off.

(3) Suppose a beam of light is completely circularly polarized. As the converse of the work on the composition of S.H.M. at right angles shows, *a circular vibration may be resolved into or is dynamically equivalent to two linear vibrations of equal amplitudes along any two lines at right angles, with a phase difference equal to $\pi/2$.* When, therefore, a beam of circularly polarized light falls on a Nicol prism, there is no change in the intensity of the emergent light as the Nicol is

rotated. That this is so should be clear from Fig. 14.4, where $OB = OA = a$ represent the amplitudes of the component linear vibrations, as well as their vibration planes, while OP is the vibration plane of the light transmitted by the Nicol. If the angle $POB = \theta$, we see that the Nicol transmits two components, one of amplitude $a \cos \theta$, the other, of amplitude $a \sin \theta$. Since the phase difference between these two is $\pi/2$, the resultant amplitude A is, therefore, given by (see section 7.11)

$$A^2 = a^2 \cos^2 \theta + a^2 \sin^2 \theta + 2a^2 \cos \theta \sin \theta \cos \frac{\pi}{2} = a^2.$$

Hence, regardless of the value of θ, the emergent intensity is always the same. The rotating Nicol, therefore, shows no change in intensity, and hence does not distinguish between ordinary and circularly polarized light.

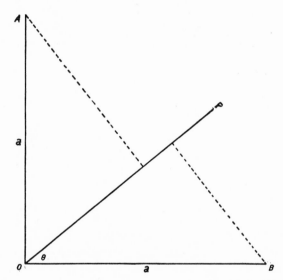

Fig. 14.4. Diagram used in proving that, when circularly polarized light falls on a Nicol prism (or Polaroid film), the intensity of the emergent light is independent of the position of the Nicol.

Suppose, however, that we introduce into the path of the circularly polarized beam a quarter-wave plate. Then a further phase difference of $\pi/2$ is introduced between the components so that on emergence from this plate, the phase difference is either 0 or π. In either case, plane polarized light results, and now, when the beam falls on a rotating Nicol, complete extinction occurs for certain positions. If, however, a quarter-wave plate is introduced into the path of ordinary light, plane polarized light does not emerge and the rotating Nicol shows no changes in intensity.

(4) Consider next a beam of elliptically polarized light. Although an elliptical vibration, as we have seen, is the general resultant of any two linear mo-

tions at right angles, it can always be built up by combining two linear along lines parallel to the major and to the minor axis, and differing in phase by $\pi/2$ (see Fig. 7.17). Conversely, an elliptical motion is dynamically the equivalent of two linear vibrations of unequal amplitude, along lines parallel to the axes, and differing in phase by $\pi/2$. When, therefore, elliptically polarized light falls on a rotating Nicol, it is not difficult to see that there are changes in intensity, a maximum existing when the principal plane is parallel to the major axis of the

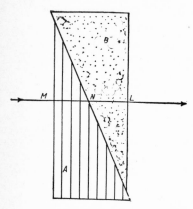

ellipse, a minimum when it is parallel to the minor axis. But this is just what is observed when a beam consists of a mixture of plane polarized and ordinary light. To distinguish between the two, a quarter-wave plate may be used in the same way and for the same reason as in the analysis of circularly polarized light.

More exact and more detailed analysis of the general nature of beams of light with respect to the kind and degree of polarization can be made by the use of a Babinet Compensator. Essentially this consists of two small-angled, wedge-shaped pieces of quartz, placed as in Fig. 14.5, so as to form a rectan-

Fig. 14.5. A Babinet compensator.

gular piece of uniform thickness. The pieces are cut so that in each the optic axis is parallel to the surface, but in A, in the plane of the paper; in B, perpendicular to this plane. If a ray of polarized light is incident normally in the direction of the arrow, in general an E and an O beam result, between which a phase difference is introduced

$$= \frac{2\pi}{\lambda} (n_E - n_O) \; MN, \text{ in the first piece,}$$

and

$$= \frac{2\pi}{\lambda} (n_E - n_O) \; NL, \text{ in the second piece.}$$

Now since the principal planes of the two pieces are at right angles, that component which traverses A as an E beam (that is, with vibrations in the principal plane) becomes the O beam for the second piece. The velocities, therefore, are interchanged in the second piece, and so the resultant phase difference is given by the difference of the foregoing expressions, that is, by

$$\frac{2\pi}{\lambda} (n_E - n_O) \; (MN - NL).$$

It follows that if the piece B can slide with respect to the other, the path length

NL can either be increased or decreased, and so the phase difference on emergence at L can be made any desired value. Consequently the light emerging at L can be made either linearly or elliptically or circularly polarized.

If circular polarized light is wanted, or if it is desired to introduce at L a phase difference exactly equal to $\pi/2$, this device has an advantage over a quarter-wave plate in that the latter gives the required phase difference exactly for only one wavelength, whereas the compensator can be set accurately for any wavelength.

As the use of this device in the general analysis of the state of polarization of a beam of light involves principles similar to those discussed in connection with the quarter-wave plate, further details will not be given.

14.7. Test of Strain in Glass. Ordinary glass is isotropic and exhibits no sign of double refraction. When glass is subject to great strain, however, it becomes doubly refracting. A convenient test of the presence of such strains is found, therefore, by placing the specimen between a crossed analyzer and polarizer. If the glass has strains, it is doubly refracting, two beams are transmitted, and the strains are rendered evident by the appearance of interference colors.

An important application of this fact has been made to determine the distribution of stresses in solid opaque materials used in engineering construction. To do so, models of the material to be examined are made in glass or in a transparent plastic substance like lucite or bakelite. The models are then placed between analyzer and polarizer, and from a study of the color pattern corresponding to the strains in the transparent material, the actual stresses can be determined. This phenomenon, with its application in this way, is called *photoelasticity*.

In photoelasticity it is customary to use a circular polariscope. This consists of a combination of the usual polarizer and analyzer plus two quarter-wave plates, one associated with the polarizer, the other with the analyzer. Suppose that, before the introduction of the plates, the analyzer and polarizer are set in the crossed position. As we have seen in section 14.5, the instroduction of a quarter-wave plate (properly oriented) next to the polarizer gives circularly polarized light and light is transmitted by the analyzer. A second quarter-wave plate is now inserted in front of the analyzer and rotated to such a position that there is again no light transmitted through the analyzer. With this arrangement the two quarter-wave plates have counteracted each other, that is, they are now so placed that the component whose phase was 90° ahead after traversing the first plate is delayed 90° by the second, the net difference in phase between the two components now being zero. (See section 7.13 and Fig. 7.14.) Although, as far as extinction of transmitted light goes, the final result is the same as if there were no quarter-wave plates this combination has the very great advantage that, if after this preliminary adjustment has been made, the combination of the analyzer and its quarter-wave plate is rotated, there is still no light transmitted for any position.*   (See again (3) section 14.6.)

When stresses are being examined in photoelasticity and the specimen is placed between the polarizing and analyzing units of a circular polariscope, it has the very great advantage that the interference pattern remains constant for all positions of the specimen.   Figure 3, Plate VII, facing p. 224, is a photograph of such a pattern, reproduced through the courtesy of the Polaroid Corporation.

14.8. It was pointed out in (2) of section 13.7 that, when two approaching cars are not on the same horizontal level, the arrangement there described is not entirely satisfactory.   The difficulty may be overcome by the use of circularly polarized light.   Suppose that the pieces of Polaroid over the headlights and the Polaroid viewing screen are covered with a thin plastic layer whose thickness is so chosen that it is a quarter-wave plate for a wavelength in the region of maximum sensitivity of the eye.   The beams leaving the headlights are then circularly polarized, provided the quarter-wave plate is mounted so that condition (2), section 14.5, is fulfilled.   Moreover, circularly polarized light emerges whether the car is on absolutely level ground or not.   When this circularly polarized light falls on the viewing piece of Polaroid similarly covered (on its outer surface) with a quarter-wave plate, no light is transmitted to the eye of the observer in an approaching car.   As explained at the end of (3) in section 14.6, the second quarter-wave plate converts the circularly polarized beam into plane polarized light and this is cut off by the Polaroid plate next to the eye.

14.9. Interference with Highly Convergent Light.   In the arrangement for the study of interference with polarized light which we have been considering, approximately parallel rays have been used.   We shall now briefly consider the type of interference phenomenon when the incident light is highly convergent. Suppose, then, by means of an arrangement such as is shown in Fig. 14.6, where L_1 and L_2 represent lens *systems*, a uniaxial crystal C is placed in the path of a

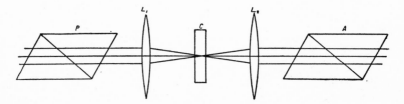

Fig. 14.6. Arrangement for observing interference patterns with doubly refracting crystal when highly convergent light is used. P and A are polarizer and analyzer; L_1 and L_2, convergent lenses; C, the crystal.

* Constant *transmission* of light may be obtained with this arrangement, if the quarter-wave plate in front of the analyzer is rotated through 90°.   In this case the same component is delayed 90° by each quarter-wave plate, thus causing a net phase difference of 180°.   See section 7.13 and Fig. 7.18.

beam of convergent white light, plane polarized by the Nicol prism P, and subsequently analyzed by the analyzing Nicol A. Consider first the special case when the analyzer and polarizer are crossed so that in Fig. 14.7, which represents the face of the crystal, the vibration plane of the incident light is represented by PP', that of the light transmitted by the analyzer by AA', at right angles to PP'. In this figure L represents the point at which the axis of the incident beam intersects the face of the crystal.

If now the crystal is cut with the optic axis perpendicular to the face on which the light is incident, along the axis of the beam of light (through L) the O and

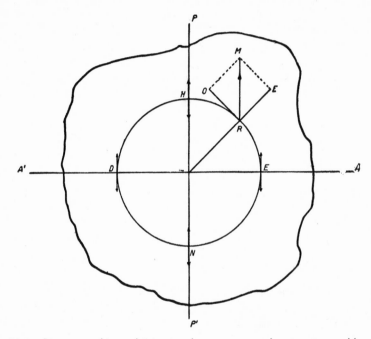

Fig. 14.7.   Diagram used in explaining interference patterns showing rings and brushes.

the E beams travel with equal velocity and no phase difference results. Indeed, in this direction, for a reason which will appear presently, there is only one beam transmitted through the crystal. Consider, however, any point R where the incident light is not normal to the face of the crystal. The original disturbance of amplitude RM, with vibrations parallel to PP', is at this point broken into two, an E beam with vibrations in the principal plane and therefore parallel to RE (since the principal plane contains the optic axis and the incident ray), and an O beam with vibrations perpendicular to RE, or along RO. The direction of a ray incident at R not being parallel to the optic axis, the two disturbances travel through the crystal with unequal velocities, and on emergence a phase difference results. Since the velocity of the E ray varies with the direction and is the same for all lines making equal angles with the optic axis, the magnitude of the phase difference for a crystal of uniform thickness is the same for all points on a circle with center L and radius LR. When, therefore, the emergent light is analyzed by the analyzing Nicol, the color resulting from interference is the same for all points on this circle, except for the four points H, D, N, and E, which are always black. At the points H and N, the vibration plane of the incident light is in a principal plane and so the O beam is entirely absent. When, therefore, the light from such points falls on the analyzer with its vibration plane perpendicular to PP', none at all is transmitted. Since the same can be said with regard to any point on the line PP', we see that the complete light pattern transmitted will be crossed with a black line or band parallel to PP'. Similarly, at the points D and E and all points on the line AA', the vibration plane of the incident light is perpendicular to the principal plane, and so is transmitted unchanged as an O beam. Corresponding to these points, therefore, a black band parallel to AA' is observed in the transmitted light.

Again, since for all other points on the crystal face, the phase difference between the O and the E disturbances steadily changes as circles of radii greater or less than LR are taken, in addition to the dark bands, there is a series of circular colored interference fringes. A photograph of the appearance is given in Fig. 3, Plate V, facing p. 168.

If the analyzer is placed so that its vibration plane is parallel to that of the polarizer, the single beam for all points along PP' and AA' is completely transmitted, and the black bands are replaced by bright ones.

If the crystal is cut with the optic axis parallel to the surface, general analysis shows that the fringes are now hyperbolic, while for an oblique section they are elliptic or hyperbolic.

14.10. Buckley, an English crystallographer, has drawn attention to a simple arrangement whereby, with the aid of Polaroid plates or films of fairly wide aperture, interference patterns with highly convergent light may be obtained. In this arrangement light from a projection lantern falls on the first piece of Polaroid, the polarizer, and is then strongly converged by a lens system such as the Abbe microscope condenser. The doubly refracting crystal is placed as in Fig. 14.6, but unlike the arrangement in that illustration the only additional apparatus necessary is the analyzer, in this case the second piece of Polaroid, placed in the path of the diverging beam, and a screen. A good-sized image of the interference pattern is seen on the screen.

XV

Rotatory Polarization

15.1. Rotation of the Vibration Plane. Suppose, with a monochromatic source such as a sodium flame, a polarizer P, Fig. 15.1, and an analyzer A have been placed *in the crossed position.* If, now, a piece of quartz Q, a millimeter or two thick, and *cut with its face perpendicular to the optic axis,* is inserted between the polarizer and the analyzer, it is found that light is transmitted by the latter. On the other hand, rotation of the analyzer through a definite angle θ (about 22° if the quartz is 1 mm thick and yellow light is used) once more completely cuts off the light. It follows, therefore, that the vibration plane of the light leaving

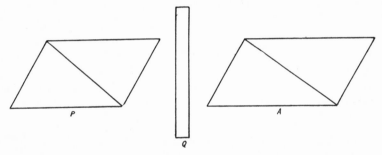

Fig. 15.1. Arrangement for observing rotatory polarization. Q is a small slab of quartz cut with faces perpendicular to the optic axis.

the quartz must make an angle equal to θ with that of the light incident on it. In other words, as a result of the passage of the light through the crystal along the optic axis, the vibration plane has been rotated through a definite angle. If yellow light is replaced by red, the same general result is obtained except that the angle of rotation is less, about 17° for red light of wavelength 6500 A, for a crystal 1 mm thick.

Such an experiment, first performed by Arago (France, 1786–1853) in 1811, illustrates the phenomenon of rotatory polarization. An extended examination of substances having the property of rotating the vibration plane has shown that it is possessed by (1) crystalline quartz along the optic axis; (2) certain liquids such as turpentine, as well as solutions of sugar, tartaric acid; (3) certain isotropic substances when placed in a strong magnetic field.

Quartz and *optically active* substances in general, that is, liquids, and those which in solution have this property may rotate the vibration plane either to the right or to the left, and consequently are classified as dextro-rotatory or laevo-rotatory. The same substance may exhibit both kinds, some crystals of quartz, for example, rotating to the left, others to the right.

Concerning the actual amount of rotation, the following simple laws have been experimentally found:

(1) In the case of quartz and pure liquids, for a fixed wavelength, the angle of rotation is directly proportional to the thickness. For solutions, the angle for a given thickness is proportional to the concentration of the optically active substance.

(2) For a fixed thickness, the angle of rotation increases as the wavelength decreases, roughly inversely as the square of the wavelength.

Thus, for a crystal of quartz 1 mm thick, we have the values for the angle of rotation given in Table X.

Table X.   Rotation of Vibration Plane by 1 mm quartz, at 20° C

Wavelength	6708	6563	5893	5351	4861	4102
Rotation	16.4°	17.3°	21.7°	26.5°	32.7°	47.5°

It will be noted that these values apply only at 20° C. For other temperatures, a correction must be made; thus for D light, the rotation at any temperature $t°$ may be found from the relation

$$\theta = 21.°72 \left[1 + 0.000147 \, (t - 20) \right].$$

15.2. An interesting illustration of the variation in the rotation with wavelength is had when the monochromatic source is replaced by white light. In this case, rotation of the analyzer can never produce extinction of the light, but for each position, a colored beam emerges. The color results from the fact that, for every position of the analyzer, there is, in general, one wavelength for which the vibration plane is exactly at right angles to that of the light transmitted by the analyzer. This wavelength, therefore, is completely cut off, while a certain percentage of the intensity of all other wavelengths (whose vibration planes are not perpendicular to that of the analyzer) is transmitted. The resultant light transmitted is, therefore, colored.

The variation of the amount of rotation with changing wavelength can be nicely shown by using a tank of water containing fine scattering particles in suspension somewhat after the manner described in section 11.22. Suppose that, with white light as source, we place between a polarizing Nicol P, Fig. 15.2, and the tank, a piece of quartz Q cut perpendicular to the optic axis. The plane polarized beam of white light incident on Q then gives rise, on emergence, to vibration planes, in different azimuths for different wavelengths. Consequently, if an observer is looking at right angles to the beam traversing the tank, that is, along the line AB, there always is, in general, some wavelength for which the vibrations are parallel to AB, and another wavelength for which the vibrations are perpendicular to this direction. Light corresponding to the first wavelength is, therefore, entirely absent; to the second, present with maximum intensity; and the resultant beam observed is colored. As the polarizing Nicol is rotated, the color shade alters, because that wavelength for which no light is transmitted along AB is then continuously changing. Of course, the exact shade of the beam seen in direction AB depends also on the excess scattering in this direction of the shorter wavelengths.

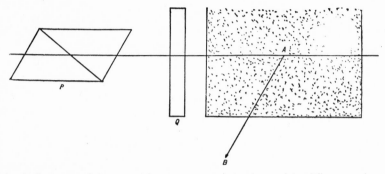

Fig. 15.2. Light scattered from particles in suspension is observed in different colors as the polarizer P is rotated. Q is a piece of quartz cut with faces perpendicular to the optic axis.

This experiment may be varied so as to give, if successfully done, a striking and very beautiful phenomenon, by removing the quartz and using in the tank— or, better, in a long tube—a strong sugar solution containing scattering particles in suspension. In this case, since the vibration plane of any particular wavelength is being continuously rotated as the light traverses the solution, the resultant shade seen when looking at right angles is also constantly changing along the length of the tube. The net result is to give a colored spiral appearance to the whole tube.

15.3. Tint of Passage. Another illustration of color phenomenon due to the same general cause is obtained by taking a piece of quartz of such a thickness that the rotation for a wavelength in the greenish-yellow region, that is, in the brightest part of the spectrum, is 90°. If, for example, the thickness is 3.75 mm, the rotation per millimeter is

$$\frac{90}{3 \cdot 75} = 24°,$$

and Table X shows that the corresponding wavelength is about 5600 A. Suppose, then, that such a piece is inserted between a polarizer and an analyzer, the vibration plane of the former being represented by *POP′*, Fig. 15.3. In the same figure, then, the vibration plane for light of wavelength 5600 on emergence from the crystal is represented by *MOM′*, the angle *POM* being equal to 90°. For a longer wavelength, 6000, for example, the vibration plane is represented by *NON′*, the angle *PON* being considerably less than 90°. For a shorter wavelength such as 5200, the vibration plane is rotated through a greater angle, and hence is represented by *ZOZ′*.

If, now, the analyzer is turned so that its vibration plane is parallel to that of the polarizer, light of wavelength 5600 is completely cut off, the resultant shade of the transmitted light being a grayish-violet. A slight rotation one way from this position evidently increases the transmitted intensity of 6000 and other

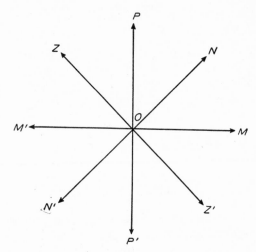

Fig. 15.3. Diagram used in explaining the meaning of sensitive tint when a piece of quartz cut with faces perpendicular to the optic axis is placed between an analyzer and polarizer.

wavelengths toward the red end of the spectrum, but decreases that of 5000 and the shorter waves at the blue end. The grayish-violet tint is then replaced by a deep pink. A slight rotation in the opposite direction, however, decreases the intensity of the longer waves, increasing that of the shorter, and so causes a quick change from the grayish-violet to a deep blue. As the contrast between pink and blue is very marked and takes place as the result of a slight rotation, the gray-violet shade is called the *tint of passage* or *sensitive tint*. Because of this fact, even with white light as a source, it is possible to set an analyzer in a critical position, if a piece of quartz of such a thickness is placed before it.

If the simple piece of quartz is replaced by two adjoining pieces of equal thickness, one dextro-, the other laevo-rotatory, a still more sensitive arrangement, called a *biquartz* is provided. In this case, when the polarizer and analyzer are parallel, the sensitive tint is obtained in each piece. A slight rotation of the analyzer, however, increases the intensity of the longer wavelengths in one, at the same time increasing that of the short wavelengths in the other, and thus causes one piece to become pink, the other blue. Rotation in the opposite direction interchanges the colors. A slight rotation through the critical position, therefore, when the two adjoining pieces have the same shade, causes such a very marked change in the two halves that a setting in this position can be accurately made. Reference will again be made to this point in the next section.

15.4. Analysis of Optically Active Substances. Since the angle of rotation of an optically active substance in solution is proportional to the concentration, a quantitative means is thus provided for studying the strength of such solutions. In the case of sugars, this fact is particularly important because "commercial

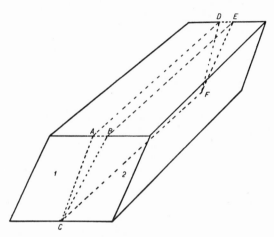

Fig. 15.4. A Cornu-Jellett Nicol, made by cutting a wedge-shaped piece from an ordinary Nicol.

sugars are bought and sold and the import duties collected upon tests" of the amount of rotation. "There are upwards of one hundred sugars known and nearly all of those in solution rotate the azimuth of a rectangular vibration in one direction or the other." (Skinner.) For the exact measurement of the amount of rotation, the observer uses a *saccharimeter*, another name given a polarimeter when used for measuring optical rotations of this kind. In the simplest form, all that is required is a polarizer, an analyzer whose exact position can be read from a circular scale, and, between the two, a tube with transparent ends containing the optically active solution. In this form, with monochromatic light as source, the analyzer is set for extinction before and after the introduction of the solution, the angle of rotation of course being equal to the difference in the two readings. The position of extinction, however, cannot be set exactly enough for accurate measurements, and, in actual practice, settings are generally made by what is called the brightness half-shade method. In essence, this consists in so altering the simple polarimeter arrangement that a field of view is obtained with at least two contiguous parts, the final setting of the analyzer being made when these are of equal brightness.

A particular example, in which a Cornu-Jellett half-shade Nicol is used to obtain the necessary two portions, should make the principle clear. This form of Nicol is made by taking an ordinary Nicol prism, and cutting along its full length a thin *wedge-shaped* piece, somewhat as represented by $ABCDEF$ in Fig. 15.4, after which the two parts 1 and 2 are cemented together. As a result the principal planes of these two parts are now slightly inclined to one another, and therefore, also, the vibration planes of the light transmitted by each. If, then, a beam of plane polarized light is incident on a Cornu-Jellett Nicol used as an analyzer, and it is set so that no light is transmitted by part 2, a feeble

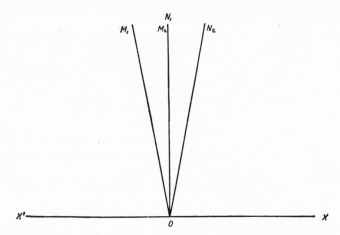

Fig. 15.5.   Diagram used in explaining the use of a Cornu-Jellett Nicol.

intensity will be transmitted by part 1. Thus, if in Fig. 15.5, XOX' represents the vibration plane of the incident light, and, for a certain position of the analyzer, OM_1 represents the vibration plane of light transmitted by 1, ON_1 that by 2, part 2 is dark (since the angle N_1OX is 90°), while some light is transmitted by 1. Again, if the analyzer is rotated through the angle M_1ON_1, so that ON_1 (or OM_2) represents the vibration plane of 1, and ON_2 that of 2, part 1 is now dark, part 2 transmitting a little light. In between these positions there is obviously one place for which each part transmits a feeble intensity of the same brightness, and because of the contrast between the two halves resulting from a slight rotation either way, this position can be set with great accuracy. With monochromatic light and this form of Nicol as analyzer, accurate measurements of angles of rotation can be made.

From the work of the preceding section, it should be clear that with white light as a source and the use of a biquartz between an ordinary analyzer and polarizer, settings of the analyzer may be made. In this case, measurements of the amount of rotation are evidently made for that particular wavelength whose vibration plane is rotated through 90°. What this wavelength is can be found by examining the light transmitted by either half of the biquartz with a spectroscope when the principal planes of analyzer and polarizer are parallel.

15.5. Specific Rotation. To compare the optical activity of different substances, a unit must be adopted. This is done by defining the term *specific rotation* in the following way:

$$\text{Specific rotation} = \frac{\text{angle of rotation for a thickness of 10 cm}}{\text{density of solution in grams per cc}}.$$

A few actual values, for a temperature of 20° C, are given in Table XI. (Taken from Kaye and Laby's Tables.)

Table XI. Specific Rotations of Certain Substances

Substance	Solvent	Specific Rotation	Condition
Glucose	water	−94.4° after 7 min −51.4° after 7 hr	when 4 g dissolved in 100 g of solution
Turpentine	pure liquid	−37°	
Nicotine	pure	−162°	at temperature 10° to 30° C
Rochelle salt	water	+29.73° −0.0078 c	c = concentration in g per 100 cc of solution.

The plus sign indicates dextro-rotatory, that is, anti-clockwise when looking along the beam away from the source, the minus sign, laevo-rotatory.

15.6. Rotation by Magnetic Field. In 1845, Michael Faraday (England, 1791–1867) showed that, when a piece of glass of high refractive index traversed by a beam of plane polarized light, is placed in a strong magnetic field, a rotation of the vibration plane occurs. Since the original discovery, further experiments by Faraday and by later investigators have shown that a similar phenomenon is observed, although sometimes in a very slight degree, by many solids, liquids and gases. The actual angle of rotation θ is directly proportional to (1) the strength H of the magnetic field and (2) the length l of the path traversed in the field. The amount of rotation may, therefore, be expressed by the law

$$\theta = cHl,$$

where c is a constant, called Verdet's constant.

If the direction of the light is reversed, the sense of rotation is also reversed. Thus if a clockwise rotation occurs when light travels in the direction of the lines of force, the rotation is contra-clockwise when the beam is reversed. In consequence of this, if a beam is reflected back and forth along the lines of force, the amount of rotation is greater, the greater the number of times the path is traversed. For this reason rotations may be measured for substances which exhibit this property to only a very slight extent. In the case of optically active substances, the rotation is always in the same sense regardless of the direction of the beam of light, in consequence of which a reversal of the beam annuls the original rotation.

15.7. Explanation of Rotation of Vibration Plane. We have seen in Chapter XIV that for thin crystals an incident beam of plane polarized light can emerge as a plane polarized beam with the vibration plane turned through an angle.

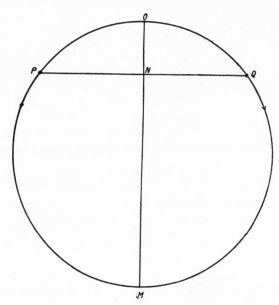

Fig. 15.6. A linear vibratory motion along *ONM* is the equivalent of two equal and opposite circular motions of the same period.

For this to be the case, the phase difference between the O and the E components vibrating at right angles must be some odd multiple of π, that is, it occurs only for crystals of very special thicknesses. In rotatory polarization, however, plane polarized light emerges for any thickness of the substance, with an angle of rotation which steadily increases with increasing thickness. We must, therefore, look elsewhere for the explanation.

There is another way in which plane polarized light can result when two disturbances act on a particle, and that is when the two are each circularly polarized but in opposite senses. Thus a rectilinear vibration along a line may be the resultant of two circular vibrations, and, conversely, a rectilinear vibration may be resolved into or is dynamically the equivalent of two equal and opposite circular vibrations. This being the case, it is possible to explain the phenomena we are discussing on the supposition that we have to do with a class of substances which may be said to be *circularly doubly refracting* in that they transmit only circular vibrations, and these with velocities which are unequal for the two senses of rotation. This was the explanation first proposed by Fresnel, who showed, in a way presently to be described, that in quartz along the optic axis there are two such disturbances.

First of all it is necessary to see that, according to this explanation, the difference between dextro- and laevo-rotatory substances arises from the fact

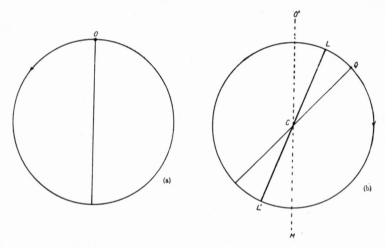

Fig. 15.7.   When two circular vibrations of the same period traverse a crystal at different velocities, the emergent equivalent linear motion *LCL'* makes an angle with the equivalent incident motion along *O'CN'*.

that, in the one, the contra-clockwise vibration is propagated the faster and, in the other, the clockwise vibration. Consider, then, a particle executing a rectilinear motion parallel to the line OM, Fig. 15.6. Such a motion is the equivalent of two equal and opposite circular motions of the same period, for, as far as any displacement perpendicular to OM is concerned, the effect of one is always equal and opposite to that of the other. For example, the displacement PN neutralizes QN. Conversely, the resultant of two circular motions of the same period acting on a single particle is a rectilinear vibration along OM if the two circular disturbances pass each other (when imagined acting independently) at O and M.

Suppose, now, that plane polarized light, with vibration plane parallel to OM, Fig. 15.6, is incident on a medium which transmits only circular vibrations and these with unequal velocities. The original vibration is then replaced by two equal and opposite circular motions, which, at the instant the disturbance strikes the medium, may be considered to be in position O. If, then, the two travel through the medium at different rates, on emergence, at the instant the contra-clockwise disturbance is represented by the particle at O, Fig. 15.7(a), the particle for the clockwise will be at some other position, such as Q, Fig. 15.7(b). The two disturbances on emerging will continue to travel at equal rates and hence will combine into a rectilinear vibration along the line LCL', where LC bisects $O'CQ$, for at right angles to this line there can be no resultant displacement. As a result of the unequal velocities in the medium, therefore, the vibration plane has been rotated through the angle $O'CL$. Moreover, it is not difficult to see that if the velocity of *propagation* (not the period of rotation) of the clockwise motion is the slower, the rotation of the vibration plane is to the right (looking in the direction of propagation). Conversely, if the clockwise motion is the faster, the rotation of the vibration plane is in the opposite sense.

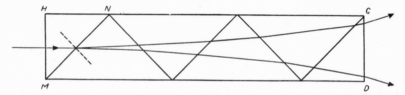

Fig. 15.8.   Fresnel combination of dextro- and laevo-quartz prisms for demonstrating the existence of two disturbances which travel at unequal rates along the optic axis.

As already mentioned, Fresnel demonstrated experimentally the existence of two disturbances in quartz, traveling with unequal rates along the optic axis. To do so, he took several pieces of both dextro- and laevo-quartz, in the form of prisms, placing them together, alternately right and left, to form a rectangular solid as in Fig. 15.8. In each the optic axis was parallel to the sides CH and MD. On the foregoing theory, then, if plane polarized light is incident normally on the face at the left, two disturbances travel in this direction with unequal velocities. On striking the inclined surface MN and entering the second prism, the disturbance which was faster in the first prism now becomes the slower. Hence, by the ordinary laws of refraction one beam is bent away from the normal to MN, the other toward it. Since at the other inclined surfaces similar effects take place, it is not difficult to see that two distinctly separated beams should emerge from the right face. Fresnel showed that this actually was the case.

15.8. That the phenomenon of rotatory polarization is absent in fused quartz is experimental evidence that it is in some way related to the crystalline structure of this substance. In the case of liquids and of solutions of optically active substances, no crystalline structure is, of course, possible, but for these it is found that the molecules possess an asymmetric carbon atom. Moreover, since such molecules, for some substances, can occur in two forms, one of which is the mirror image of the other, it is not surprising that different specimens of the same substance can exhibit sometimes dextro- and sometimes laevo-rotations.

PROBLEMS

1. Plane waves fall normally on the face of a crystal of Iceland spar. By the use of wavelets and Huygens' Principle, explain the formation of O and E rays. Make a careful diagram.

2. Define *extraordinary index of refraction*, discussing your answer with respect to cross-sectional diagrams of an O and an E wavelet in a suitable plane.

3. Make a diagram which shows clearly how it is possible in double refraction to have E rays which are not perpendicular to the corresponding wave-fronts.

4. Plane waves fall perpendicularly on the face of a piece of Iceland spar. By making suitable sectional diagrams show that, corresponding to a single incident ray, an O and an E ray will emerge from the opposite face. Show also that, depending on how the crystal is cut and placed with respect to the incident light, each of the following cases is possible (a) The O and the E beam travel in different directions. (b) The O and the E beam travel in the same direction and with the same velocity. (c) The O and the E beam are in the same direction, but travel with different velocities. Specify the conditions necessary for each. In all cases the incident and emergent faces of the crystal are parallel.

5. A narrow beam of light falls on a piece of Iceland spar that separates the emergent beams. If the light passes through a second thick crystal of the same substance (the principal planes of the two crystals making an angle of 40° with each other) and is received on a screen, describe the appearance seen, and find quantitatively the relative intensities of the images observed.

6. Two Nicol prisms are set so that maximum light is transmitted. Find through what angle the analyzer must be rotated to reduce the intensity to (a) one-half and (b) one-third of the original emergent intensity.

7. Light passes through a polarizing and an analyzing Nicol prism. Find the percentage reduction in intensity when the analyzer is rotated through 10° (a) if initially its principal plane makes an angle of 20° with that of the polarizer; (b) if initially its principal plane makes an angle of 70° with that of the polarizer. (In each case the angle is increased after rotation.)

8. Two sources of light are viewed, one after the other, through two Nicol prisms (polariscope arrangement). It is found that the intensities of the emergent beams in the two cases are equal when the angles between the principal planes of the Nicols are 36° and 48° respectively. Compare the intensities of the original sources.

9. Prove that, when circularly polarized light leaves a quarter-wave plate and falls on a Nicol prism, the same intensity is transmitted for all positions of the Nicol.

10. A horizontal beam of light traverses a tank containing water with a suspension of colloidal particles. An observer looks through a Nicol prism along a direction at right angles to the beam. By how much is the intensity of the light he sees reduced by turning the Nicol prism through an angle of 40° from the position where maximum intensity is observed?

11. When a narrow beam of light is incident on a glass block and the reflected light is examined to determine the extent to which it is polarized, it is found that maximum polarization occurs for an angle of incidence equal to 57°. Find the index of refraction of the glass.

12. When light is incident on a glass block at the angle which gives maximum polarization in the reflected beam, prove that the angle between the reflected and the refracted beams is 90°.

13. Two S.H.M. of the same period and of amplitudes a and b, which act along lines at right angles, are superimposed. (a) If the difference in phase is 30°, find the nature of the resultant motion. (b) Describe an optical arrangement of realizing such a super-position in light and obtaining such a phase difference. (c) With such an optical arrangement, find the ratio a/b.

14. (a) When plane polarized light falls on a thin piece of doubly refracting crystal, what two conditions must be fulfilled in order that circularly polarized light emerges? (b) Under what conditions will (i) plane polarized and, (ii) elliptically polarized light emerge?

15. If you were provided with a piece of Polaroid film (or a Nicol prism) and a thick piece of doubly refracting crystal such as Iceland spar, explain how you could obtain two narrow beams of light with intensities in the ratio of 2 to 1.

16. A parallel beam of plane polarized monochromatic light of wavelength (in air) 5.89×10^{-5} cm falls normally on a thin piece of doubly refracting crystal, of thickness 0.01618 mm, cut with optic axis parallel to the surface. (a) If $n_E = 1.5533$ and $n_O = 1.5442$, find the phase difference between the O and the E beams on emergence. (b) If the vibration plane of the light incident on the crystal makes an angle of 36° with the principal plane of the crystal, find the ratio of the intensities of the O and the E beams. (c) By plotting, find the nature of the vibrations of the emergent light (due to the superposition of the O and the E beams).

17. (a) Two S.H.M. disturbances, with amplitudes in the ratio of $\sqrt{3}$ to 1, with periods equal, with phase difference = 180°, are superimposed. Find graphically the nature of the resulting motion if the individual S.H.M. are along lines at right angles. (b) Given a Nicol prism, a thin section of a doubly refracting crystal whose faces are parallel to the optic axis, and whose principal plane is known, show how you would obtain two beams with amplitudes in the foregoing ratio. (c) Find the minimum thickness of the crystal for which the phase difference is 180°, for wavelength 5.46×10^{-5} cm ($n_E = 1.5533$; $n_O = 1.5442$.)

18. A parallel beam of plane polarized light for which $\lambda = 5.89 \times 10^{-5}$ cm is incident normally on a thin quartz wedge whose angle is 45 min. The wedge is cut so that the optic axis is parallel to the thin edge of the wedge. Find the distance between any two interference fringes seen on the face of the wedge. (Take $n_E = 1.5533$; $n_O = 1.5442$.)

19. Plane polarized light falls normally on a thin piece of doubly refracting crystal of uniform thickness, so cut that the optic axis lies in the surface of the crystal. On emergence the light is elliptically polarized in such a way that one of the axes of the ellipse is parallel to the principal plane of the crystal. What is the least thickness of the crystal for which this is the case? (Take $n_E = 1.556$; $n_O = 1.546$; $\lambda = 6.24 \times 10^{-5}$ cm.)

20. A parallel beam of plane polarized light for which $\lambda = 5.89 \times 10^{-5}$ cm is incident normally on a piece of doubly refracting crystal in the form of a wedge, so cut that the optic axis is parallel to the thin edge of the wedge. If the angle of the wedge is 36 min, find the distance from the edge to the place along the wedge at which the emergent light is first plane polarized. ($n_E = 1.5533$, $n_O = 1.5442$.)

21. A line is marked on each of three pieces of Polaroid film, A, B and C, to indicate the principal plane. They are set on top of each other so that looking down on them the principal plane of B is 45° to the right of that of A, and the principal plane of C is 45° to the left. Show that no light emerges from the combination. (Assume that the films are as perfect as Nicol prisms.)

22. In the previous question, if the angles are 30° instead of 45°, find the ratio of the intensity of the light incident on A to that of the light emerging from C.

23. In a Babinet compensator a narrow beam of light is incident perpendicularly on the face of the wedge A (Fig. 14.5) at a place where its thickness is 3 mm. Find the length of the path the beam must travel in the wedge B if circularly polarized light emerges. ($n_E = 1.5533$; $n_O = 1.5442$.)

24. Explain how, with the aid of a quarter-wave plate and a Nicol prism, you could distinguish between a beam of unpolarized light and one circularly polarized.

25. State one set of conditions under which *no* light will emerge when a parallel beam of white light falls normally on a piece of Polaroid film, a thin piece of doubly refracting crystal, and a second piece of Polaroid film.

26. Explain under what conditions light will emerge through the arrangement in the previous questions without any color.

27. Explain how you could obtain complementary colors with a Nicol prism (or Polaroid film), a thin piece of doubly refracting crystal of uniform thickness, and a piece of Iceland spar.

28. Explain how you could obtain complementary colors with a Nicol prism (or Polaroid film), a piece of quartz *cut perpendicular to the optic axis*, a tank of water containing scattering particles in suspension, and a plane mirror set at an angle above the tank.

29. A flat piece of quartz, cut with its faces perpendicular to the optic axis, has such a thickness that the vibration plane of 5600 A is rotated 90° when the incident light is plane polarized. If this piece is placed between two Nicol prisms and a beam of white light is used, explain under what conditions the *sensitive tint* or *tint of passage* is obtained.

30. By plotting the numbers given in Table X, section 15.1, find what thickness of quartz is necessary in problem 29.

XVI

The Electromagnetic Theory
of Light

16.1. In the preceding chapters of this book, particularly in those dealing with interference, diffraction, and polarization, much has been said about waves and vibrating particles. That the propagation of light is subject to the laws of wave motion has been pointed out many times. Moreover, since the conception of wave motion is invariably associated with a periodic vibration of a portion of some medium, an all-pervading ether has been postulated. The vibrations of the ultimate particles of this hypothetical medium may then be considered as constituting light disturbances. Throughout the greater part of the nineteenth century the ether was supposed to have the properties of an elastic solid, a conception which played a very important part in the development of the subject of light. Although this elastic solid theory of light ultimately was abandoned, it is necessary to examine one or two features in connection with it.

In the first place the student should recall that in an elastic solid, when a particle is displaced from its normal position, stresses or what we may call *restoring forces* are brought into play. If the displaced particle is released, and the displacement is not too large, it will eventually return to its normal position. Moreover, for all cases with which the theory of elasticity has to do, Hooke's Law gives the relation between the resulting stress and the displacement (or strain). According to this law, the stress is proportional to the strain, the factor of proportionality being called an *elastic modulus* or coefficient of elasticity. In an elastic solid, two kinds of strain are possible. (1) All the particles in a thin "slice" may be displaced with reference to a parallel layer, constituting what is called a *shear*. When a rod, fixed at one end, is twisted at the other, this is the kind of strain which results. (2) An elastic solid may be uniformly compressed or dilated. As Hooke's Law is applicable in either case, there are two corresponding coefficients of elasticity: n, the shear or rigidity or distortion modulus, and k, the coefficient giving the ratio of the stress to a strain which is a uniform dilatation.

If a disturbance is created at a local region in an elastic solid, a wave motion will travel outward in a manner much as we have described by the elementary method of section 7.2. An exact treatment of the problem, in which the dynamical equations of motion of an individual particle of the solid are set up, shows that there are two resulting wave disturbances: (1) one with transverse vibrations traveling with a velocity equal to $\sqrt{\dfrac{n}{\rho}}$; (2) a second, with longitudinal vibrations traveling with velocity $\sqrt{\dfrac{k + \dfrac{4n}{3}}{\rho}}$, where ρ is the density of the elastic solid. *Now in light the experimental facts discussed under the subject of polarization have shown us that longitudinal vibrations cannot exist.* Here, then, is a first difficulty, if ether has the properties of an elastic solid. What becomes of the longitudinal vibration? The difficulty was removed by considering that the longitudinal vibration traveled with infinite velocity; or, in other words, as will be seen from the foregoing expression for the velocity, that the ether was incompressible.* There then remained only the transverse wave traveling with a velocity which depended on the elasticity and the density. Making use of such a conception, the great theoretical physicists of the nineteenth century, like Green, Stokes, and Rayleigh, sought to deduce the known properties of light such as reflection, refraction, and double refraction. Although their work forms an important part of the theoretical development of the subject of light, the elastic solid theory led to difficulties and even to contradictions and, with the advent of Maxwell's famous Electromagnetic Theory, was discarded.

16.2. The Electromagnetic Theory. To understand the basic ideas in connection with this theory some knowledge of the principles of electricity is necessary. Faraday, in dealing with the attraction and repulsion between electrified bodies, introduced the conception of tubes of force or, better, Faraday tubes, to visualize strains in an ether surrounding an electrified body. It was impossible for him, as it is for many physicists, to think of an electrified body repelling or attracting another at some distance from it, with nothing taking place in the intervening space. Electric attraction and repulsion, therefore, were considered to be the result of strains transmitted through an ether, and Faraday tubes were used not only to give the mind a picture of such strains, but also, after Faraday's time, as a means of attacking electric problems quantitatively. Before the time of Maxwell (Great Britain, 1831–1879), this ether was not the luminiferous ether, the subjects of electricity and of light constituting two very distinct branches of physics. The great unification, which we are about to explain, was the result of the work of Maxwell, who set out to find out the properties of a medium that would transmit electric action. In establishing his mathematical equations, Maxwell introduced the somewhat revolutionary conception of *displacement* currents. According to this, when Faraday tubes are being established in free space, in air or any dielectric, there exists a momentary current which,

---

* The late Lord Kelvin showed that the difficulty could be removed and the theory developed by assuming a contractile ether in which the longitudinal velocity was zero.

while it lasts, has all the properties of a steady current. The idea will perhaps be clear by a consideration of Fig. 16.1 where A and B represent the plates of a

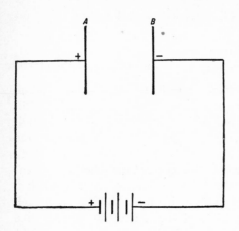

condenser joined to the terminals of a battery. In the static condition, the condenser plates are charged—one positive, the other negative—and Faraday tubes exist in the region between them. In this case there is, of course, no current, for we have what is ordinarily called an open circuit. But, according to the new view introduced by Maxwell, during the short initial time in which the condenser plates are being charged, or the Faraday tubes established, there exists in the dielectric between the plates a displacement current whose magnitude is proportional to the rate at which the number of tubes is increasing. Moreover, just as a steady current is surrounded by a steady magnetic field, so Maxwell assumed that the momentary displacement current gave rise to a *momentary* magnetic field in its neighborhood. If now it is recalled that an induced electromotive force results whenever there is a *change* in a magnetic field, it will be seen that the momentary magnetic field must give rise to an electric intensity. This electric intensity will then cause another momentary displacement current which, in its turn, will cause another momentary magnetic field, and so on. It follows, therefore, that granted an initial displacement current such as Maxwell postulated, an electromagnetic disturbance should be propagated from the region of the original displacement. All this Maxwell put in the form of equations, by means of which it is not difficult to show that the velocity of such a disturbance is equal to $c/\sqrt{\mu k}$, where c, the electromagnetic constant, is the number of electrostatic units of electricity in one electromagnetic unit quantity, k is the dielectric constant of the medium, and μ the magnetic permeability. In free space, where $k = 1$ and $\mu = 1$, we have $v = c$.

Fig. 16.1. A momentary displacement current exists in the region between the plates A and B of a condenser during the initial period of charging by the battery.

The value of c can readily be found by standard *electrical* means. For example, the quantity of electricity stored in a condenser can be determined in electrostatic units from the product of the potential difference between its plates multiplied by the capacitance calculated from its dimensions; and in electromagnetic units, by observing the current in a galvanometer when the condenser is rapidly charged and discharged an observed number of times a second. Results obtained, whether by this or other means, give the value of $c = 3 \times 10^{10}$ cm per sec. But the observed velocity of light is 3×10^{10} cm per sec. The electromagnetic disturbance predicted by Maxwell, therefore, travels at the same speed as that of light.

Maxwell's equations also show that in such a disturbance the waves are transverse, as is the case for light. It is natural, therefore, to draw the conclusion that light is an electromagnetic phenomenon. The student, however, must guard against thinking that the electromagnetic theory in any way undermines the wave theory. It throws overboard the conception of mechanical vibrations of ether particles, but the periodicity of a light disturbance remains as before a fundamental characteristic. The ether, too, is still the seat of the disturbance, which, however, is now considered to be a periodic change in electric (and magnetic) intensity.

16.3. When the electromagnetic theory was developed by mathematical physicists, it was found that the laws of reflection and of refraction could readily be deduced from Maxwell's equations; that the facts of double refraction could be satisfactorily explained—in short, that the serious difficulties encountered in using an elastic solid theory disappeared when this powerful theory was put to the test. Nor should it be forgotten that two hitherto unrelated branches of science—light and electricity—were by means of it brought together by an underlying fundamental conception.

Direct experimental verification also followed, two outstanding examples being provided by the work of Boltzmann (Germany, 1844–1906) and Hertz (Germany, 1857–1894). According to the expression deduced by Maxwell, the velocity of an electromagnetic disturbance in a medium with dielectric constant $= k$ and permeability $= 1$ is given by the relation

$$v = \frac{c}{\sqrt{k}}.$$

It follows that

$$\frac{\text{velocity in free space}}{\text{velocity in this medium}} = \sqrt{k}$$

or, if n is the index of refraction, that

$$n^2 = k. \tag{16.01}$$

Here, then, is a relation which may readily be put to an experimental test as far as light is concerned, for it is a simple matter to measure n by optical means, and k by electrical. That it is true for some media was pointed out by Boltzmann in 1873. Some actual numerical values are given in Table XII, where the indices are for yellow light.

In other cases, such as water, where $n = 1.33$ and $k = 81$, there is no agreement whatever. This lack of agreement can be explained, however, when the fact of dispersion is taken into consideration—that is, the fact that different wavelengths travel at different rates in a dielectric. Reference will be made to the theory of dispersion later, but here it may be indicated that,. in obtaining the value of k for water, the electrical field is static, a condition corresponding to infinite wavelength, whereas n as we have seen in Chapter VI (Cauchy's formula)

Table XII.

	n	$\sqrt{k}$
air	1.000294	1.000295
hydrogen	1.000138	1.000132
carbon dioxide	1.000449	1.000473
carbon monoxide	1.000346	1.000345

is a function of the wavelength, and in light has values corresponding to short wavelengths.

16.4. The Work of Hertz.   About the year 1885 remarkable experimental confirmation of the truth of the electromagnetic theory was given by Hertz, who

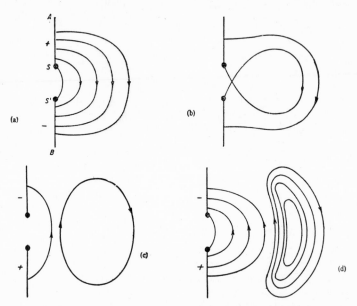

Fig. 16.2.   Use of Faraday tubes to picture the generation of electric loops by an oscillating discharge between the metallic conductors A and B.

generated electromagnetic waves by purely electrical means and showed that they possessed many of the properties of light waves.   In generating electrical waves, Hertz made use of the well-known fact that the discharge of a condenser in a low resistance circuit is oscillatory. In such a case the periodic time is given by the relation

$$T = 2\pi \sqrt{CL},$$

where C is the capacitance of the circuit and L its inductance. When a Leyden jar is discharged, the apparently single spark which we see is, in reality, a succession of sparks (as can be shown by a rapidly revolving mirror), corresponding to the successive alternating currents during the process of discharge. According to Maxwell's ideas electromagnetic waves should spread out from the region of the spark.

By the aid of Faraday tubes we may form a useful picture of the generation of such waves. Suppose, for example, that A and B, Fig. 16.2(a),* are metallic plates joined to the terminals of a static electric machine, so that when the potential difference is sufficiently great a spark passes between the two small spheres S and S'. Just before the spark passes, if A is positively charged, B negatively, Faraday tubes pass from A to B, somewhat as represented in Fig. 16.2(a). The arrow indicates the direction of the electric intensity, that is, the direction in which a small body carrying a unit positive charge would move if placed in the electric field. When the spark first passes and the discharge begins to take place, many of the Faraday tubes disappear, the corresponding energy reappearing as sound, light, and heat, but if the discharge is sufficiently rapid, that is, if the ends of the tube move quickly enough, the ends of some may cross, forming closed loops as is shown for a single tube in Fig. 16.2(b). As the ends continue to move, the condenser being charged in the reverse sense, the loops break off, the original tube giving rise to a condition represented in Fig. 16.2(c). Since in reality many tubes will take part in such a process, at the end of the reversal, the state of affairs may be represented somewhat as in Fig. 16.2(d).

After several to-and-fro oscillations we may picture the condition somewhat as in Fig. 16.3. We now see that, as a result of this rapid oscillatory discharge, in the region surrounding the oscillator, at any instant we have places with the electric intensity in one direction alternating with others where the electric intensity is in the opposite direction. Moreover, it is not difficult to see that, if we fix our attention on any given place, as time goes on the electric intensity at that place will periodically change. *In other words we have the periodicity in time and in space which, as we have seen in Chapter VII, characterizes a wave motion,* and we may represent such waves at any instant by the dotted curve shown in Fig. 16.3 depicting the changes in electric intensity from point to point in the surrounding medium. To complete the picture, the magnetic lines associated with and running at right angles to the moving Faraday tubes should also be represented. Although, for simplicity, these are omitted, it should not be forgotten that in electromagnetic waves we have to do with periodic changes in both

* Figs. 16.2 and 16.3 are reproduced in part from "The Principles Underlying Radio Communication" by the kind permission of the Signal Corps, U. S. Army.

electric and magnetic intensities, that these vector quantities are at right angles to each other, and that each is at right angles to the direction of propagation— in other words, that we are dealing with transverse vibrations.

Now Hertz took such an electric arrangement and by means of a detector

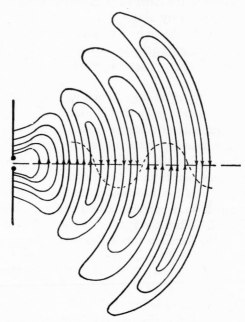

Fig. 16.3.   A picture at a certain instant of a group of electric loops and the corresponding periodic alternations in space in the direction of the electric field.

proved the actual existence of electromagnetic waves.   Moreover, he showed, experimentally, not only that such waves had many of the properties of light waves, but also that they traveled with the velocity predicted by Maxwell.   They could be reflected; they could be refracted and the value of the index determined; they were polarized when obtained from such an oscillator, and they gave rise to interference phenomena.   The work of Hertz thus completely established the general truth of the electromagnetic theory of light.   *Light waves and waves generated electrically are of the same nature.*   Many of their properties are, of course, totally different.   For example, some electrical waves will readily pass through a brick wall, whereas light waves will not.   Differences in properties arise from the very marked differences in wavelength, but the essential nature of both is the same; for both are electromagnetic periodic disturbances traveling at a fixed speed in ether.

16.5. Range of Electromagnetic Waves.   The student is familiar with the fact that, in addition to visible light waves, there is an infrared region of longer, and an ultraviolet region of shorter, invisible optical wavelengths. In days when radio is a household word, the reader will scarcely need to be told that since the time of Hertz an enormous amount of work has been done in connection with electrical waves, and that they can be generated with lengths ranging from miles to milli-meters. We thus have short electrical and long optical waves. How near do the two regions approach? The answer is provided by an investigation of Nichols and Tear (United States) who obtained from an electric oscil-lator wavelengths as short as 0.22 mm; at the same time, by suitably screening a mercury arc, they found infrared waves as long as 0.4 mm. There is then no gap between the longest infrared radiations and the shortest electrical waves. We thus have a continuous range of electromag-netic radiations extending from electric waves almost as long as we wish to have them, through wireless* and Hertzian waves until we reach the infrared; then visible light, followed by the shorter ultraviolet region in which wavelengths as short as 40 A have been measured. But the family does not end there, for *x-rays* and *gamma rays* from radioactive sources extend the range much further. Table XIII gives approximate values for the various re-gions of electromagnetic waves; Fig. 16.4 gives the same information in a graphical form.

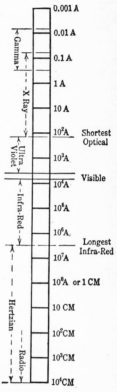

Fig. 16.4. Range of electromagnetic waves.

16.7. Electric Vector the Light Vector. In section 16.4 it was pointed out that in an electromagnetic wave train we have to do with a periodicity in both the electric and the magnetic intensity, and that the directions of these two vector quantities are at right angles. Again, in the chapter on polarization, we have seen that, in plane polarized light, the vibrations are confined to a single definite plane. Now, on the electromagnetic

Table XIII.   Range of Electromagnetic Wavelengths

Electric and Hertzian		20+ miles	to	0.22 mm
Infrared		0.4 mm	to	0.0007 mm
Visible Light		0.0007 mm	to	0.0004 mm
	or	7000 A	to	4000 A
Ultraviolet and				
Extreme ultraviolet		4000 A	to	40 A
X-rays		500 A	to	0.06 A
Gamma		0.3 A	to	0.006 A

vibrations are confined to a single definite plane. Now, on the electromagnetic

* Radio waves used in radar are sometimes of the order of a few centimeters or less in length, in which range they are called microwaves.

theory, if the electric vibrations are at all places in the same plane, the magnetic vibrations must be in a plane at right angles to this one. Is it then the periodic changes in the electric intensity we are to think of as light vibrations, or the corresponding changes in the magnetic intensity? The answer to that question is provided when the reflection of light from the surface of a transparent medium like glass is considered on the electromagnetic theory. In the mathematical treatment, which is beyond the scope of this book, it is shown that, when reflection takes place at the polarizing angle, the electric vibrations are normal to the plane of incidence. But, in Chapter XIII, we saw that light vibrations must be perpendicular to the plane of incidence in polarized reflected light. It follows, therefore, that it is the electric vibrations which are the light vibrations.

Experimental confirmation of the truth of this was provided by Wiener in an experiment which showed the existence of stationary light waves in a thin film of silver chloride in collodium, when direct and reflected beams of light meet. Since at a node the sensitive film is not acted on, while at an antinode there is a reaction, the film contains layers alternately black and light (regions where the silver is separated out alternately with those where it is not). Now when electromagnetic waves are reflected and stationary waves result, the magnetic and electric nodes are a quarter of a wavelength apart, and Wiener's experiment showed that the position of the nodal regions corresponded to the predicted position of the electric nodal places, not the magnetic.

16.7. Theory of Dispersion. Hitherto, although much has been said about the phenomenon of dispersion, no attempt has been made to explain why the velocity of light in transparent bodies varies with the frequency. The general reason lies in the fact that in such cases we are dealing with the effect of particles of matter on the propagation of the wave disturbance through the ether in which the matter may be considered to be imbedded. Just what effect this is, we shall briefly consider from the point of view of the electromagnetic theory.

In the first place, the student should recall that an atom consists of a positively charged nucleus surrounded by one or more negatively charged electrons. When an atom is a constituent part of a body *which is a conductor of electricity*, and an electric force is applied, one or more of the electrons may readily be passed on to a neighboring atom, thus giving rise to an electric current. On the other hand, *if the body is a dielectric*, and that is the kind in which we are here interested, the electric force causes only a displacement of the electron. If the electric force is constant, the electron comes to rest when the magnitude of the *restoring forces*, called into play as a result of its displacement, is equal and opposite to the electric force. If such a displacement is caused by the application of a force which is at once removed, the restoring forces may be considered to cause the electron to vibrate to and fro much as a released mass at the end of a stretched spring executes a periodic motion. The period of an electron, when so displaced and left free to vibrate, represents a *natural frequency* of vibration. In a dielectric such as glass, therefore, we can think of certain electrons in the constituent atoms as having natural frequencies of oscillation, provided they have suffered, for some reason, an initial displacement. In the present work we shall confine our attention to the case where there is only one such natural frequency for a given dielectric. (The theory can readily be extended to include the more general case of several such frequencies.)

Consider now what happens when a rapidly *alternating* electric force is applied to such an electron, a condition which occurs on the electromagnetic theory, when the dielectric is traversed by a beam of light. The electron is then forced to execute oscillations with the period of the applied force, and consequently the amplitude of these forced oscillations depends on how nearly the frequency of the applied force approaches the natural frequency of the electron. If the two are about equal, we have the phenomenon of *resonance*, with which work in sound should have made the student familiar. In that case, the electron vibrates with a very large amplitude, almost all of the energy of the incident disturbance being then absorbed. If in the exciting beam there is a large range of frequencies (or wavelengths), we then have an *absorption band* in the spectrum of the emerging light—a point to which reference is made in section 17.5. As such absorption represents a loss of energy from the original beam, it is natural to assume, when dealing with the motion of the vibrating electron, that there is a factor akin to friction whose magnitude is proportional to the velocity of the electron. In the case of resonance, that is, of an absorption band, amplitudes and hence velocities are very large, and the frictional losses very marked. If, however, we deal with frequencies well away from the natural frequency of the electron, the amplitude of the forced vibration is small, and therefore also the effect of friction.

When these ideas are put into mathematical form, and Maxwell's equations are extended to include currents due to the movement of the electrons, then, instead of the simple relation $n^2 = k$ deduced previously, one obtains the expression

$$n^2 = 1 + \frac{A_1 \lambda^2}{\lambda^2 - \lambda_1^2},$$ \hfill (16.02)

where n is the index of refraction of the dielectric for wavelength λ, where A_1 is a constant whose value depends on the charge on the electron, on its mass, on its natural frequency, and on the number of electrons in unit volume; and where λ_1 is the wavelength in free ether corresponding to a frequency equal to the natural frequency of the electron.

(If there is more than one natural frequency, additional similar terms must be added to this expression.)

Now let us examine relation (16.02) a little more carefully with reference to one or two cases.

(1) **For very long waves,** that is, when λ is many times greater than λ_1.

In this case, the expression reduces to

$$n^2 = 1 + A_1, \tag{16.03}$$

which corresponds to the $n^2 = k$ discussed in section 16.01. Dispersion does not now enter into the question.

(2) **When λ is sufficiently long, that the ratio λ_1/λ is small.** For example, if, in a transparent substance like glass, the absorption band (λ_1) is well in the ultraviolet, and we confine ourselves to visible wavelengths, we approximate to this condition.

Rewriting equation (16.02), we have

$$n^2 = 1 + \frac{A_1\lambda^2}{\lambda^2 - \lambda_1^2}$$

$$= 1 + \frac{A_1}{\left(1 - \frac{\lambda_1^2}{\lambda^2}\right)}$$

$$= 1 + A_1\left(1 - \frac{\lambda_1^2}{\lambda^2}\right)^{-1}$$

$$= 1 + A_1\left(1 + \frac{\lambda_1^2}{\lambda^2}\right),$$

if we neglect higher powers than the second of λ_1/λ, as we may do with little error when its value is small. We have, then

$$n^2 = 1 + A_1 + \frac{A_1\lambda_1^2}{\lambda^2},$$

which we may write

$$n^2 = A + \frac{B}{\lambda^2}, \text{ by putting} \tag{16.04}$$

$$A = 1 + A_1, \quad \text{and} \quad B = A_1\lambda_1^2.$$

In other words, equation (16.02) reduces to the simple Cauchy formula which, as was pointed out in section 6.3, applies with a fair degree of accuracy to ordinary cases of dispersion.

(3) **Anomalous Dispersion.** When the range of λ's includes λ_1, that is, when we have to do with an absorption band in the region considered.

In this case it will be evident that, as we pass from large values of λ in the direction toward λ_1, the value of the index increases more and more rapidly until, for wavelengths such that $\lambda^2 - \lambda_1^2$ is a small quantity, the value becomes extremely large. For wavelengths, therefore, which are just *greater* than that corresponding to the absorption band, the index is abnormally high, as is roughly indicated by the portion MN of the curve in Fig. 16.5. On the other side of the band, that is, when λ is a little *less* than λ_1, the term $A_1\lambda^2/(\lambda - \lambda_1^2)$ is negative, and we obtain abnormally low values of n which, however, gradually increase as λ becomes still smaller—somewhat as shown by the portion LK of Fig. 16.5. For wavelengths on one side of an absorption band, therefore, the index should be abnormally high; on the other side, abnormally low.   This means, if one used a prism of a material which had an absorption band in the green, for example, that wavelengths beyond the band on the violet side should be refracted *less* than those near the band on the longer wavelength side.   As a matter of fact, such

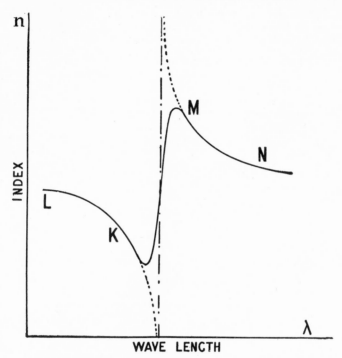

Fig. 16.5.   Dispersion curve for a medium which has an absorption band in the region plotted. The parts *MN* and *K* are on either side of the absorption band.   See Plate VIII, Fig. 5, facing p. 321.

cases of so-called *anomalous dispersion* are well-known.   Thus a prism made of an alcoholic solution of fuchsine, an aniline dye with an absorption band in the green, refracts violet light less than red, although red, orange, and yellow appear in the normal order.

In Chapter XVII attention is directed to the selective absorption of sodium vapor, which gives a dark band (strictly speaking, two close together) in the yellow part of the visible spectrum.   That sodium vapor exhibits anomalous dispersion should be clear from an inspection of the photograph reproduced in Fig. 5, Plate VIII, facing p. 321.   In taking this photograph a glass prism, which refracted a beam of white light into a narrow *horizontal* spectrum, was used in conjunction with an exhausted cylindrical horizontal tube containing pieces of metallic sodium.   On strongly heating this tube at its *lower* surface the sodium was vaporized, evidently in such a way that the vapor density was much greater at the bottom of the tube than at the cooler top.   The column of vapor then acted as a prism with base at the bottom and refracting edge at the top. In this way what was equivalent to a sodium vapor prism deviated the light vertically, thus making evident, in the manner shown in the photograph, the phenomenon of anomalous dispersion. In spite of the name "anomalous," the student should realize from the preceding explanation that ordinary dispersion and anomalous are just two particular features of the same general phenomenon.

A complete theoretical treatment of dispersion involves the use of quantum mechanics and work which is beyond the scope of this book.

XVII

The Origin of Spectra

PRELIMINARY DISCUSSION

17.1. Before considering somewhat in detail the whole question of the ultimate source from which light waves emanate, it is necessary to add to the information about the spectrum given in Chapters VI and XVI. In the following sections a brief reference is made to a few elementary but fundamental facts.

17.2. Light Sources. It is first of all desirable for the student to be familiar with methods frequently used for making a substance luminous. The more important of these are the following.

(*a*) **The Incandescent Solid.** Any solid substance, if sufficiently heated, first begins to glow with a reddish color, and eventually, if the temperature goes high enough, becomes "white hot." An incandescent filament lamp is a familiar example of such a light source. The spectrum of such a source is continuous, that is, does not consist of a number of distinct spectral lines.

(*b*) **The Gas Burner.** By introducing many substances into the flame of a non-luminous Bunsen or other gas burner, luminosity characteristic of the substance results. The spectrum of such a source is called the *flame spectrum* of the substance. It consists of only a few spectral lines, sometimes only a single line.

(*c*) **The Arc.** The familiar electric arc between two carbon rods illustrates the basis of another common light source. A photograph of the luminous vapor between the rods gives the carbon arc spectrum, while, if some volatile metal or metallic salt is introduced into the arc, the resulting spectrum shows arc spectral lines of such a metal. If the carbon rods are replaced by iron ones, an iron arc results, while if a special arrangement is used so that an electric current can pass through mercury vapor in an evacuated vessel, we have a mercury vacuum arc. In general there are various ways in which arc spectra may be obtained but all are characterized by currents usually of several amperes, with a voltage drop (potential difference) probably considerably less than 100 volts between the terminals.

(*d*) **The Spark.** If two pieces of metal such as MM', Fig. 17.1, are joined to the terminals of an induction coil or small transformer, the spark which "jumps" between them on discharge is a source of light, which, when analyzed, gives the *spark spectrum* of the metal. The intensity of the spark is greatly increased by placing a capacitor C in parallel with the coil, while it may be

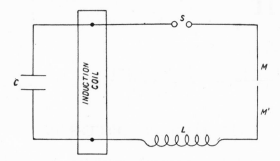

Fig. 17.1. An arrangement for examining the spectrum of the light emitted by a spark between the metal terminals *M* and *M'*.

further altered by varying (1) the length of an auxiliary spark gap S and (2) the amount of inductance L in the circuit. In the case of a spark, electrical conditions are very different from those obtaining in the arc. In the spark we have to do with small currents, fractions of an ampere, but with voltages which may be as high as many thousands. In Fig. 3, Plate II, facing p. 96, b is a small portion of the arc spectrum of the metal tin, taken with a prism spectrograph, while a is the spark spectrum for the same region taken on the same photographic plate in such a way that it overlaps, to a considerable extent, the arc spectrum. Reference will again be made to this figure.

Fig. 17.2. A common source for the spectral analysis of light emitted by a luminous gas at low pressure.

(*e*) **The Vacuum Tube.** This is a very common source for the analysis of the light emitted by luminous gases and vapors. If a tube with electrodes E, E', Fig. 17.2, containing a gas at low pressure (of the order of 1 mm) is joined directly to an induction coil or transformer, a brilliant luminosity results. Tubes of various shapes may be used, but in all the principle is the same. In Fig. 1, Plate II, a reproduction of the vacuum tube spectrum (visible) of hydrogen is given; Fig. 2, Plate II, is a similar spectrum for helium.

(*f*) **Electronic Bombardment.** To understand this method which, although not so frequently used as the others, has provided valuable spectroscopic information, the student must recall again the view that an atom is a planetary system on a microscopic scale. It consists of a nucleus which has a positive charge and represents almost the whole mass of the atom, together with negatively charged electrons grouped about the nucleus. In the normal atom the total negative charge of the electrons just neutralizes the positive charge on the nucleus. The number of electrons steadily increases one at a time, from 1 in hydrogen, 2 in helium, until we reach such numbers as 80 for mercury and 92 for uranium. The hydrogen nucleus is sometimes called a *proton*, and there is much evidence that the nuclei of all atoms are built up of protons and neutrons. A *neutron* is a particle without any electrical charge which has a mass nearly but not quite the same as that of a proton. The nucleus of helium, for example, has two protons and two neutrons, and so has a net positive charge of 2 units or an *atomic number* of 2, as distinguished from a *mass number* of 4. By various means one or more electrons may be removed from the parent atom, thus leaving a positive *ion*.

Sometimes it is desirable to have a stream of free electrons. One means of accomplishing this consists in (1) heating a metallic filament to incandescence in a highly evacuated vessel, (2) in having the filament negative with respect to a nearby electrode in the vessel. Suppose, for example, that *FF'*, Fig. 17.3, repre-

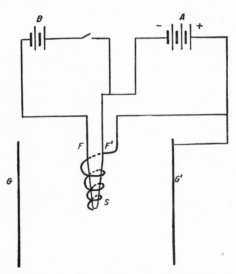

Fig. 17.3. An arrangement for examining the spectrum of the light emitted by a vapor in the vessel GG' when it is bombarded by electrons of controlled speed emitted by the hot filament FF'.

sents an incandescent filament, heated by being placed in an electric circuit with the battery *B*, and that it is surrounded by the metallic spiral *S*, the whole being in a highly exhausted vessel. If the filament is joined to the negative terminal of a second battery *A*, while the spiral is joined to the positive, electrons will pass from the filament to the spiral. Moreover, if an outer electrode *GG'* is electrically joined to the spiral so that no potential difference exists between *G* and S, then most of the electrons will pass through the spiral and traverse the outer region *with a speed controlled by the potential difference between the filament and the spiral.* Suppose, now, that the vapor of some metal is present in this region—and this may readily be the case if the whole apparatus is heated sufficiently. The atoms of the metallic vapor will then be bombarded by the stream of electrons and so may be excited to luminosity. Obviously by varying the speed of the electrons, and thus their mean kinetic energy, changes in the spectrum brought about by more and more violent bombardment may readily be examined. Photographs of spectra taken in this way are reproduced in Fig. 1, Plate III, facing p. 97. The single line spectrum shown in (*a*) was obtained when the potential difference through which the electrons fell was 3.2 volts; the two line spectrum in (*b*), for a potential difference of 6.5 volts; while the many line spectrum in (*c*) resulted from 10 volts. These photographs were taken by Drs. P. D. Foote, W. F. Meggers, and F. H. Mohler (all United States), through whose kindness it is possible to reproduce them in this book.

Although the use of such a method requires much greater experimental skill than the others we have given, it has been thus briefly described because the results obtained by it are extremely important on account of the information provided concerning the origin of spectra.

(*g*) **The Electrodeless Discharge.** Another source which the author has found extremely useful in the study of spectra is obtained by means of high frequency electrical currents. If a partially exhausted tube *without electrodes* is placed inside a coil carrying such currents, at suitable pressures a luminosity which is sometimes very brilliant takes place in the tube. By varying the pressure, or the intensity of the currents, changes in the spectra may be observed. Fig. 2, *b*, *c*, Plate III, and Fig. 4, Plate II, to which reference will again be made, give examples of spectra obtained in this way, with a tube containing mercury vapor.

High frequency currents may also be used to give bright luminous discharges in tubes to which *external* electrodes are applied. In this case the electrodes are joined to two points on a coil carrying the high frequency current.

The foregoing list by no means exhausts the number of light sources which are used in the examination of spectra, for any source which emits light may be useful. As additional sources, of a more or less special nature, Meggers lists the interrupted arc, the high frequency spark, the high voltage alternating-current arc, the pulsating direct-current arc of variable time and current, and still others.

17.3. Emission Spectra. We are now in a position to consider more carefully some of the results obtained by the use of the foregoing luminous sources. Since we are at present considering only the analysis of light *emitted* by a source, we are dealing with *emission spectra.* Of these we have two general classes, continuous and discontinuous. Continuous spectra, consisting of a wide range of unseparated wavelengths, are emitted by incandescent solids and, under very special circumstances, by fairly dense luminous gases.

Discontinuous spectra may be subdivided into two classes: line spectra and band spectra. Reference has already been made to the figures of Plate II, which provide good examples of line spectra, and attention need scarcely be directed to the sharply defined isolated wavelengths which characterize them. Such spectra are emitted by substances in the gaseous or vapor state.

Sometimes the spectrum of a luminous source is characterized by groups of individual lines whose distance apart, never great, becomes less and less until frequently it is impossible to separate them. In Fig. 4, Plate III, the student will find a reproduction of such a group—a single band—taken by Dr. R. W. B. Pearse (England) with an instrument of high dispersion. With an instrument of low dispersion, frequently the individual members of a single band are not separated, so that, when one views a number of them, the spectrum has a fluted appearance, as illustrated by Fig. 3, Plate III, a portion of the band spectrum of nitrogen. The sharp edges where the individual members are closest together are called *band heads*.

17.4. Plurality of Spectra. A very little experience in using a spectroscope is sufficient to emphasize the fundamental fact of spectrum analysis, that every luminous source or substance emits a characteristic spectrum. Thus an observer with very little experience could tell at a glance that luminous hydrogen was the source in the case of Fig. 1, Plate II, and luminous helium, in the case of Fig. 2, Plate II. As an extremely small amount of a substance in a luminous source is often sufficient to bring out its corresponding spectrum lines, the use of the spectroscope or spectrograph as a means of analysis is obvious.

Important as this fact is, it is still more important for the student to grasp the idea underlying the phrase *plurality of spectra*. By this is meant the fact that the same substance may give a variety of spectra when excited to luminosity by different means. Take the case of sodium, for example. If a little common salt or sodium itself is put in the non-luminous flame of a Bunsen burner, the resulting spectrum shows only a single yellow line or, more accurately, with good dispersion and a narrow slit, two yellow lines close together. If, however, the sodium arc spectrum is photographed, many spectral lines are observed. Again, if the spark between two pieces of sodium is analyzed, some of the arc lines will be found to have disappeared, while certain new wavelengths are present. We have then at least three different kinds of spectra, all characteristic of sodium, with some lines in common, but no two exactly alike.

In Fig. 2, Plate III, reproductions are given of three spectra of mercury vapor taken when the same tube was made luminous with different degrees of excitation. The increase in the number of lines as one passes from spectrum (*a*) to spectrum (*c*) is at once apparent. Reference has already been made to another example of plurality in the case of magnesium vapor when bombarded by electrons possessing varying amounts of kinetic energy. (See again Fig. 1, Plate III.)

In the early days of spectroscopy careful examination was made of the arc and the spark spectra of many elements. It was found that some lines, present with feeble intensity in the arc, came out with greatly increased intensity in the spark. Such lines were said to be *enhanced*. In this connection note again Fig. 3, Plate II, where the spark spectrum of tin is superimposed on the arc spectrum, the two photographs being made on the same plate by allowing the light from the sources to fall on two different, but overlapping portions of the slit of the spectrograph. While allowance must be made for differences in exposure, the student should notice: (1) lines such as 2706, 2421, 2429 are present in both arc and spark, but weaker in the spark; (2) lines such as 2531, 2524, 2455, 2381 are present in arc, absent in spark; (3) lines such as 2658, 2643, 2631, absent in the arc, appear with marked intensity in the spark. The latter group are typical spark lines.

Because of modern theoretical developments, the term "enhanced" has fallen somewhat out of use. Anticipating later work, we may here state that spark lines are now known to be due to the atom in an ionized state, arc lines to the neutral atom. In the case of an element X, the arc spectrum is described as the X I spectrum, while X II refers to the spectrum of a singly ionized atom (one electron lost), X III to that of a doubly ionized atom (two electrons lost), and so on. In the case of chlorine, whose atom may lose from one to seven electrons, lines corresponding to all the different ionized states have been observed.

17.5. Absorption Spectra. If between the slit of a spectroscope and a source emitting a continuous range of wavelengths a non-opaque substance is interposed, certain wavelengths are sometimes absorbed, giving rise to corresponding dark regions in the spectrum. In such a case we are dealing with the *absorption spectrum* of the substance. As in the case of emission spectra, we may distinguish different kinds of absorption spectra.

A pure red glass, absorbing everything but red, gives a continuous absorption spectrum.

Dilute solutions of blood, of neodymium nitrate, and of many other substances give rise to isolated dark bands whose number, width, and position are characteristic of the absorbing substance. This is a case of *selective* absorption, of which use may be made in the analysis of solutions of such substances.

In the case of an absorbing gas or vapor, isolated wavelengths, giving rise to lines as sharp as emission lines, may be observed. An excellent example of such an absorption spectrum is found when the sun is used as a source. With any instrument of even moderate dispersion and a narrow slit, it is easy to show that the spectrum of the sun is not continuous, but is crossed with narrow black lines. These lines are called Fraunhofer lines after their discoverer, the German optician who made the first gratings and died in 1826 at the early age of thirty-nine.

In the early days of spectroscopy letters were assigned to a few of these lines. As an example, we may mention the A, C, D_1, D_2, F, and H wavelengths of which some use was made in Chapter VI. The actual number of Fraunhofer lines is very great, as will be evident from an inspection of Figs. 1 and 2, Plate VIII, facing p. 224, which show reproductions of small portions only of the complete visible solar spectrum. The original photographs from which these figures were made were taken by Dr. R. E. DeLury at the Dominion Observatory, Ottawa, Canada.

By taking spectral photographs of the emission spectra of certain substances with the same instrument as was used to obtain solar spectra, a very important fact comes to light. *Some of the bright emission lines coincide with certain of the dark Fraunhofer lines.* For example, the two bright yellow lines of luminous sodium correspond exactly to the dark lines called D_1 and D_2; two prominent lines in the spark spectrum of calcium correspond exactly to the dark lines called H and K.

The explanation is found by a consideration of the following simple experiment. Suppose light, emerging from a slit illuminated by any intense white source S, Fig. 17.4, is allowed to pass through the column of vapor above pieces

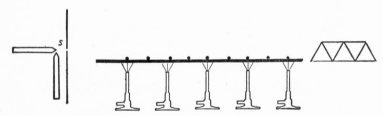

Fig. 17.4. White light from the source S passes through the column of vapor above heated particles of sodium or fused salt before falling on the slit of a spectroscope.

of fused salt or sodium strongly heated by burners below the plate on which the pieces rest. If the emergent light is examined by a spectroscope, the spectrum being thrown on a screen, it is found that in exactly the place normally occupied by the bright sodium line (or lines) a black image of the slit appears on the screen. This means that the sodium vapor absorbs just those wavelengths which it emits when acting as a luminous source—a particular example of what is known as Kirchhoff's law. On the theoretical side we may, for the present, consider the phenomenon a case of resonance, the ultimate particles, whatever they are, absorbing the energy corresponding to each frequency in the continuous source which is the same as a natural frequency of vibration of the particles. (See, also, section 16.7.)

To return to the solar spectrum, we see that if a continuous spectrum is emitted by the hottest portion of the sun, and if enveloping this portion is a layer containing vapors of substances like sodium and calcium, we have a simple explanation of the presence of the D_1, D_2, H, and K (and other) Fraunhofer lines. A complete analysis of all the Fraunhofer lines reveals the existence of substances present in the solar atmosphere.

When, due to absorption, the absence of a bright spectral line is marked by a dark line, as in the sodium experiment, the line is said to be *reversed*. A special case of reversal is found in what is known as the *self-reversal* of a line. This happens when a spectral line appears bright, although frequently broader than usual, with a narrow dark center. If the vapor in an arc, for example, is sufficiently dense, the spectral line may be broadened, while the cooler, less dense vapor in the outer portions of the arc absorbs the wavelength corresponding to the center of the line.

17.6. Doppler Effect. Suppose a vibrating source is moving with a velocity v in the direction of the arrow, Fig. 17.5. Suppose, further, that at a certain in-

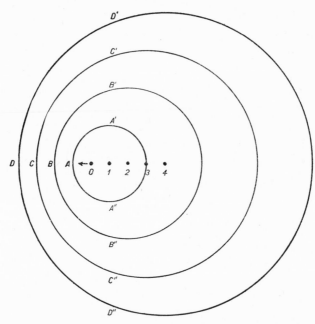

Fig. 17.5. The Doppler effect. Diagram shows the shortening of wavelengths received from an approaching source and the lengthening when the source is receding.

stant, the source is at the position marked 0; that T sec before, it was at 1; $2T$ sec before, at 2; $3T$ sec before, at 3; and so on. The diagram represents, at the moment that the source is at 0, the positions of wave-fronts which left the source when it was in positions 1, 2, 3, etc. The wave-front which left the source when at 1 will have advanced to the position $AA'A''$, where $1A = VT$, V being the velocity of the wave disturbance; the wave-front originating at 2 will have reached $BB'B''$, where $2B = 2VT$. Similarly, $3C = 3VT$, $4D = 4VT$. If T is the periodic time, then these wave-fronts are a wavelength apart.

Obviously, then, the wave-fronts are crowded more closely together in the direction toward which the source is moving, but are farther apart than normally in the opposite direction. If the source is a luminous one and we accept light as a wave phenomenon, then an observer towards which the source is moving will receive wavelengths shorter, an observer from which the source is receding, wavelengths longer, than those emitted by the source if stationary. The actual change in wavelength is readily found.

Let λ' = wavelength from an approaching source,

λ_0 = wavelength from a stationary source.

Then, since $0D = 4\lambda'$

and $0D = 4D - 04$

$\therefore\ 4\lambda' = 4D - 04$

$= 4VT - 4vT$

or

$$\lambda' = VT\left(1 - \frac{v}{V}\right)$$

$$= \lambda_0\left(1 - \frac{v}{V}\right). \tag{17.01a}$$

For a receding source,

$$\lambda' = \lambda_0\left(1 + \frac{v}{V}\right). \tag{17.01b}$$

Such changes in wavelength are observed with moving light sources, but, because of the high value of V, the actual displacement of any spectral line is extremely small. To realize this, take a concrete case. To obtain a displacement of one-tenth of an angstrom unit for light of wavelength 5000 angstroms, the application of relation (17.01) shows that a source would have to move with a velocity of 5 kilometers per sec (remember that $V = 3 \times 10^{10}$ cm per sec), or about 1340 miles per hour. Such a displacement is about one-sixtieth of the separation of the D lines of sodium. But small as it is, much smaller displacements can be measured, and in many astronomical observatories, measurements of Doppler displacements, and subsequent calculation of velocities are part of the regular routine work. As examples of phenomena on which such observations are made, we note briefly the following:

(a) **The Mapping of the Path of Certain Stars in the Heavens.** By photographing the spectrum of the light from a star, night after night, any possible motion of the star toward or away from the earth is made evident by the corresponding shift in the position of any line occurring in the spectrum. It is found, for example, that for a period of a few months a spectral line may show a displacement toward the violet end of the spectrum, the amount of which gradually decreases until finally it drops to zero. Continued observation then shows a gradually increasing displacement toward the red end. Such a star is at first approaching the earth, afterwards receding from it.

(b) **Measurements Relating to the Rotation of the Sun.** The two spectra of Fig. 2, Plate VIII, facing p. 321, provide an excellent example of such observations. To obtain spectrum a (only a small portion of the complete visible region), light from the west limb of the sun, at the equator, fell on a portion of the slit of the instrument, while, for spectrum b, light from the east limb fell on an adjacent portion of the slit. Because of the rotation of the sun, one limb is approaching the earth, and the other is receding. Hence in one case there is a slight shortening of each wavelength, whereas for the other there is a slight lengthening. The resulting displacement of corresponding lines in the two spectra, while not of great magnitude, is clearly shown in the figure. Actual measurement (obtained by placing the photographic plate under a high power traveling microscope) shows that this displacement corresponds to a value of somewhat less than 2 kilometers per second.

17.7. The Zeeman Effect. When a source of light is placed between the poles of a powerful electromagnet, it is found that, when the magnetic field is thrown on, a single spectral line is replaced by a number of others, that is, breaks up into components. This separation resulting from the action of a magnetic field on the source is called the *Zeeman Effect*, a name given in honor of its discoverer, Prof. P. Zeeman, of Holland. The number of components depends on the spectral line examined, and when the spectroscope is directed in a line at right angles to the lines of force, the result is not the same as when the direction is along the lines of force. Further discussion of this phenomenon will be given in this chapter, but at this point attention may be directed to Fig. 3 and Fig. 4, Plate VIII, facing p. 321. Figure 3, an example of the so-called normal Zeeman effect (for zinc λ6362), shows the characteristic group of three when observation is at right angles to the lines of force (the transverse position). Figure 4 is an example of longitudinal observation and shows how the single line in Fig. a, where there is no magnetic field, is replaced in b, where the field is applied, by two components, one of either side of the normal position of the line.

17.8. Stark Effect. As might be expected, an electric as well as a magnetic field has an influence on the light emitted by a luminous source. If the electric field is sufficiently powerful, a single line is replaced by components as was first shown by J. Stark (Germany). A good example of the Stark effect is shown in Fig. 2, Plate VII, facing p. 224, where the single line at the top of the spectrum

PLATE VIII

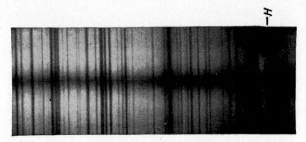

Fig. 1. A portion of the spectrum of the sun in the neighbor-hood of a sunspot. (DeLury)

Fig. 2. A portion of spectrum of east limb of the sun side by side with corresponding portion of west limb. To show displacement of lines due to Doppler effect. (DeLury)

Fig. 3. Normal Zeeman effect. (McLennan)

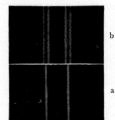

Fig. 4. Zeeman effect. (a) magnetic field off; (b) field on, vision in direction of field. (McLennan)

Fig. 5. Anomalous dispersion of sodium vapor.

is replaced (at the bottom, in the region of the strong electric field) by a number of components.*

17.9 Origin of Spectra. We wish now to see, in the light of the facts so far presented, what can be said about the ultimate source or origin from which light waves emanate.

(1) **The ultimate source, whatever it is, must in some way be related to the atom.** Consider the evidence.

(a) The mere fact that the frequency of any kind of visible light is so high *suggests* that the dimensions of the "vibrator" are extremely small in comparison with those of ordinary pieces of matter. Thus, for $\lambda = 5 \times 10^{-5}$ cm, since the velocity of light $= 3 \times 10^{10}$ cm per sec, the frequency $= \dfrac{3 \cdot 10^{10} \cdot 10^5}{5}$, or about 6×10^{14} per sec. If, therefore, anything material is oscillating, mechanical considerations suggest that it is extremely small, and it is natural to think of the atom as a possible source.

If the electromagnetic theory is accepted, the shortness of the waves suggests the same thing, for, in generating the very short electric waves which closed the gap between the infrared and the electric region, oscillators of minute dimensions are necessary. (Spark lengths as short as a few thousandths of a millimeter were used.) If, then, electric waves as short as those encountered in light are generated, it is not improbable that the oscillator is of atomic dimensions.

(b) This view is supported by the fact of spectrum analysis. When just a trace of a compound such as sodium chloride is placed in a Bunsen burner, lines characteristic of the metallic element are emitted—a fact which is to be expected if the resulting radiation is from atoms. (It may not be amiss to state here that later we shall present evidence that we also obtain light as a result of radiation from molecules. This, however, in no way contradicts the general proposition we are discussing.)

(c) The hypothesis that the ultimate source has to do with the atom provides a ready explanation of many observed facts, when it is considered with reference to the translatory motion of atoms and molecules postulated by the kinetic theory of gases. To understand the nature of this evidence the student should recall the work of Chapter VI, where it was shown that, in an ordinary prism spectrograph, each spectral line is an image of the illuminated slit of the instrument. It follows that the narrower the slit, the narrower the observed spectral line, a conclusion which is in general accord with experiment. If, however, an extremely narrow slit is used, the observed width of the line is found to vary with certain factors. For example, in the case of a luminous gas or vapor, the width of the spectral line varies with the pressure, being narrower at low pressures.

* For the original photograph the author is indebted to Dr. J. Stuart Foster, of McGill University, Montreal, a physicist who has made an extended study of this phenomenon.

On the other hand, no matter how low the pressure, a certain limiting width is ultimately reached. Again, if a vacuum tube containing a luminous gas such as helium is plunged into liquid air, it has been shown by the use of high power spectroscopes that the spectral line is narrower than at room temperatures, or, more accurately, *that the light corresponding to a single spectral line is more nearly absolutely monochromatic at the low temperature than at the high.*

Finally, if two vacuum tubes are taken, one with luminous helium of low atomic weight and the other with luminous mercury vapor of high atomic weight, it can be shown that *a single spectral line is narrower*, that is, *more nearly monochromatic, in the case of mercury than of helium.*

All these facts find a ready explanation in terms of the kinetic theory of gases. According to it, in a gas or vapor, the atoms (or molecules) are moving about in an irregular "zig-zag" fashion with velocities grouped about a mean square velocity whose magnitude is greater, the higher the temperature, and the smaller the mass of the atom. Suppose now that a single atom, or a part of one, is radiating light of a single definite frequency, as well as a few million other atoms of the same kind. Because of the motion of translation postulated by the kinetic theory, some of these atoms will be moving toward the slit of a spectrograph receiving the light, others away from it, others along a line at right angles to the axis of the collimator of the spectrograph, and still others in other directions. If the Doppler effect is evident, as it should be under such conditions, it follows that the instrument will record a small range of wavelengths grouped around that particular wavelength corresponding to the frequency in the source. In other words, no matter how narrow the slit, some finite width is to be expected—as is actually the case.

Again, if the temperature of the luminous gas is suddenly lowered, the velocities of the atoms become less, hence the changes in wavelength arising from the Doppler effect become less, and the spectral line becomes more nearly monochromatic. The helium tube in liquid air should radiate light more monochromatic than at room temperature.

If two groups of atoms of different elements, such as helium and mercury, are radiating light while at the same temperature, the heavier mercury atoms, moving more slowly, emit light more nearly monochromatic than the lighter helium atoms.

Finally, if a luminous gas is at higher and higher pressures, it can readily be seen that collisions between atoms become more and more frequent until ultimately an individual atom, because of frequent "shocks" and the resulting short mean free path, is no longer left isolated sufficiently long to emit monochromatic radiation. In this connection we may recall that an incandescent solid emits a continuous spectrum.

We conclude, then, that many facts find a ready interpretation, if the source of light is closely related to the atom.

(2) **The ultimate source must be electrical in nature.**

(a) If the electromagnetic theory is accepted, this conclusion is inevitable. Electric waves demand an electric source.

(b) This view is supported by the Stark effect, a luminous source being influenced in a marked degree by a strong electric field, and

(c) by the Zeeman effect, where the field is magnetic.

17.10. If, then, the source is electric, and if it is intimately connected with the atom, what is it? To that question, a very natural answer suggests itself. Why not the electron, a constituent part of every atom, as well as a negatively charged particle? Certainly it is easy to form a *qualitative* picture in which an electron, displaced from its normal position by some external agency, is acted on by a restoring force as a result of which it vibrates to and fro, radiating light; or, a somewhat different picture, in which the electron rapidly revolving around the positive nucleus, much as the planets encircle the sun, radiates waves whose length is determined by the period of revolution. According to the electromagnetic theory, whenever charges are accelerated, as in either of these two pictures, radiation results. "Acceleration of electric charges is the only known mode of originating ether disturbances"—so wrote Sir Oliver Lodge at the beginning of this century. It was natural, then, that such pictures should be examined quantitatively to see if observed facts of light could be deduced from such hypothetical sources.

Before pointing out the objections to accepting either of these plausible pictures, let us consider the explanation of the Zeeman effect from the above point of view, an explanation which, although presented in an elementary fashion, embodies ideas somewhat similar to those originally given by Lorentz shortly after the discovery of this phenomenon in 1896. To understand what follows, the student needs to recall the "motor principle," the law that a portion of a circuit (carrying a current), which is free to move and which lies in a magnetic field, is acted on by a force, at right angles both to the direction of the current and to that of the field, of a magnitude directly proportional both to the strength of the magnetic field and to that of the current. If we have not an ordinary *wire* circuit but a current due to a flight of charged particles, each of mass m and each bearing a charge e, moving with velocity v, then the force acting on the particle is equal to Hev, where H is the intensity of the magnetic field. An electron, therefore, which rotates in an orbit of radius r about the nucleus of an atom with positive charge E, in a plane perpendicular to the lines of a magnetic field in which the atom lies, is acted on by the force Hev in addition to the electrostatic force of attraction Ee/r^2. Moreover, the direction of this force is either toward or away from the center, depending on the sense of rotation. If the force Hev is toward the center, the resultant force is greater than when no magnetic field is present, and consequently the rotating electron moves at a higher speed. When the force is away from the center, the opposite is the case and the speed is slower.

Now, without going into dynamical details, it can be shown that the most general motion of a particle like an electron about a center of attraction is dynamically equivalent to the superposition of a linear vibration along any specified direction, and two equal and opposite circular motions in a plane at right angles to this direction. If, then, we have a few million million atoms in a magnetic field, we can think of one group with electrons oscillating along the lines of force (the specified direction), another group with electrons executing circular oscillations in one sense, in planes perpendicular to the lines, and a third group with circular motions in the opposite sense. The first motion is unaffected by the

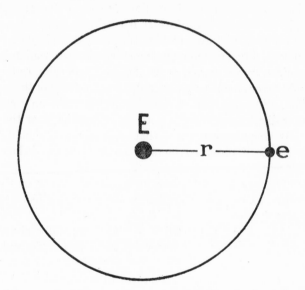

Fig. 17.6.   An electron with charge e rotates in a circular orbit of radius r about a nucleus with charge E.

magnetic field (being along the lines of force), but the circular motions, originally of equal periods, have their periods altered, one slightly decreased, the other slightly increased. If, then, an observer or an instrument is receiving light in a direction perpendicular to the lines of force, instead of one beam of approximately monochromatic light (a single spectral line), three should be received, one with wavelength the same as that transmitted in the absence of the magnetic field, a second with wavelength slightly greater, and a third with wavelength slightly less than the first. In the so-called normal Zeeman effect this is exactly what is observed, the original spectral line being replaced by three others as is nicely shown in Fig. 3, Plate VIII, facing p. 321. It should be understood that the change in wavelength is very slight, actually being equal to 0.011 A in the case illustrated. The effect would not be visible, therefore, in an ordinary prism spectrograph, an instrument of very high dispersion and resolving power being necessary.

A little reflection should make it clear that all three wavelengths are linearly polarized, the vibration plane of the central line being along the lines of force, that of the other two at right angles to this direction. This can be readily shown by observation through a Nicol prism or double-image prism.

If the instrument is directed along the lines of force, there is no light received corresponding to the linear motion, for the vibrations are longitudinal with respect to this direction. Corresponding to the two circular motions, however, two disturbances are received, one with wavelength slightly greater, the other slightly less than the normal, the two beams being circularly polarized in opposite senses.

The Zeeman effect for longitudinal observation is nicely shown in Fig. 4, Plate VIII, where the upper photograph has been taken with field on, the lower with field off. Note that the original single line is now replaced by a pair.

When the preceding ideas are incorporated into equations of motion, an important result follows. Suppose, as depicted in Fig. 17.6, an electron of mass m and charge e rotates in a circular orbit of radius r about a nucleus of charge E, no magnetic field being present. If v is the linear velocity of the electron and ω its angular velocity, then by ordinary mechanics

$$\frac{mv^2}{r} = mr\omega^2 = \frac{Ee}{r^2}.$$

When a magnetic field of intensity H oersted is applied we have the additional force Hev, directed, for motion in one sense, toward the center; for motion in the opposite sense, away from the center. If ω_1 is the angular velocity for the one case, ω_2 for the other, we have now the equations

$$mr\omega_1^2 = mr\omega^2 + Hev$$
$$= mr\omega^2 + Her\omega_1$$

and $\qquad\qquad mr\omega_2^2 = mr\omega^2 - Her\omega_2.$

These two equations reduce to

$$\omega_1^2 = \omega^2 + H\frac{e}{m}\omega_1,$$

$$\omega_2^2 = \omega^2 - H\frac{e}{m}\omega_2.$$

Subtracting we have

$$\omega_1^2 - \omega_2^2 = H\frac{e}{m}(\omega_1 + \omega_2)$$

or $\qquad\qquad \omega_1 - \omega_2 = H\frac{e}{m}.$

Now *if* the frequencies of the light radiated are equal to the orbital frequencies, and λ_1, λ, λ_2 are the corresponding wavelengths, we have

$$c = \frac{\omega_1 \lambda_1}{2\pi}, \quad c = \frac{\omega \lambda}{2\pi}, \quad \text{and} \quad c = \frac{\omega_2 \lambda_2}{2\pi},$$

where c = velocity of light.

Hence we can write

$$\frac{2\pi c}{\lambda_1} - \frac{2\pi c}{\lambda_2} = H \frac{e}{m}$$

or

$$\frac{\lambda_2 - \lambda_1}{\lambda_1 \lambda_2} = \frac{H}{2\pi c} \cdot \frac{e}{m}.$$

Since $\Delta\lambda$, the difference in wavelength between λ_1 and λ (or λ_2 and λ) is small, we may write

$$\frac{2\Delta\lambda}{\lambda^2} = \frac{1}{2\pi} \cdot \frac{H}{c} \cdot \frac{e}{m}$$

or

$$\Delta\lambda = \frac{H}{4\pi c} \cdot \frac{e}{m} \cdot \lambda^2 \qquad (17.02)$$

If, then, the value of $\Delta\lambda$ is observed for a measured magnetic field, this expression provides us with a means of evaluating e/m. *It is most significant that values obtained in this way agree with those determined by purely electrical methods.* When, therefore, Lorentz* derived (in a more general and somewhat different way) this relation shortly after the discovery of the Zeeman effect, and when this striking agreement for the values of e/m was obtained, it seemed *as if* strong confirmation had been obtained for the truth of the picture we have been presenting concerning the origin of spectra.

17.11. Let us, however, look at some objections to this view.

(1) Suppose we consider, as we have done, that in the normal (unexcited) state of an atom, an electron is revolving in a fixed orbit around the nucleus, as a planet revolves about the sun. At once we encounter an objection to the electromagnetic theory, for, since in the motion of the electron, we have a case of accelerated motion of an electrical charge, radiation should result *without excitation by any external agency.* But substances in their normal unexcited state do not radiate.

(2) If, disregarding this difficulty, we assume that such a radiation does take place (as we have done in the discussion of the Zeeman effect), we at once en-

---

* Lorentz made use of a type of atom in which planetary motion is not necessary, for the electrons occupy positions of equilibrium within a sphere of positive electricity. Radiation was considered to take place when an electron, displaced from its equilibrium position by some external agency, vibrated to and fro because of quasi-elastic forces supposed to be proportional to the amount of displacement. The work of Rutherford on scattering of alpha particles showed that this view of the strucutre of an atom could not be maintained.

counter another difficulty, for the resulting radiation should give rise to a *continuous* spectrum. As energy is radiated, the total energy of the atomic system (the positive nucleus plus the rotating negative electron) must become less. This means that the electron must be continuously attracted nearer and nearer to the nucleus, hence that the radius of the orbit and the frequency of rotation continuously change. If, therefore, the orbital frequency is the radiation frequency, as is the case on the view we are considering, the spectrum observed should be continuous. But, if there is one feature which characterizes the ordinary spectrum of a luminous gas or vapor more than any other, it is the appearance of well-defined isolated spectral lines.

(3) Suppose, however, that we adopt the picture of the atom used by Lorentz, considering that an electron is not in rotation but is in some static position of equilibrium as a result of all the forces acting on it. We may then assume that radiation results only when, because of shocks or collisions provided by an external agency, the electron is displaced from its position of equilibrium, radiation taking place as it executes vibrations about this position. When mathematical analysis of such a condition is made, it can be shown, as was done in 1906 by the late Lord Rayleigh, that relations *not* in agreement with the observed laws of spectral series are obtained. In all such calculated relations the square of the frequencies appears, not the simple first power as in series relations. (See section 19.1.)

There are serious difficulties, therefore, when it comes to dealing with the mode of production of light waves, whether it is assumed that radiation results from the orbital motion of an electron, or from the vibrations of an electron displaced from an equilibrium position. In spite of the wonderful success of the electromagnetic theory in so far as questions relating to the propagation of light are concerned, the ablest mathematical physicists at the close of the nineteenth century and the beginning of the twentieth were unable, *as long as they adhered rigidly to the dynamical principles involved*, to find a satisfactory picture of the origin of spectra.

But, it may be asked, what about the striking agreement in the value of e/m obtained from the Zeeman effect compared with those by other methods? A twofold answer may be given to that question. In the first place, the Zeeman effect is by no means as simple a phenomenon as has thus far been represented. The majority of spectral lines do not give rise to the characteristic group of three explained, apparently so simply, on the view discussed before. The pattern for most lines is more complex, sometimes much more so, and finds no such ready explanation.

In the second place, the quantum theory, a discussion of which will be given in the next chapter, not only is able to provide the same expression for the normal group of three but also to account for the more complex so-called anomalous Zeeman effect observed with other lines.

We conclude, then, that, while there must be much truth in many of the ideas put forward in this chapter, in particular, that the source of radiation is intimately related to the electron, a satisfactory explanation of the origin of spectra cannot be found—at any rate, has never been found—in any combination of the modern atom with the classical electromagnetic theory of light.

XVIII

Radiation and the Quantum Theory

18.1. Birth of the Quantum Theory. To understand something of the way in which this very important theory originated, the reader is asked first to recall the nature of the spectrum of an incandescent solid. If the light radiated from the filament of a lamp is analyzed by a prism, a continuous spectrum is obtained. By means of an instrument such as a bolometer or a thermopile, a quantitative examination may be made of the way in which the energy is distributed throughout the whole range of wavelengths. When this is done, curves somewhat similar

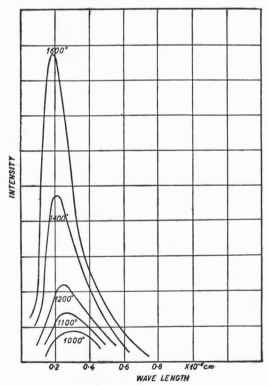

Fig. 18.1. Curves showing the distribution of energy in the continuous spectrum of a black body at different temperatures.

329

to those given in Fig. 18.1 are obtained. Thus, for a particular temperature of the source, there is always a certain wavelength λ_m, for which the intensity of radiation is a maximum. Moreover, as the graphs of Fig. 18.1 show, the higher the temperature, the smaller the value of λ_m.

Now no scientist is content simply with the obtaining of an experimental curve. His search is always for causes and for origins, and when curves such as those in Fig. 18.1 are obtained, the next step is to deduce *theoretically* from fundamental considerations a law which is in agreement with the observed facts. In the case under discussion, it will not do to obtain the spectral distribution energy curve for any incandescent solid, for, even at the same temperature, in general, incandescent solids do not give identical curves. The radiation depends on surface conditions, as well as on temperature. There is, however, one kind of luminous solid which emits radiation whose spectral distribution is a function only of the temperature. Such a substance, called a *black body*, is one which completely absorbs all electromagnetic waves incident on its surface, and theoretical considerations are always made with reference to it. There is, then, in this field of work, a two-fold problem: (1) to examine experimentally with the utmost care the radiation from a black body; and (2) to see, if, by a consideration of radiation processes, and of the equilibrium state obtaining among various wavelengths, a law can be deduced in agreement with the experimental results.

To obtain in actual practice a black body, use is made of the fact that, in an enclosed cavity kept at constant temperature, the energy is distributed among the various wavelengths in the same way as in the radiation from an ideal black body. The radiation from such an enclosure is independent of the material of which its walls are made. One such cavity, by means of which accurate measurements have been made, consists of three concentric porcelain cylindrical tubes, the region within the inner of which is kept at constant temperature by electric heating and the most rigid precautions. The radiation emerging from a small opening from the interior of this inner tube is a close approximation to black body radiation. (See, also, section 18.3.) Analysis of the radiation at different temperatures gives curves of the type shown in Fig. 18.1.

18.2. Photometry. Since the subjects of radiation and photometry have a common link in the black body, it is desirable at this stage, before discussing the theoretical interpretation of the curves of Fig. 18.1, to make a brief reference to a few basic ideas in modern photometry. In photometry we are concerned with only that portion of the total amount of energy radiated from a source, such as an incandescent lamp, to which the eye is sensitive. With this in mind we speak of a *flux of luminosity* from the source. The unit of *luminous flux* (symbol F) is the *lumen* which is defined below. Some idea of its size may be had from the statement that a 100-watt incandescent lamp emits about 1650 lumens.

Since the sensitivity of the eye varies greatly with the wavelength of the incident light, an exact knowledge of the relative sensitivity of different wavelengths is necessary. This is given by the international *relative luminosity curve* in Fig. 18.2, which is the result of tests made by a large number of observers. The curve, drawn to approximate accuracy only, shows the relative response of the eye to equal total amounts of radiant flux of different wavelengths. It will

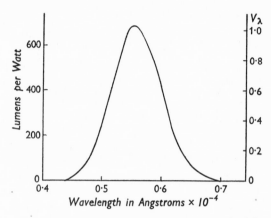

Fig. 18.2. The international relative luminosity curve. The scale on the left is in lumens per watt; on the right, values are shown of the relative luminous efficiency.

be noticed that the eye has a maximum sensitivity for wavelength 5540 A. In the figure, two scales of vertical ordinates have been used. On the right-hand side the numbers give the values of V_λ, the *relative luminous efficiency*, the value 1 being assigned to the wavelength for which the efficiency is a maximum. The scale on the left side is in lumens per watt, the peak corresponding to 680 lumens per watt. The definition of the lumen and an explanation of the origin of the number 680 are given below.

18.3. The Candela. The definition of the lumen links it with an agreed unit source of *luminous intensity* (symbol I). Historically, the unit goes back to the paraffin wax candle and to a period of many years during which, first, actual candles, then oil-burning lamps, and finally electric lamps were used as standard sources. Some thirty years ago, as a result of interchanges of special electric lamps used as standards by such national laboratories as the Bureau of Standards in Washington, the National Physical Laboratory in London, and the Physikalisch-Technische Reichsanstalt in Germany, an international candle was adopted, its value being defined in terms of carbon filament lamps in the possession of the national laboratories. There was, however, no primary standard independent of electric lamps and reproducible in all countries. This position has now been altered by the adoption of a black body as the primary source of luminosity. Reference has already been made to one type of black body. Another, essentially similar, consists of a tube of thoria immersed in a crucible where it is surrounded by molten platinum. (See Fig. 18.3.) Black body radiation is emitted from the mouth of the thoria tube, the standard unit source of luminosity, the *candela*, being based on the luminous flux from the tube *at the temperature of freezing platinum*. By definition, 1 sq cm of the mouth of the tube

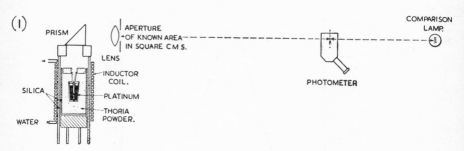

Fig. 18.3.   An arrangement for comparing the luminous intensity of a lamp with the primary (black body) standard of light.   (Courtesy, Director, National Physical Laboratory.)

corresponds to 60 candela. The following more exact definition, adopted by the General Conference of Weights and Measures in 1948, was recently tentatively approved by the International Commission on Illumination. A candela is a "unit of luminous intensity: it is of such a value that the luminous intensity of a full radiator at the freezing point of platinum is 60 units of luminous intensity per cm²."

The candela differs somewhat in magnitude from the international candle, and at the various standard laboratories measurements have been and are being made to determine the exact ratio of the old and the new unit and "to assure international uniformity of values for lamps of various types."

The International Commission on Illumination has also agreed on the definition of a lumen (sometimes called the new lumen) as "the flux emitted in a solid angle of one steradian* by a uniform point source having an intensity of one candela." It follows from this definition that a *point* source of one candela emits 4π lumens. Actually most sources have an extended area.

The Mechanical Equivalent of Light. An important fundamental quantity (M) is the number of lumens per watt of radiant energy emitted by a source of luminosity. In this connection the term *lightwatt* is used to designate the number of lumens per watt for the wavelength 5540 A which, as we have seen, is the region of maximum sensitivity of the eye. This number (M) may be found in two ways, both of which depend ultimately on the black body source of luminous intensity.

Method 1. The luminous intensity of the standard black body is 60 candela per sq cm. For an extended surface, as distinguished from a point source, the

* The student will recall that one steradian is the solid angle subtended at a point by unit area at unit distance, the area being perpendicular to the line joining the point to the center of the area.

total flux emitted per sq cm equals 60π lumens. Now let $E(\lambda_{max}) \cdot d\lambda$ be the power in watts per sq cm radiated by the standard black body at wavelength 5540 by a band of width $d\lambda$. Then, for any other wavelength λ, for the narrow band between λ and $\lambda + d\lambda$,

$$\text{the power radiated} = V_\lambda E(\lambda) \cdot d\lambda \text{ watts per sq cm.}$$

Therefore, the total power radiated $= \int_0^\infty V_\lambda E(\lambda) \cdot d\lambda$ watts per sq cm. To evaluate this integral, one must substitute values of V_λ obtained from Fig. 18.2 and make use of Planck's formula for E_λ given in relation 18.03, section 18.10. The value of M is then given by

$$M = \frac{\int_0^\infty V_\lambda E(\lambda) \cdot d\lambda}{60\pi} \text{ lumens per watt.}$$

Since the calculations involve the use of the relative luminosity curve of Fig. 18.2, the values of the constants C_1 and C_2 in Planck's formula, and an accurate value of the melting point of platinum, the value of $M = 680$ * we have given above has not yet been accepted internationally. An evaluation of this number is still the subject of investigations at the National Laboratories.

Method 2. A more direct determination of the value of M can be made by taking a light source whose luminous intensity has been measured carefully and measuring the distribution of energy in its spectrum in absolute units. Few such determinations have been made.

A striking illustration of the importance of the temperature of a black body source is provided by the following numbers taken from a table given by de Groot (Holland). If we take the absolute temperature of melting platinum as 2041.7° K and the corresponding 60 candela per sq cm as the luminous intensity, then at 2000° K, the luminous intensity of a black body radiator is 46.5 candela per sq cm, and at 2200° K, 145 candela per sq cm.

18.4. Color Temperature. The quality of the light emitted by a source also depends markedly on the temperature, a fact which is the cause of one of the greatest difficulties in making accurate measurements in photometry. To describe the quality of a source use is made of the term *color temperature*, which, to quote Walsh of the N.P.L. (England), may be defined as "the temperature of a full radiator (black body) which matches the source in color and which emits radiation of substantially the same spectral distribution within the visible region." For example, gas-filled tungsten lamps have color temperatures ranging from 2800° to 3000°. Direct comparison of a lamp of this type with the primary standard (whose color temperature, of course is 2041.7°) is not usually made.

* This value was given the author by Mr. L. J. Collier of the National Physical Laboratory.

In measuring the luminous intensity of any lamp to be tested, the procedure adopted in standard laboratories like the N.P.L. is something like this. First, the primary standard is compared with a sub-standard lamp A (as in Fig. 18.3), which has been constructed to have a color temperature of 2042°. Lamp A is then compared with another sub-standard lamp B, of color temperature 2353°, compensation for the difference in color being made by the use of a blue glass filter. Lamp B is then compared with a "working standard" lamp, against which finally the test lamp is measured.

18.5. Illumination.   The illumination (symbol E) of a surface is possibly the most practical of all problems in photometry.   The illumination at a point is measured by the number of lumens received per unit area in the neighborhood of the point in question or, in the more exact words of the definition adopted by the International Commission, is the "ratio of the luminous flux incident on an infinitesimal element of surface containing the point under consideration, to the area of this element."   It is measured in lumens per square meter, the unit being called a *lux*.   When details of objects or fine print are being observed, the illumination should not be less than 500 lux.

Actual values of illumination may be obtained readily by the use of a photoelectric cell of the barrier layer type, whose response matches that of the eye. The scale of the meter in such an instrument can be calibrated, by the use of a source of known luminous intensity, to read directly in lux.   In passing, it is worth noting that the elementary photometers described in textbooks of physics have now largely only a historical value, the photoelectric cell and the integrating sphere* making them almost obsolete, as far as the measurement of total flux is concerned.

Before returning to the general question of radiation a brief reference is made to two or three other fundamental quantities in photometry, the definitions given being those recommended for adoption by the International Commission on Illumination.

18.6. Luminous Emittance.   This quantity (symbol H) from a point on a surface is defined as the "ratio of the luminous flux emitted from an infinitesimal element of surface containing the point under consideration to the area of this element."   It is measured in lumens per square meter.

The *luminance* (symbol L) at a point on a surface and in any direction is "the ratio of the luminous intensity in that direction of an infinitesimal element of the

---

* In the integrating sphere, whose diameter is of the order of a few feet, sometimes as large as 10 ft, in standardization laboratories, the interior wall is white and the light diffusely reflected.   When a source is placed near the center, the illumination on a small window in the wall of the sphere is directly proportional to the total flux emitted by the source, provided the window does not receive direct radiation from the source.   Comparison between the total flux emitted by a standard and a test source is, therefore, readily made by the use of a photoelectric cell placed in front of the window.

surface containing the point under consideration, to the orthogonally projected area of this element on a plane perpendicular to that direction." Luminance corresponds to what was formerly called *brightness*.

18.7. Radiation Laws. We return now to the problem of interpreting theoretically the curves of Fig. 18.1. When attempts were made to deduce a law in agreement with the experimental curve grave difficulties were encountered. Indeed, at the outset, it may be stated that so long as no departure was made from the laws of Newtonian mechanics and classical electrodynamics, it proved impossible to deduce a law representing all the facts. Radiation laws were, of course, derived, and two of these it is well to note.

18.8. Wien's Radiation Law. Making certain assumptions, Wien proved that

$$E_\lambda = \frac{c_1}{\lambda^5} \cdot e^{-\frac{c_2}{\lambda T}} \qquad (18.01)$$

where E_λ is the intensity of radiation for wavelength λ, c_1, c_2 are constants, and T is the absolute temperature. Experiment shows, however, that this law holds only for the region of short wavelengths.

18.9. Rayleigh's Radiation Law. According to this

$$E_\lambda = \frac{c_1 T}{c_2 \lambda^4} \qquad (18.02)$$

where c_1, c_2 are constants, T is the absolute temperature. This law holds approximately for long wavelengths, but not at all for short, as can be seen at once, for according to this relation, the smaller λ, the greater the intensity of radiation, a deduction most certainly not in accordance with the curves of Fig. 18.1.

18.10. Planck's Radiation Formula. In 1900 Max Planck (Germany), a man who had devoted years of study to problems of radiation, showed that a radiation formula in agreement with the facts could be derived if a certain startling assumption were made. According to this, *interchanges of energy in processes of emission and absorption take place only in multiples of discrete energy units.* As in his theoretical investigations he made use of electronic vibrators or oscillators, this hypothesis not only introduced the new idea that energy is atomistic but also assumed that accelerated motion of charges does not always give rise to radiation. It may, therefore, properly be described as revolutionary. The unit of energy is called a *quantum*, the magnitude of which, for a frequency ν is equal to $h\nu$, where h is a universal constant, now called Planck's constant. The value of this constant Planck showed to be

$$h = 6.62 \times 10^{-27} \text{ (erg} \times \text{sec)}.$$

The radiation formula which he derived is given by

$$E_\lambda = \frac{hc^3}{\lambda^5} \cdot \frac{1}{e^{\frac{h\nu}{kT}} - 1}, \qquad (18.03)$$

where c = velocity of light,

   ν = frequency,

   T = absolute temperature.

   k = a constant, whose value = $\dfrac{R}{N}$,

where R is the absolute gas constant, and N is Avogadro's number. In passing it may be noted that, taking the value of R from other work, and the value of k from radiation measurements, Planck obtained a value for N in excellent agreement with values obtained by very different methods.

Planck's radiation formula has been proved by the most careful observations to represent the facts accurately. Moreover, it can readily be shown that, for small values of λ, it reduces to Wien's formula; for large values, to Rayleigh's. It is the one and only relation, therefore, which fits the facts, and it is derived by assuming quanta of energy, and that an electromagnetic oscillator may "oscillate" without radiating.

18.11. Photoelectric Effect and Quantum Theory. Although the birth of the quantum theory coincided with the opening of the twentieth century, other evidence in support of it had to be established before the theory became of outstanding importance. In 1905, Einstein (Germany) suggested that the idea of quanta need not be restricted to discontinuity in emission and absorption processes, but that it was quite possible that light might be propagated in little bundles of energy (light quanta), each of which maintained its identity throughout its path. It was not, however, until the photoelectric phenomenon discovered by Hertz in 1889 was subjected to a careful quantitative examination by Lenard (Germany), Hughes (Great Britain), Millikan (United States), and others that evidence became overwhelming that *certain* facts could only be explained in terms of Planck's unit of energy $h\nu$. Let us look at some of these facts.

When an insulated metallic plate, negatively charged, is illuminated by light of suitable wavelengths, it loses its charge because of a photoelectric emission of electrons. Careful investigations concerning the relations between the kind of light, the velocity, and the number of electrons emitted, have established the following laws:

(1) A certain critical wavelength is necessary before the photoelectric emission takes place at all. To illustrate, for some metals, red light is ineffective, while with ultraviolet light, the effect is marked. The incident light, therefore, must contain wavelengths below a critical value.

(2) While the total number of electrons emitted per second varies with the intensity of the incident light, *the maximum velocity with which an electron emerges from the surface of the metal, for a given kind of light, is independent of the intensity.* This very important fact means that when a source of light is moved from a distance of 1 ft to 10 ft from the metal surface, there is no difference in the maximum velocity with which the electrons emerge.

(3) In the region of effective wavelengths, this maximum velocity depends directly on the frequency of the incident light. In other words, the shorter λ the wavelength (or the higher the frequency), the greater the velocity. In symbols this law, sometimes known as Einstein's Law, is then written.

$$E_{\max} = a\nu - P, \tag{18.04}$$

where $E_{\max}$ = maximum kinetic energy of an emerging electron, where a is a constant independent of the metal, and where P is another constant whose value depends on the nature of the metal.

Now look at the significance of these laws. On the wave theory, energy is spread uniformly and continuously over a wave-front. Therefore, the amount of energy incident on a given surface area, 1 sq mm for example, must become less and less the farther the source of light is removed. Now it is obvious that an electron comes out of an atom because of the energy supplied by the incident light—and yet it emerges with the same energy whether the source is 1 ft or 100 ft away. On a continuous wave-front theory it is difficult to explain this fact, but the explanation is at once forthcoming if light energy travels in discontinuous bundles, that is, in light quanta, which may be assumed to travel not unlike the corpuscules of the old corpuscular theory. A quantum theory, according to which energy is distributed over a wave-front anything but continuously, then provides a ready explanation.

What about the magnitude of the energy in a quantum in this case? Experiment and relation (18.04) provide the answer to that question. To understand how this is the case, it is necessary to know that in order to measure the maximum velocity of a photoelectron, an opposing electric field is applied with a potential difference of just such a value as will prevent any electrons leaving the metal. Suppose, then, that the application of a potential difference of V_1 volts keeps electrons from escaping when the incident light has a frequency ν_1, and that V_2 volts are required for a frequency ν_2. Then, remembering that the work done when a particle with electronic charge e falls through a potential difference of V is Ve, we have

$$V_1 e = a\nu_1 - P$$
$$V_2 e = a\nu_2 - P,$$

from which

$$(V_1 - V_2)e = a(\nu_1 - \nu_2)$$

or

$$a = \frac{(V_1 - V_2)e}{\nu_1 - \nu_2}.$$

The constant a can be evaluated, therefore, from the observed potential values V_1 and V_2, from the frequencies ν_1 and ν_2 of the incident light, and the charge e on an electron. The result of careful measurements made in this way by Millikan and others gives the value of $a = 6.62 \times 10^{-27}$ (erg $\times$ sec), and it is the same for all metals. It is seen, then, that a is in reality Planck's constant h, and that relation (18.04) should be written

$$E_{\max} = h\nu - P. \tag{18.05}$$

The conclusion is obvious. The photoelectric effect receives a ready explanation in terms of a quantum theory, according to which light energy is restricted to multiples of a quantum of magnitude $h\nu$.

18.12. Quantum Theory and Emission of a Single Spectral Line. Further evidence supporting a quantum theory is provided by certain experiments in which light emission results from the bombardment of a gas or a vapor by electrons. In section 17.2 it was pointed out that, as the speed of the bombarding electrons is gradually increased, more and more spectral lines are emitted, a point illustrated by Fig. 1, Plate III, facing p. 97. In a, Fig. 1, it will again be noted that the spectrum of magnesium consists of a single line, a phenomenon which can be reproduced with other elements. One of the first elements investigated was mercury, in which case it was shown by Franck and Hertz (Germany) that a quantum relation again connects the frequency of the single line emitted with the energy of the colliding electron. (For other elements, the same relation was shown by other observers.)

In mercury, experiment shows that the wavelength 2536 A is alone emitted when the bombarding electron has a velocity acquired by falling through a potential difference of 4.9 volts. Now let us make one or two simple calculations, being given that $e = 4.80 \times 10^{-10}$ absolute electrostatic units of quantity, that 300 volts = 1 absolute electrostatic unit of potential difference.

For wavelength 2536 A, we have

$$\nu = \frac{c}{\lambda} = \frac{3 \times 10^{10}}{2536 \times 10^{-8}},$$

where c is the velocity of light *in vacuo*. Therefore, the corresponding quantum of energy is

$$h\nu = \frac{6.62 \times 10^{-27} \times 3 \times 10^{10}}{2536 \times 10^{-8}}$$

$$= 7.83 \times 10^{-12} \text{ ergs.}$$

If, now, we assume that

$$Ve = h\nu,$$

we have

$$V = \frac{7.83 \times 10^{-12}}{4.80 \times 10^{-10}} \text{ absolute units}$$

$$= \frac{300 \times 7.83 \times 10^{-12}}{4.80 \times 10^{-10}} = 4.89 \text{ volts.}$$

We see, then, that on the assumption that a quantum of energy is radiated when the colliding electron loses an equivalent amount of kinetic energy, there is agreement between observed and calculated values.

XIX

Spectral Series and Origin of Spectra

19.1. Spectral Series. The discovery of the existence of *spectral series* was outstanding in work which led to the modern interpretation of spectra. A glance at the regular spacing of the important spectral lines in the spectrum of hydrogen (Plate II, facing p. 96, Fig. 1) suggests the existence of some relationship con-

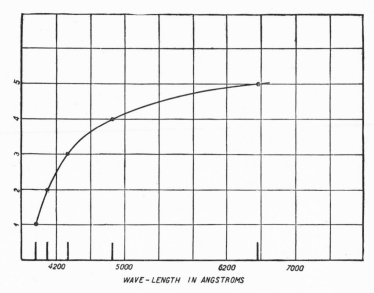

WAVE-LENGTH IN ANGSTROMS

Fig. 19.1.   Curve obtained by assigning successive integral numbers to the Balmer lines of hydrogen and plotting these numbers against wavelengths.

necting their wavelengths. This suggestion is confirmed by assigning any sequence of integral numbers to successive lines and making a graph, with one ordinate these numbers, the other wavelengths. As Fig. 19.1 shows, a smooth curve results.

In 1885 it was shown by Balmer (Germany) that the wavelengths of these hydrogen lines could all be calculated from the relation

$$\lambda = 3645.6 \, \frac{m^2}{m^2 - 4}, \tag{19.01}$$

where m takes values 3, 4, 5 $\cdots$, and λ is in angstroms. For reasons which will appear later, this relation may more conveniently and accurately be expressed

$$\bar{\nu} = \frac{1}{\lambda} = 109678 \left(\frac{1}{2^2} - \frac{1}{m^2} \right), \tag{19.02}$$

where $\bar{\nu}$, the number of wavelengths in 1 cm, is called the *wave-number*. In (19.02) λ is in centimeters.

Since $c = \nu\lambda$, where c is the velocity of light in free space and ν is the frequency of the light, we have $\nu = c\bar{\nu}$.

In dealing with wave-numbers, note that wavelengths *in vacuo* are always used. To change from λ *in vacuo* to λ in I.A. (see section 6.3) the index of refraction of air at 15° C and 760 mm pressure must be known, since $\lambda_{\text{vac.}} = $ index $\times \lambda_{\text{air}}$. Books giving the wavelengths of spectral series lines, however, usually include a table of conversion values.

In Table XIV a comparison is made of a few hydrogen wavelengths (expressed in I.A.) as calculated by relation (19.02) with values observed.

Table XIV.   A Few Wavelengths of the
Balmer Hydrogen Series

	Observed	Calculated
H_α	6562.84	6562.79
H_β	4861.36	4861.33
H_γ	4340.48	4340.47
H_δ	4101.76	4101.74

A group of wavelengths, any one of which may be calculated by using the appropriate *integral* value of the variable m, constitutes a *spectral series*. The foregoing hydrogen lines constitute the first four members of what is usually called the Balmer hydrogen series. As many as thirty-five members of this series have been observed, that is, as far as $m = 37$.

It may not be amiss at this place to point out that the Balmer formula, like all other series relations, involves not the first power of the variable m, but the second power.

Since the pioneer work of Balmer, a tremendous amount of work has been done in the analysis of spectra, with the result that not only have spectral series been discovered for most elements, but, also, for one and the same element, several different series are known.

In hydrogen, for example, there is another group of lines in the ultraviolet whose wavelengths may be calculated from the relation,

$$\bar{\nu} = 109678 \left(\frac{1}{1^2} - \frac{1}{m^2} \right), \tag{19.03}$$

where m takes values 2, 3, 4 $\cdots$. This group constitutes the Lyman series named after its discoverer, Prof. Lyman, an American physicist. The student can easily show by calculation that lines observed at 1216, 1026, and 972 constitute the first three members of this series.

In the infrared region three other hydrogen series have been observed. As these are of the same kind as the Balmer and the Lyman series, they may be represented by the general formula

$$\bar{\nu} = 109678 \left(\frac{1}{k^2} - \frac{1}{m^2} \right). \tag{19.04}$$

When $k = 3$ and $m = 4, 5, 6, \cdots$, we have the Paschen series. The observed wavelengths range from $18751(m = 4)$ to $8863(m = 11)$.

When $k = 4$ and $m = 5, 6, 7, \cdots$, the Brackett series is obtained. This includes lines with wavelengths as long as 40500.

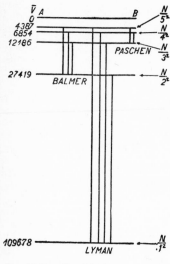

Fig. 19.2. Graphical representation of hydrogen spectral series. The figures on the left are wavenumbers; N is the Rydberg constant.

Finally, when $k = 5$ and $m = 6, 7, \cdots$, there is the Pfund series, in which only a single member has been observed. Its wavelength is 74600.

The number 109678 which occurs in all relations, and will appear in all other series relations, is called the Rydberg constant, and will be represented by N.*

Graphical Representation of Hydrogen Series. Suppose, in Fig. 19.2, that the distances between the horizontal lines or levels from an arbitrary zero line AB are proportional to the magnitudes $N/1^2, N/2^2, N/3^2, N/4^2 \cdots$. Then the Balmer series may be represented by the vertical lines joining the $N/3^2, N/4^2, N/5^2 \cdots$ levels to the $N/2^2$ level; the Lyman series by the group of vertical lines joining $N/2^2, N/3^2 \cdots$ levels to $N/1^2$; and the Paschen series by the lines joining $N/4^2, N/5^2 \cdots$ to $N/3^2$. The advantage of thus representing spectral series will appear when questions relating to the origin of spectra are under consideration.

General Series Relations. Some of the more important ideas in connection with series for elements other than hydrogen may be explained by taking the case of lithium. In this element, there are three important series of arc lines.

---

* Strictly speaking this number varies slightly in different series relations for reasons which will be apparent in section 19.6.

(a) The *principal* series,

$$\bar{\nu}_P = 43486 - \frac{N}{(m + 0.9597)^2}, \quad m = 1, 2, 3, \tag{19.05a}$$

(b) The *diffuse* series,

$$\bar{\nu}_D = 28582 - \frac{N}{(m + 0.9990)^2}, \quad m = 2, 3, 4, \cdots \tag{19.05b}$$

(c) The *sharp* series,

$$\bar{\nu}_S = 28582 - \frac{N}{(m + 0.5888)^2}, \quad m = 2, 3, 4, \cdots. \tag{19.05c}$$

As in hydrogen, the wave-number for each wavelength is equal to the difference between a fixed number, called the *limit*, and a variable *term*, which involves the universal Rydberg constant N and the variable *sequence* number m. It is well to note several other things.

(a) The variable term is no longer of the simple form N/m^2, but $N/(m + c)^2$, where c is a constant whose value varies with the particular series under consideration.

(b) The same number gives the limit of the sharp and of the diffuse series. This is indicated in Fig. 19.3, where the dotted lines represent limits and where

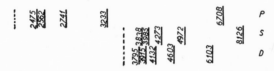

Fig. 19.3. The short vertical lines in the horizontal rows, P, S and D, represent three groups of wavelengths in the spectrum of lithium, each group being part of a spectral series.

an individual wavelength is indicated by drawing a short vertical line on a horizontal *wave-number* scale.

(c) The limit of the principal series, namely, 43486, is numerically equal to the first term of the sharp series. Thus, when $m = 1$,

$$\frac{109678}{(m + 0.5888)^2} \doteq 43486.$$

The common limit of the sharp and the diffuse series is equal to the first term of the principal. Again, when $m = 1$,

$$\frac{109678}{(m + 0.9597)^2} = 28582.$$

These are particular examples of a very important general law, which states that the limit of any series is a term of some other series.

Bearing the preceding result in mind, we may now rewrite equations (19.05) as

$$\bar{\nu}_P = \frac{N}{(1 + 0.5888)^2} - \frac{N}{(m + 0.9597)^2} \qquad (19.06a)$$

$$\bar{\nu}_D = \frac{N}{(1 + 0.9597)^2} - \frac{N}{(m + 0.9990)^2} \qquad (19.06b)$$

$$\bar{\nu}_S = \frac{N}{(1 + 0.9597)^2} - \frac{N}{(m + 0.5888)^2}. \qquad (19.06c)$$

We see, then, that the wave-number of any spectral line (which is a member of a series) is equal to the difference between two terms. This is a statement of

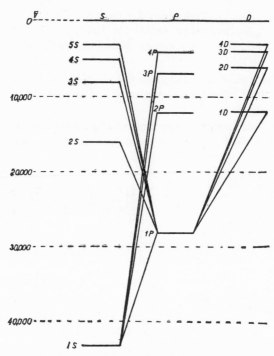

Fig. 19.4. Graphical representation of three spectral series of lithium. Each vertical column of short horizontal lines represents term values. The wave-number of a spectral line is always equal to the difference between two term values.

the Ritz *combination* law. For convenience in writing, the function $N/(m + c)^2$ is written mc, in consequence of which we may write the series relations as follows:

$$\bar{\nu}_P = 1S - mP \qquad (19.07a)$$

$$\bar{\nu}_D = 1P - mD \qquad (19.07b)$$

$$\bar{\nu}_S = 1P - mS, \qquad (19.07c)$$

where P, D, and S are used to represent the constants of the principal, diffuse and sharp series.

By means of the same method as used for hydrogen, these three series have been represented graphically in Fig. 19.4. The second column represents the P term values or levels, that is,

$$\frac{N}{(1 + 0.9597)^2}, \quad \frac{N}{(2 + 0.9597)^2}, \quad \frac{N}{(3 + 0.9597)^2}, \quad \cdots;$$

the first column, the S terms; and the third, the D terms, while as before lines connecting levels represent wavelengths in accordance with relations (19.07). The student should not have difficulty in interpreting the diagram for himself. (See also Chapter XX.)

The terms *principal, sharp,* and *diffuse* were originally chosen because of certain physical differences in the lines which belonged to the individual series.

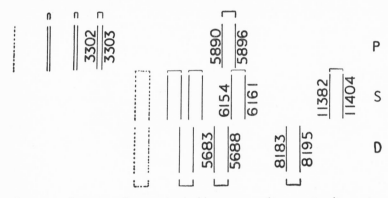

Fig. 19.5. Diagram to illustrate the doublet structure of important sodium series.

Thus, members of principal series were strong lines, members of the diffuse were lines with ill-defined edges, while sharp series lines were sharply defined. As this is not always the case, however, and as still other types of series are known, the only exact description of any series is to be found in the relation which describes it, as well as in its connection with other series.

Doublet, Triplet and Multiplet Series. The study of series is intimately bound up with another important fact which must now be explained. The student's attention has already been directed to the two yellow sodium lines (D_1 and D_2) in the flame spectrum. Now a glance at the arc spectrum of this element shows the presence of other pairs of lines. For many of these pairs the difference in the wave-numbers of the two lines is exactly the same, while for other pairs this difference becomes less, the farther one goes in the ultraviolet. Such pairs of lines are called *doublets.* Similar pairs occur in all the members of the sodium family, although in lithium the lines are so close that they appear unresolved in ordinary spectrographs. Now these doublet lines are all members of series. Thus in the sodium arc spectrum we have six important series: two principal—the first members of which are the D lines—two diffuse, and two sharp. The doublet separation is the same for all pairs belonging to the diffuse

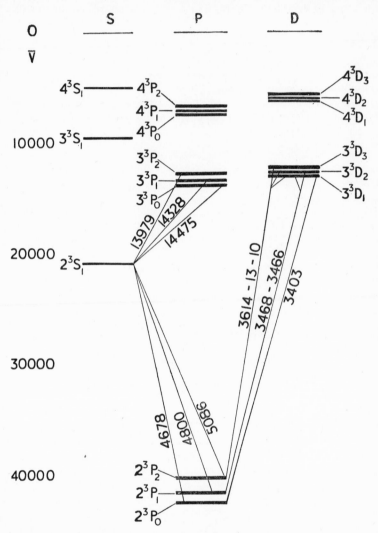

Fig. 19.6. Graphical representation of the sharp, principal and diffuse triplet series of cadmium.

and the sharp series, thus giving rise to parallel series, while, in the case of the principal series, the doublet separation gradually decreases until the two series reach a common limit.

Because of the comparatively small separation of the doublet pairs in the sodium series, it is not possible to represent them to scale by a diagram similar to Fig. 19.3. In Fig. 19.5, however, the general nature of the important sodium series has been indicated by assuming a much larger separation between the doublets than that which actually exists.

In other elements there are related lines appearing in triplets. In still others we may have quadruplets, quintets, etc.

19.2. On page 344 reference has been made to the Ritz combination law according to which the wave-number of a spectral line is equal to the difference between two terms. In one sense *term* values, therefore, are more fundamental than the wave-numbers of *lines*, and the analysis of a spectrum into series consists essentially in establishing term values, that is, in constructing diagrams like Fig. 19.4. The question now arises: What alteration must be made in such diagrams when we pass from singlet to multiplet series? Although a knowledge of the theoretical significance of spectral series is necessary before this question can be satisfactorily answered, at this stage we may indicate the chief change that is necessary, postponing further discussion until section 19.9.

As a concrete case, consider the principal, sharp and diffuse triplet series lines of cadmium, some of which are marked in Fig. 1, Plate IX, facing p. 352. The wave-numbers of all these lines can be represented as in Fig. 19.6 (drawn roughly to scale) by a series of single S term values, which we may designate mS, with m having successive integral values, just as in Fig. 19.4; a series of P term values, each of which consists of three sub-terms; and a series of D terms, each of which has also three sub-terms. To distinguish sub-terms the notation of page 344 must be extended. This is done by the use of subscripts and superscripts. Thus, in Fig. 19.6, the lowest group of P terms is designated 2^3P_0, 2^3P_1, and 2^3P_2. Here the serial number m has the value 2 and the three sub-levels are distinguished by the subscripts 0, 1, 2 at the lower right of P. The superscript 3 to the upper left of P is used simply to indicate that we are dealing with a triplet system. The next P group is designated 3^3P_0, 3^3P_1, 3^3P_2; the lowest D group 3^3D_1, 3^3D_2, 3^3D_3; and so on. Although the S terms are single, since they are part of the whole triplet system they are usually marked m^3S_1. The first

A Sharp Triplet of Cadmium

Wavelength	$\bar{\nu}$	Notation
5085.88	19656.8	$2^3P_2 - 2^3S_1$
4799.91	20827.9	$2^3P_1 - 2^3S_1$
4678.19	21369.8	$2^3P_0 - 2^3S_1$

three members of the sharp series of cadmium, that is, the lines whose wavelengths are 5086, 4800, 4678 (see Fig. 1, Plate IX) are therefore described as in the accompanying table.

Since both the P and the D terms occur in groups of three sub-terms, we might expect diffuse lines to occur in groups of nine. This would certainly be the case if each of the three D sub-terms combined with each of the three P sub-terms. Actually the D lines occur in groups of six, because a selection principle, which we shall discuss later (section 19.9), rules out three of the possible combinations. The first group of six D lines and their designation are in the following table.

A Diffuse Triplet of Cadmium

Wavelength	$\bar{\nu}$	Notation
3614.43	27659.0	$2^3P_2 - 3^3D_1$
3612.89	27670.8	$2^3P_2 - 3^3D_2$
3610.51	27689.0	$2^3P_2 - 3^3D_3$
3467.61	28830.1	$2^3P_1 - 3^3D_1$
3466.18	28842.0	$2^3P_1 - 3^3D_2$
3403.60	29372.3	$2^3P_0 - 3^3D_1$

In Fig. 1, Plate IX these six lines appear as three, because the dispersion of the spectrograph used in making the spectrogram was not great enough to separate 3614, 3613, and 3610, nor 3467.6 and 3466.2.

In cadmium, in addition to the foregoing triplet system of lines, there are many lines which belong to a singlet system. That is, we have a singlet S series, a singlet P series, a singlet D series, etc. and corresponding to these lines, a series of single S terms (marked m^1S_0), a series of single P terms (marked m^1P_1), and a series of single D terms (m^1D_2). To avoid confusion, the singlet system term values have not been included in Fig. 19.6.

The same ideas apply to the term analysis of a doublet system like that of sodium and the other alkali elements, where the wave-numbers of the S, P and D series lines can all be found from a series of single S term values; a series of double-valued P terms, and a series of double-valued D terms.* To distinguish the sub-levels of the P terms the subscripts $\frac{3}{2}$ and $\frac{1}{2}$ are used, whereas $\frac{5}{2}$ and $\frac{3}{2}$† are used to distinguish the D sub-levels. The D lines of sodium, that is, 5896 and 5890, the first members of the doublet P series, are described by

$$1^2S_{1/2} - 1^2P_{1/2} \qquad \text{and} \qquad 1^2S_{1/2} - 1^2P_{3/2}.‡$$

To represent completely, therefore, all the S, P and D doublet series of sodium, Fig. 19.4 should be extended in the same manner as has been done for a triplet system in Fig. 19.6. In the doublet system all S terms would remain single as in Fig. 19.4 but, in accordance with the notation already explained, would now be marked $m^2S_{1/2}$ (where $m = 1, 2, 3$ etc.); the P terms would all occur

---

* In some elements these double term values are too close to be separated.
† The significance of the half numbers will appear in section 19.10.
‡ The superscript 2 at the upper left of the letter indicates the doublet nature of the system.

in pairs marked $m^2P_{3/2}$ and $m^2P_{1/2}$; and the D terms in pairs marked $m^2D_{5/2}$ and $m^2D_{3/2}$. In the case of the element lithium, the doublet lines are all so close that the sub-terms appear as one in such diagrams. In passing it is interesting to note that in a chemical family like the alkalies, all of which give doublet spectra, the doublet separation steadily increases with increasing atomic weight. For example, if we take the separation (in wave-numbers) of the first pair of the principal series, we have 0.34 for lithium, 17.2 for sodium, 57.8 for potassium, 237 for rubidium, and 554 for caesium.

For convenience, the designation of sharp, principal and diffuse terms for singlet, doublet and triplet systems has been summarized in Table XV.

With respect to a singlet system it will be noted that this notation (which is now used internationally) differs slightly from that used in section 19.1. In accordance with this more modern usage, relations 19.07a, b and c would be written

$$\bar{\nu}_P = 1^1S_0 - m^1P_1$$

$$\bar{\nu}_D = 1^1P_1 - m^1D_2$$

$$\bar{\nu}_S = 1^1P_1 - m^1S_0.$$

Table XV.   Designation of Terms

Terms	Sharp	Principal	Diffuse
Singlet	m^1S_0	m^1P_1	m^1D_2
Doublet	$m^2S_{1/2}$	$m^2P_{3/2}$ $m^2P_{1/2}$	$m^2D_{5/2}$ $m^2D_{3/2}$
Triplet	m^3S_1	m^3P_2 m^3P_1 m^3P_0	m^3D_3 m^3D_2 m^3D_1

19.3. The general analysis which has been made of the spectra of elements shows: (1) In any system of series for a single element, we have often to consider more *types* than the sharp, principal, and diffuse; these are designated F, G, H, etc. (2) In addition to singlet, doublet and triplet systems, we have also, for the more complex spectra, quadruplet, quintet, sextet, etc. systems. Further discussion of such details is beyond the scope of this book and we shall conclude this section with a statement of two other interesting facts. In a given chemical family, for all elements the arc spectra are of either even or odd multiplicity—never both, but as we pass from one vertical column in the periodic table to the next, the character of the group alternates. Thus in the sodium family, doublets only occur in arc spectra; in the magnesium, triplets and singlets.

19.4. Quantum Defect. In Fig. 19.4 the lowest S, P and D terms are marked 1S, 1P and 1D, whereas in Fig. 19.6 they are marked 2S, 2P and 3D.

The question then arises, What determines the value of m for the lowest terms? Two things should be noted. (1) For calculations, all that matters is the value of $(m + c)$. For example (see Table XVII), the lowest D term in one of the sodium series is 12,276, from which $(m + c)$ equals 2.990. In calculations it is immaterial whether we take $m = 2$, $c = 0.990$; or $m = 1$, $c = 1.990$; or $m = 3$, $c = -0.010$. (2) As suggested in section 19.9, the number m is identified with the total quantum number n. In hydrogen, therefore, where to a first approximation $c = 0$, there is no ambiguity. For the lowest term m or $n = 1$.

With elements like sodium the same value of m is not always used. For theoretical reasons $(m + c)$ is often written $(n - \mu)$ where μ is the *quantum defect*. When μ is small as in the above D term where it is equal to 0.01, the term $N/(3 - \mu)^2$ differs only slightly from the hydrogen term $N/3^2$ and it is natural to designate the lowest D term $3D$. When $(m + c)$ or $(n - \mu)$ departs appreciably from integral values, as in the S and P terms of the foregoing sodium series, the choice of the lowest m is not always the same.

19.5. Bohr's Theory and Origin of Spectra.

The most striking evidence in favor of a quantum theory was given by the Danish physicist Niels Bohr, who in 1913 deduced from theoretical considerations the Balmer series relation for hydrogen spectral lines. As a foundation on which to base his views, Bohr accepted (1) the planetary view of the atom which Rutherford's work on alpha particles necessitates and (2) the idea of quanta of radiant energy. Since a planetary electron means an accelerated charge, the difficulties given at the end of the last chapter had to be met. This was done by making the bold assumption that an electron revolving around the nucleus of an atom could occupy *without radiating* certain definite orbital paths—non-radiating orbits or *stationary states* we shall call them. Now, while this view is nothing but a flat denial of one aspect of the electromagnetic theory (according to which accelerated charges must radiate), it is quite in accordance with the work of Planck on black body radiation.

In an orbit the ordinary laws of mechanics are supposed to hold, that is, the attraction of the nucleus for the electron provides the necessary central force to keep the latter in its path. In the normal state of a non-luminous gas or vapor, the electron occupies an innermost *stable* orbit. When, however, the gas or vapor is "excited" to luminosity by some external agency, the electron is moved farther away from the nucleus, to do which work must be done against the attraction of the nucleus. The total energy of the atom then increases having values E_1, E_2, E_3, ... E_n, as the electron occupies the first (or innermost orbit), the second, the third ... the nth orbit. According to the ideas we are now presenting, radiation results when, after such an increase in energy has been brought about, an electron drops back from an outer orbit to one nearer the nucleus. The frequency of the radiation is given by the condition (known as Bohr's *frequency condition*)

$$h\nu = W_n - W_k, \tag{19.08}$$

where W_n and W_k are the energy values corresponding to the nth and the kth orbit.

Since $\nu = c/\lambda$ we may write equation (19.08)

$$\frac{1}{\lambda} = \frac{1}{hc}(W_n - W_k). \tag{19.09}$$

On this view, then, *each wavelength corresponds to a definite change in energy values, or in what we may call energy levels* and, as we shall see presently, a spectral series consists of a group of wavelengths, each one of which results from a drop of the electron from an outer to the same inner orbit. Thus we might have a series consisting of wavelengths $\lambda_1, \lambda_2, \lambda_3, \lambda_4, \ldots$ where

$$\frac{1}{\lambda_1} = \frac{1}{hc}(W_2 - W_1); \; \frac{1}{\lambda_2} = \frac{1}{hc}(W_3 - W_1); \; \frac{1}{\lambda_3} = \frac{1}{hc}(W_4 - W_1); \text{ etc.}$$

Again, if the external agency exciting the atom to luminosity is such that the electron is displaced from the innermost orbit to the next, obviously only one subsequent change in energy value is possible; in other words, a single spectral line is emitted.

To fix the definite discrete orbits in which an electron may revolve without radiating, that is, to fix the energy levels, another condition is necessary. This is the so-called *quantum condition* according to which the angular momentum of the atom for the nth non-radiating orbit is $n \cdot (h/2\pi)$, where n can have only integral values, and h is Planck's constant. In thus restricting the angular momentum to multiples of a fundamental unit involving h, this physical quantity is said to be *quantized*.

Now let us apply these ideas to the hydrogen atom, in which case a single electron with negative charge e revolves in an orbit about a nucleus with positive charge $E = e$. In the simplest case the orbits are circular, and we shall so consider them in this elementary treatment. We shall also assume that, because the mass of the nucleus is over 1800 times that of the electron, it is at rest. Our problem then is to see what quantitative relations can be deduced, accepting the foregoing conditions.

Let a = radius of any orbit,
ω = angular velocity of electron.

Since the central attraction of the nucleus for the electron is Ee/a^2, we have, applying ordinary mechanics,

$$ma\omega^2 = \frac{Ee}{a^2} \quad \text{or} \quad ma^2\omega^2 = \frac{Ee}{a}. \tag{19.10}$$

Before the frequency condition can be applied, an expression giving the energy for any orbit must be found. Since a portion of the energy is potential, its magnitude must be measured with reference to some arbitrary zero, just as elevations are given with respect to sea-level as zero, or just as the potential energy of a raised weight is expressed with reference to its value at the surface of the earth. The arbitrary zero chosen is the state when the electron has been removed completely away from the attraction of the nucleus. *The potential energy for any orbit, therefore, bears a negative sign and is numerically less the farther the orbit is from the nucleus.*

If then $E_{pot.}$ = potential energy of the atom, we have (since the potential at a distance a from a charge E is E/a)

$$E_{pot.} = -\frac{Ee}{a}.$$

(19.11)

Again, the kinetic energy $E_{kin.}$ is given by

$$E_{kin.} = \tfrac{1}{2}mv^2$$

$$= \tfrac{1}{2}ma^2\omega^2.$$

(19.12)

$\therefore$ W, the total energy $= E_{pot.} + E_{kin.}$

$$= -\frac{Ee}{a} + \tfrac{1}{2}ma^2\omega^2$$

$$= -\frac{Ee}{2a}, \text{ from relation (19.10)}$$

or

$$= -\tfrac{1}{2}ma^2\omega^2.$$

This expression for the total energy then tells us that the *smaller a*, the radius of an orbit, the larger the (negative) number giving the value of the total energy. This is, of course, because of the zero chosen for the measure of the potential energy.

Next let us apply the quantum condition according to which

$$ma^2\omega \text{ (angular momentum)} = n \cdot \frac{h}{2\pi},$$

if a is the radius of the nth orbit.

Since $ma^2\omega^2 = eE/a$, by relation (19.10), we have at once

$$a\omega = \frac{2\pi eE}{nh}$$

(19.13)

or

$$\frac{eE}{a} = \frac{4\pi^2 me^2 E^2}{n^2 h^2}.$$

(19.14)

Therefore, if W_n = energy for the nth orbit,

$$W_n = -\tfrac{1}{2}\frac{4\pi^2 me^2 E^2}{n^2 h^2} = -\frac{2\pi^2 me^2 E^2}{n^2 h^2}.$$

(19.15)

In passing we note that, by relation (19.14),

PLATE IX

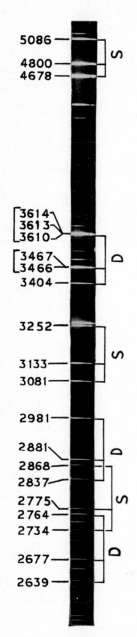

5086 —
4800 —
4678 —

S

3614
3613
3610

3467
3466
3404 —

D

3252 —

3133 —
3081 —

S

2981 —

2881
2868 —
2837

D

2775
2764 —
2734 —

S

2677 —

D

2639 —

Fig. 1. Cadmium arc
spectrum. (Quartz
Spectrograph)

Fig. 2. Electron diffraction pattern.
(G. P. Thomson)

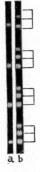

a b

Fig. 3. Fabry-Perot
fringes. (a) line with-
out structure; (b) line
with three components.
(E. Gwynne Jones)

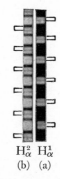

H_α^2 H_α^1
(b) (a)

Fig. 4. Fabry-Perot
fringes. (a) H_α^1 showing doublet structure;
(b) H_α^1 along with H_α^2.

H_α^2 H_α^1

Fig. 5. Grating photograph
of H_α^1 and H_α^2.
(Harris, Jost and Pearse)

$$a = \frac{n^2h^2}{4\pi^2meE}. \tag{19.16}$$

Since $e = 4.80 \times 10^{-10}$ and $E = e$ for the hydrogen atom, and since

$$h = 6.62 \times 10^{-27},$$

$$\frac{e}{m} = 5.3 \times 10^{17},$$

(all electrical units being in the electrostatic system), relation (19.16) gives for the first or innermost orbit the value

$$a = 0.53 \times 10^{-8} \text{ cm.}$$

This value is in good agreement with results for the radius of a hydrogen atom estimated in other ways.

Relation (19.16) also tells us that the radii of the orbits increase as the square of the natural numbers.

We are now in a position to apply the frequency condition (19.09)

$$\frac{1}{\lambda} = \frac{1}{hc} (W_n - W_k),$$

where λ is the emitted wavelength corresponding to an electron drop from the nth to the kth orbit, or less pictorially, to a change in the atomic energy of amount $W_n - W_k$. Using the value of W_n given by relation (19.15) this gives us

$$\frac{1}{\lambda} = \frac{1}{hc} \left(-\frac{2\pi^2me^2E^2}{n^2h^2} + \frac{2\pi^2me^2E^2}{k^2h^2} \right)$$

$$= \frac{2\pi^2me^2E^2}{h^3c} \left(\frac{1}{k^2} - \frac{1}{n^2} \right) \tag{19.17}$$

or, using the notation of section 19.1,

$$\bar{\nu} = \frac{2\pi^2me^2E^2}{h^3c} \left(\frac{1}{k^2} - \frac{1}{n^2} \right)$$

$$= N \left(\frac{1}{k^2} - \frac{1}{n^2} \right), \quad \text{where } N = \frac{2\pi^2me^2E^2}{h^3c}. \tag{19.18}$$

It will at once be noticed that this relation is of exactly the same form as that describing any of the hydrogen series given in section 19.1. Moreover, if k is taken equal to 2 (and if the value of N proves to be the same as the Rydberg constant), the relation is *identical* with the Balmer series formula. Now, since e, e/m, h and c are all fundamental quantities (whose magnitudes have already been given), and since $E = e$ in the hydrogen atom, the value of N can readily be calculated. On substituting the values of these constants, we find

$$N = \frac{2\pi^2me^4}{h^3c} = 1.09 \times 10^5 \text{ cm.}^{-1}$$

When this result is compared with the empirical value 109678 given in section 19.1, the striking agreement is apparent.

One great achievement of Bohr's theory then lies in the theoretical deduction of empirical series relations. Thus lines of the Lyman series arise when an electron drops from outer orbits to the innermost, or normal orbit, for which $k = 1$. For the emission of the Balmer series lines (those shown in Fig. 1, Plate II, facing p. 96), as already indicated, the final position of the electron is the second innermost ($k = 2$), while for the Paschen series the orbit corresponding to the limit of the series is the third ($k = 3$). In Fig. 19.7 these ideas are represented pictorially. While pictorial representations are often a great aid in grasping

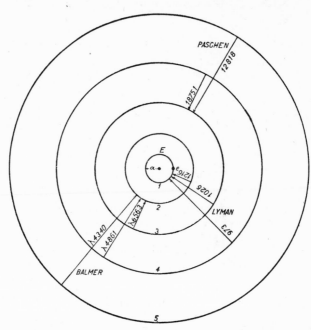

Fig. 19.7. Graphical representation of three hydrogen spectral series using electron orbits.

certain ideas, it is just as well for the student to be on his guard lest he give to these orbits a reality similar to that of concentric circular grooves in which marbles may roll around a center. Rather should he think of the orbits as representing definite energy values of the atomic system.

19.6. Bohr's theory of the origin of spectra had other remarkable successes, to a few of which a brief reference will be made. The first of these has to do with conclusions which follow when the mass of the nucleus is not considered to be infinite. In ordinary hydrogen it is known, from work which has nothing to do with spectroscopy, that M_H the mass of the atom is over eighteen hundred times m that of the electron, or that, to be exact,

$$\frac{M_H}{m} = 1838.$$

Actually, therefore, rotation takes place about the center of gravity of the nucleus and the electron, a point which, of course, is very close to the nucleus. When this fact is taken into consideration, and the same principles utilized as in the treatment for a stationary nucleus, it is found that

$$W_n = -\frac{2\pi^2\mu e^2 E^2}{n^2 h^2}, \quad \text{where } \mu = \frac{m}{1 + \dfrac{m}{M_H}}. \tag{19.19}$$

It follows that

$$N = \frac{2\pi^2\mu e^2 E^2}{h^3 c}$$

$$= \frac{2\pi^2 m e^2 E^2}{h^3 c} \cdot \frac{1}{1 + \dfrac{m}{M_H}}. \tag{19.20}$$

We see then that the value of N for hydrogen series (N_H we shall describe it) differs *slightly* from $(2\pi^2 m e^4)/(h^3 c)$, the value previously given, or what we shall now call N_∞, since it was determined on the assumption of infinite mass of the nucleus. Relation (19.20) may now be written

$$N_H = \frac{N_\infty}{1 + \dfrac{m}{M_H}}. \tag{19.21}$$

Suppose, now, that we have to do with an atom for which a single electron revolves about a nucleus *whose mass is different from that of hydrogen*. Such a system is provided when an atom of helium, normally consisting of two electrons attracted by a nucleus with a positive charge $E = 2e$, is ionized by the removal of one of the electrons. The resulting atom-ion is, therefore, hydrogen-like, and all the preceding theoretical considerations may be applied, so that we may write

$$N_{He} = \frac{N_\infty}{1 + \dfrac{m}{M_{He}}}, \tag{19.22}$$

where N_{He} = value of N for helium,
       M_{He} = mass of helium atom.
Combining relation (19.21) with (19.22), we have

$$\frac{N_{He}}{N_H} = \frac{1 + \dfrac{m}{M_H}}{1 + \dfrac{m}{M_{He}}} = \frac{1 + \dfrac{m}{M_H}}{1 + \dfrac{m}{3.98 M_H}}, \tag{19.23}$$

since $M_{He} = 3.98M_H$. But from the *empirical* spectral series relations for hydrogen and for helium, we have

$$N_{He} = 109722.26 \quad \text{and} \quad N_H = 109677.58.$$

Hence, treating M_H/m as an unknown quantity in relation (19.23), we find

$$\frac{M_H}{m} = 1838,$$

a value almost identical with that given previously as obtained by totally different methods.

19.7. Heavy Hydrogen and Application of Simple Bohr Theory. Another successful application of Bohr's original elementary theory is connected with the discovery of deuterium or heavy hydrogen. For a number of years it has been known that a large number of elements have two or more different kinds of atoms. The nucleus of each kind has the same positive charge and in each there is the same number of extranuclear electrons. But, although the atomic number (see section 17.2f) of each is thus the same, and the chemical properties are often identical, the masses are different. For example, chlorine, whose atomic weight as determined chemically is 35.46, is really a mixture of two kinds of chlorine, one of atomic weight 35, and the other, 37. Chlorine is said to have two *isotopes*, that is, to be a mixture of two different kinds of atoms which occupy the same place in the periodic table. Mercury, atomic number 80, atomic weight 200.61, has isotopes of atomic weight 196, 198, 199, 200, 201, 202 and 204; lithium, atomic number 3, atomic weight 6.94, has isotopes of atomic weight 6 and 7; and so on for many other elements.

Before 1929 it was considered that hydrogen had only one group of atoms because at that time there was almost perfect agreement between its atomic weight determined by chemical methods (which give only an average value when isotopes are present) and that determined by the mass spectrograph (a purely physical means which permits a measurement of the atomic weight of each isotope which may exist). In that year, however, it was shown (because of the discovery of isotopes in oxygen) that in reality there was a discrepancy of about 2 parts in 10,000 between the chemical and the physical values of the atomic weight of hydrogen. Birge and Menzel (United States) suggested that this discrepancy was due to the presence in ordinary hydrogen of a small amount of an isotope of atomic weight 2. Urey, Brickwedde, and Murphy, working at Princeton University, set out to look for such an isotope and in 1932 announced its discovery in a paper published in the *Physical Review*—a paper which is one of the classics in this era of physics.

From Bohr's elementary theory it is easy to predict the separation of corresponding spectral lines arising from the two kinds of hydrogen. Take, for example, H_α, the first line of the Balmer series. Using relation (19.02), and (19.21), we can write

$$\frac{1}{\lambda} = \frac{N_\infty}{1 + \dfrac{m}{M_H}} \left(\frac{1}{2^2} - \frac{1}{3^2} \right).$$

Now if hydrogen has two isotopes with $M_{H_1} = 1$ and $M_{H_2} = 2$, there are two corresponding wavelengths, H_α^1 and H_α^2, we shall call them, and it is a matter largely of arithmetic to show that if

$$\lambda \text{ for } H_\alpha^1 = 6562.79 \text{ A},$$

then $\qquad\qquad \lambda \text{ for } H_\alpha^2 = 6561.00 \text{ A}.$

The two wavelengths, therefore, according to calculation based on Bohr's simple theory, differ by 1.79 angstroms. Using a concave grating, Urey, Brickwedde, and Murphy showed that H_α^1 was accompanied by the companion line H_α^2 separated from it by this amount. Subsequently, means were found not only of increasing the concentration but also of preparing pure samples of the heavy isotope, to which the name deuterium has been given. (Although deuterium is called an isotope of hydrogen, it is well to note that its properties are by no means identical with those of the lighter isotope.)

Figure 5, Plate IX, facing p. 352, is a reproduction of a grating photograph,* which shows clearly H_α^1 and H_α^2. Reference has already been made to the Fabry-Perot photographs shown in Fig. 4, Plate IX. We may note again, however, that in Fig. 4(a), the set of fringes is due to H_α^1, whereas in Fig. 4(b), the intermediate set arises from H_α^2.

19.8. Another success of Bohr's theory has to do with the spectrum of ionized helium. Consider again an atom of this helium, for which, as already pointed out, $E = 2e$. Making use of the value of W_n given by relation (19.19), we have for the spectral series relation

$$\bar{\nu} = \frac{2\pi^2 \mu e^2 E^2}{h^3 c} \left(\frac{1}{k^2} - \frac{1}{n^2} \right)$$

$$= \frac{2\pi^2 m e^2 4 e^2}{h^3 c} \cdot \frac{1}{1 + \dfrac{m}{M_{He}}} \left(\frac{1}{k^2} - \frac{1}{n^2} \right)$$

$$= 4 N_{He} \left(\frac{1}{k^2} - \frac{1}{n^2} \right). \qquad (19.24)$$

A particular series for ionized helium is then given by $k = 4$, $n = 5, 6, 7, 8, 9, 10, \ldots$. If we consider only the members of this series which have even values of n equal to $2n'$, where $n' = 3, 4, 5, 6, \ldots$, we can then write

*Reproduced through the kindness of Dr. R. W. B. Pearse, of the Imperial College, London.

$$\bar{\nu} = 4N_{He}\left(\frac{1}{4^2} - \frac{1}{(2n')^2}\right)$$

$$= N_{He}\left(\frac{1}{2^2} - \frac{1}{n'^2}\right), \tag{19.25}$$

a relation identical with that for the Balmer series except for the slight difference between N_H and N_{He}. In other words, Bohr's theory *predicts* that, in the spectrum of helium, there should be lines almost identical with the Balmer hydrogen lines. Now, as a matter of fact, when helium is subjected to a strong electric discharge, spectral lines with wavelengths almost equal to these hydrogen lines *are* observed.

When $k = 3$, we have another spectral series for ionized helium. On giving n successive integral values, wavelengths are obtained which agree with lines, some observed by Fowler (England), others predicted by Rydberg (Germany), and at one time ascribed by both these experimenters to luminous hydrogen. Bohr's theory then leaves little doubt that the lines Fowler observed are due to helium.

Relation (19.24) also indicates that, since $E = 2e$, the Rydberg constant has the value $4N$ for ionized helium, or to be more exact, $4N_{He}$. Now it is a very significant fact that, before the advent of the Bohr theory, Fowler had shown that, to express correctly the series relations for many enhanced spark lines (section 17.4), the constant $4N$ was necessary. Bohr's view provided the explanation. Such lines are due to an element in the ionized state, while arc lines, as briefly indicated in section 17.4, arise from the atom in the neutral state. Later spectroscopic investigation has shown that, for the same element, there can exist *several* series of spark lines, for which the constants are 2^2N, 3^2N, 4^2N .... These exist in the case of atoms from which one, or two, or three or even more electrons can be removed. Singly, doubly, trebly, multiple-ionized atoms can then exist, with corresponding constants 2^2N, 3^2N .....

It is evident, then, that Bohr's theory, which accepts quanta, which assumes that accelerated charges need not radiate, which quantizes angular momentum, is responsible for an amazing advance in the interpretation of facts in spectroscopy. Its successes give overwhelming support to the view that, for the satisfactory explanation of emission processes, a quantum theory is necessary. Bohr's theory provided the foundation on which later a vast structure has been erected by theoretical physicists. The Zeeman effect, the Stark effect, and the fine structure of spectral lines have been "explained" utilizing principles of a quantum mechanics. In many respects, points of view have constantly changed, but throughout all the development, so far as the origin of spectra is concerned, there remains at least one big fundamental conception, and that is, *the identification of spectral terms with energy levels*. While mathematical considerations cannot so readily be applied to the more complicated spectra of elements with several electrons, there can be no doubt that the difference in terms which gives the wave-number of a spectral line represents a difference in the energies of two states of the atomic system. In the next chapter this point of view will be further discussed, together with additional evidence in support of it.

19.9. A Vector Model of the Atom and Further Interpretation of Spectral Series. It will be recalled that, according to Bohr's simple theory for the hydrogen atom, possible orbital paths were fixed according to the quantum condition

$$\text{angular momentum} = n \cdot \frac{h}{2\pi},$$

where n has integral values 1, 2, 3, ... Moreover, for any given orbit, the corresponding total energy, as shown by relation (19.15), depends on the value of n. We may, therefore, conveniently designate different terms or energy levels by values of n; or, alternately, we may describe the orbit in which an electron is revolving by the value of n. As we have seen, such a picture enables us to interpret the various spectral series of hydrogen.

When we try to interpret the different types of series in an element like sodium, or to show why hydrogen spectral lines are in reality close doublets (see again, Fig. 4(a), Plate IX, facing p. 352), the details of this picture must be altered. This was first done by Sommerfeld (Germany) and W. Wilson (Great Britain) by a consideration of the elliptical orbits in which an electron may revolve about a nucleus. Mathematical analysis shows that, for *each* circular orbit, there is a group of elliptical orbits, *for all of which, to a first approximation,* the total energy is the same as that given by Bohr's simple theory for the circular orbit. To distinguish between the various elliptical orbits in a particular group of this sort, as well as between different groups, two quantum numbers are necessary. A single group is designated by n, the same number used to designate a Bohr circular orbit, but now n is called the *total quantum number*. The individual orbits in a single group are distinguished by the value of a number represented by k and called the *azimuthal quantum number*. This quantum number, which may have integral values ranging from 1 to n, is defined by the relation

$$\text{angular momentum} = k \cdot \frac{h}{2\pi}.$$

The mathematical analysis shows that

$$\frac{k}{n} = \frac{\text{minor axis of ellipse}}{\text{major axis of ellipse}}.$$

We see, then, that (1) in any given group, the most elliptical orbit is that for which $k = 1$, and (2) when $k = n$, we have the Bohr circular orbit with the same quantum condition as given in section 19.5. To describe a particular orbit, therefore, values of both n and k must be known, and we may conveniently designate the orbit by the symbol n_k. In Table XVI all possible orbits are given for $n = 1, 2, 3$ and 4.

Table XVI.   Elliptical and Circular Orbits

n	k	Orbit
1	1	1_1
2	1, 2	$2_1, 2_2$
3	1, 2, 3	$3_1, 3_2, 3_3$
4	1, 2, 3, 4	$4_1, 4_2, 4_3, 4_4$

A spectral line is emitted when an electron passes from any orbit to another one of lesser energy. In the case of hydrogen, each of the transitions from either 3_1, 3_2, or 3_3 to 2_1 or 2_2 gives rise to the same line (H_α) because (but again *only to a first approximation*) the total energy depends only on $n = 3$ for the first state and $n = 2$ for the second.

In the case of an element like sodium, however, the energy value depends on both n and k. In this element, of atomic number 11, radiation is emitted as a result of the transitions from one orbit to another of a single outer valency electron which revolves about the nucleus of the atom and 10 inner electrons. The combination of the nucleus, with its positive charge of 11 units, plus the 10 inner electrons, is sometimes called the *core* of the atom. If an electron revolves in a path which is always well outside the core, then the situation is very similar to that of the hydrogen atom, for the *outside* effect of the core on the valency electron is almost exactly the same as that of a single positive charge (the resultant of $+11$ on the nucleus and -10 on the inner electrons). If, however, the valency electron in its orbit penetrates the core, the case is very different from that of the hydrogen atom and the energy values are greatly altered as compared with those of hydrogen terms.

The chance of the valency electron penetrating the core depends on two things: (1) the value of n; (2) the degree of ellipticity of the orbit, that is, the value of k. If n is great enough, that is, if the orbits are far enough out, the electron will not penetrate the core for any ellipticity. For smaller orbits, however, that is, for small values of n, the more elliptical the orbit, the greater the degree of penetration. Hence, the smaller k, the greater the penetration and the greater the departure of term values from corresponding hydrogen terms. Now the empirical analysis of such spectral series as those of sodium shows that S terms differ from hydrogen values more than P terms, and P term values more than D terms. The point is illustrated by the actual term values given in Table XVII. It is natural, therefore, to associate S terms with values of $k = 1$;* P terms with $k = 2$; D terms with $k = 3$; and so on for other series of terms,

---

* Subsequent theoretical developments made it desirable to replace k by l, where $l = k - 1$. Thus, for S terms, $l = 0$; for P terms, $l = 1$; for D terms, $l = 2$.

which, for the sake of simplicity, have been omitted. For the same reason all n_1 electron orbits are often described by the symbol ns; n_2 orbits by the symbol np; n_3 orbits by nd. That is, capital letters are used to designate *term* values and the corresponding small letters to represent electron *orbits*.

Table XVII. Comparison of Some Hydrogen and Sodium Term Values

n	Hydrogen*	Sodium		
		S	P	D
3	12186	41449	24476	12276
4	6855	15709	11176	6900
5	4387	8248	6406	4412
6	3047	5077	4151	3062
7	2238	3437	2907	2248

* These are found at once from $\dfrac{N}{3^2}$, $\dfrac{N}{4^2}$, $\dfrac{N}{5^2}$, etc., where $N = 109678$.

First Selection Principle. Although the wave-number of every spectral line is equal to the difference between two terms, the converse is not true. The difference between every two terms does not always give rise to a spectral line. For example, we do not encounter observed spectrum lines corresponding to differences between S and D terms. An examination of the lines which actually are observed leads to a rule, known as the first *selection principle*, according to which electron transitions take place only when the change in k (or in $l = k - 1$) is ± 1. For example, we observe spectral lines for transitions from $S(l = 0)$ to $P(l = 1)$ terms, or from $D(l = 2)$ to P terms but not from S to S or S to D. Occasionally, in the presence of strong electric fields, faint lines occur in violation of this principle.

19.10. Doublet Fine Structure. In section 19.2 it was pointed out that in the S, P, and D spectra series of the alkali elements, the lines occur in pairs or doublets. In the energy level or term diagrams for these elements, all P and D levels* are accordingly double, that is, for each value of n there are two sub-levels. In the short hand notation for spectral terms described in that section these sub-levels were distinguished by the use of subscripts. For example, the two sub-levels of the nth P term were there described as $nP_{3/2}$ and $nP_{1/2}$, n replacing m.

To interpret these sub-levels in terms of a model atom it is necessary to introduce still another quantum number. This is done (1) by ascribing to the valency electron a spin with an angular momentum equal to $\pm \dfrac{1}{2} \cdot \dfrac{h}{2\pi}$ (+ for ro-

*In some of the elements the terms are too close to be separated.

tation in one sense, — for rotation in the opposite); (2) by ascribing to the atom as a whole an angular momentum equal to $j \cdot \dfrac{h}{2\pi}$, where j is called the *inner quantum number.* To obtain the angular momentum of the whole atom, that is, the value of j, the spin momentum of the electron must be combined vectorially with the orbital angular momentum, which according to modern quantum mechanics is $l \cdot \dfrac{h}{2\pi}$. As already noted, l is related to the azimuthal quantum number k, by the simple relation $l = k - 1$. (Since a spinning electric charge gives rise to a magnetic field and an orbital motion of a charge is equivalent to a current with a resulting magnetic field, the spin and orbital momenta combine because of the interaction of these two magnetic fields.)

In the case of a single valency electron, because of the two possible directions of spin, for each orbit we obtain in general two values of j given by

$$j = l + \tfrac{1}{2} \quad \text{and} \quad j = l - \tfrac{1}{2}.$$

For S term values, for which $k = 1$ or $l = 0$, j can have only the value $\tfrac{1}{2}$, a negative value being inadmissible; hence S terms are single. This corresponds to the $^2S_{1/2}$ designation of section 19.2. For all P terms ($k = 2$ or $l = 1$) j has values $1 + \tfrac{1}{2}$ and $1 - \tfrac{1}{2}$, that is, $\tfrac{3}{2}$ and $\tfrac{1}{2}$ and P terms are double. These correspond to the $^2P_{3/2}$ and $^2P_{1/2}$ designation. For D terms ($k = 3$ or $l = 2$) we have $^2D_{5/2}$ and $^2D_{3/2}$.

Second Selection Principle. Transitions between different sub-levels are restricted according to this principle which states that only those occur for which the change in j is ± 1 or 0. For example, transitions $^2D_{5/2}$ to $^2P_{3/2}$; $^2D_{3/2}$ to $^2P_{3/2}$; $^2D_{3/2}$ to $^2P_{1/2}$ are allowable but not $^2D_{5/2}$ to $^2P_{1/2}$, for in the last case the change in j is $\tfrac{5}{2} - \tfrac{1}{2}$ or 2. Reference has already been made to this principle in connection with the discussion of a cadmium triplet in section 19.2.

The two selection principles may conveniently be summarized as follows.

$$\Delta l = \pm 1 \quad \text{and}$$
$$\Delta j = \pm 1 \quad \text{and} \quad 0,$$

where Δl = change in l and Δj = change in j.

Doublet or Fine Structure of Hydrogen. In section 9.10 it has already been pointed out that the analysis of the Balmer series lines of hydrogen (for example, either H_α^1 or H_α^2) by a Fabry-Perot étalon shows that each line is a close doublet (see again, Plate IX, Fig. 4 (a) and (b), facing p. 352). The doublet nature of these lines was first explained by Sommerfeld in connection with his work on elliptical orbits. When allowance is made for the fact that the mass of an electron varies with its velocity it is not difficult to show that the total energy for all elliptical orbits of the same total quantum number n is constant only to a first approximation. The solution which takes into account this relativity change of mass with velocity introduces a small correcting term whose value depends on l. The total energy of a 3_1 orbit then differs slightly from a 3_2 or a 3_3 orbit, and the value of H_α^1 as obtained from the transition 3_3 to 2_2 is not quite the same as its value for the transition 3_1 to 2_2 or for 3_2 to 2_1. When the first selection principle ($\Delta l = \pm 1$) is applied to all possible transitions between $n = 3$ and $n = 2$ orbits, it is easy to see that H_α^1 should have three components, corresponding to changes in l values 3 to 2, 2 to 1 and 1 to 2. Although early experimental work revealed only the doublet structure to which reference has been made, three components were later observed, using heavy hydrogen at low temperature.

With the advent of the spinning electron and the more recent quantum mechanics, another and more accurate explanation of the fine structure of the hydrogen lines can be given. In this work both the relativity change in mass and the spin of the electron are taken into consideration. Strangely enough the two theories lead to the same numerical values of the energy levels. There is this difference, however, that more components are predicted by the newer theory. In the case of the fine structure of ionized helium (a hydrogen-like atom) the observed fine structure agrees better with the predictions of the second theory.

19.11. Triplet and Associated Singlet System. An outline only is possible of the interpretation of a triplet system such as that of cadmium (section 19.2). The same quantum numbers are used, although not quite so simply, for with such elements we have to deal with two valency electrons. The resultant angular momentum of the atom as a whole is obtained: (1) by combining the spin momentum of each electron to get a resultant spin $S*(h/2\pi)$; (2) by combining the two orbital momenta to obtain a resultant $L \cdot (h/2\pi)$.

Since the spin momentum of a single electron is $\pm\frac{1}{2}(h/2\pi)$, the values of S can be only 1 or 0, that is, $\frac{1}{2} + \frac{1}{2}$ or $\frac{1}{2} - \frac{1}{2}$.

If the l values of each electron are designated l_1 and l_2, then the vectorial combination gives results such as are shown in Table XVIII.

Table XVIII.

l_1	l_2	$L*$
1	1	0, 1, 2
1	2	1, 2, 3
2	2	0, 1, 2, 3, 4

* In the vectorial combination of two integral quantities P and Q, where $P \geqq Q$, and the resultant can take only integral values, these values are $P + Q$, $P + Q - 1$, ... $P - Q$.

To find the resultant angular momentum of the atom as a whole, that is, the value of $J \cdot (h/2\pi)$, the S values (resultant spin) must be combined vectorially

* This letter S has nothing to do with the S used to designate a sharp term.

with the L values (resultant orbital). If we confine our attention to L values equal to 0, 1, and 2, possible J values are given in Table XIX.

Table XIX.

S	L	J	Term
1	0	1	$^3S_1$
1	1	0	$^3P_0$
		1	$^3P_1$
		2	$^3P_2$
1	2	1	$^3D_1$
		2	$^3D_2$
		3	$^3D_3$
0	0	0	$^1S_0$
0	1	1	$^1P_1$
0	2	2	$^1D_2$

Just as in the case of a single valency electron values of $l = 0, 1, 2$ correspond to S, P, and D terms respectively, so for two valency electrons $L = 0, 1, 2$, corresponds to S, P, and D terms. It will be noticed also that for S (resultant spin) values equal to 1, we have a triplet system, that is, three sub-levels for P and D terms, whereas for S values equal to 0, we have a singlet system.

To pursue this subject further would bring us far beyond the scope of this book, but it is hoped that the preceding outline will give the student a general idea of the interpretation of series spectra in terms of a model atom and quantum ideas.

19.12. Hyperfine Structure (H.F.S.). The separation of the components of a doublet may be so small that they appear as a single line in an ordinary spectrograph (for example, the lithium red line 6708 A which is in reality two wavelengths $1^2S_{1/2} - 1^2P_{1/2}$ and $1^2S_{1/2} - 1^2P_{3/2}$); or they may appear as two widely separated lines (for example, the corresponding lines of rubidium with wavelengths 8521 A and 8943 A). The term *fine structure* refers to this general complexity which can be explained in terms of the three quantum numbers, n, l, and j (or n, L, and J).

When many spectral lines are examined with a Fabry-Perot étalon or any instrument of sufficiently large resolving power and dispersion, they exhibit structure which cannot be explained in terms of these quantum numbers, the separation between components being, in general, many times less than in fine structure. Good illustrations are provided in Fig. 3(b), Plate IX, facing p. 352, where the three components of the bismuth II line 6600 A are an example of *hyperfine structure* (H.F.S.); and in Fig.(a), Plate I (frontispiece), which shows the structure of the green line 5461 when the source is a lamp containing ordinary mercury vapor. Because of the small separation of the component spectral lines analysis can be made only with instruments of high resolving power. H.F.S. is due to the vectorial combination of J values with a quantized *nuclear* spin moment designated by the quantum number I, the resultant quantized hyperfine states being denoted by the quantum number F. It should be evident that the study of H.F.S. is one of the important means of obtaining information about the nucleus of the atom.

The experimental study of H.F.S. is complicated by *isotope shifts*, that is, minute alterations in the component structure arising from the presence of different isotopes. In mercury, for example, with isotopes having mass numbers 196, 198, 199, 200, 202, and 204, slight shifts in the position of component lines are to be expected due to mass alone, and there may be other complicating factors. In section 9.12 reference has already been made to the use of mercury 198 as a pure monochromatic source.

(*N.B.* For problems relating to spectral series see end of next chapter.)

XX

Radiation Potentials; Absorption and Band Spectra

20.1. Radiating Potentials. In the case of the hydrogen spectrum, we have seen in the last chapter that, according to Bohr's theoretical considerations, the empirical spectral series relation

$$\bar{\nu} = \frac{N}{k^2} - \frac{N}{n^2}$$

is an expression of the frequency condition,

$$h\nu = W_n - W_k.$$

On this view, in support of which much evidence was given, a spectral term is therefore a measure of the energy of a corresponding state or level of the atom. When we turn to the series relations of other elements, *for all of which wave-numbers are expressed as the difference between two terms*, it is natural to assume that the same general ideas hold, that is, that the spectral series relation is just a statement of the frequency condition. Each term then corresponds to a particular energy state or level, the highest numerical term being a measure of the energy of the atom in its normal state. These energy changes are the result of the displacement of an outer *valency* electron (and possibly, in special cases, more than one) from its normal position, because of some external exciting agency. In sodium, for example, there is good evidence that the nucleus is surrounded by eleven electrons, changes in the level of the outermost one being responsible for the emission of observed spectral lines. If the atom is only feebly excited, this outer electron may be displaced just enough to cause an energy change from the most stable to the next level, in which case the subsequent radiation, when the electron reverts to its normal position, consists of a single wavelength, the familiar yellow D line. (Actually two lines D_1 and D_2 close together are emitted, thus showing the existence of two sub-levels close together.)

The soundness of the view which identifies terms with energy levels may be seen by a consideration of the following numerical example. The D lines of sodium are the first members of a principal doublet series described by the relation

$$\bar{\nu} = 41449 - \text{variable term.}$$

For the D_1 line, $\lambda = 5896$ A, we have

$$\bar{\nu} = 41449 - 24493.$$

For the D_2 line, $\lambda = 5890$ A, we have

$$\bar{\nu} = 41449 - 24476.$$

If, now, we take either of these wavelengths, and rewrite this relation in energy units, we have (using D_1)

$$h\nu = hc\bar{\nu} = hc(41449 - 24493).$$

Suppose, now, that this amount of energy is communicated to a sodium atom (which subsequently radiates 5896) as a result of bombardment by an electron. The potential V through which the electron must fall to acquire the necessary amount of energy is then given by

$$Ve = hc\bar{\nu} = hc(41449 - 24493),$$

from which, if we substitute the values of e, h, and c already given we obtain

$$V = 2.093 \text{ volts.}$$

If the term values for D_2 are used, we obtain $V = 2.095$ volts. Before sodium vapor can be excited to emit the characteristic yellow lines, therefore, each atom must have communicated to it an amount of energy equal to that possessed by an electron which has fallen through a potential difference of this amount. But this is something which may be tested by actual experiment, using a method similar to that described in (f) of section 17.2, for magnesium. Results obtained give the value of $V = 2.12$ volts, in excellent agreement with the calculated value.

The case of the D lines of sodium is, in reality, just another illustration similar to that given in the last chapter when the emission of a single line spectrum of mercury vapor was interpreted on a quantum basis. The additional point which is now being emphasized is that the quantum is emitted as a result of a change in the energy of an atom from one value or level to another, brought about by an external agency, radiation resulting when the system reverts to the original level.

The value of the energy difference corresponding to the emission of a spectral line is frequently expressed in terms of the potential difference through which an electron must fall in order to acquire such an amount of energy, and hence, as so many volts. In the example worked out, the emission of D light by sodium is the result of an energy change equivalent to 2.1 volts, or corresponds to what is called a *radiating* or *excitation potential* of 2.1 volts.

The second member in the series for which D_1 is the first is $\lambda\,3303$, described by

$$\bar{\nu} = 41499 - 11181.$$

By applying exactly the same method, the corresponding radiating potential is found to be 3.74 volts. Actually, as already pointed out more than once, it has been shown experimentally that more and more lines appear with increasing energy of colliding electrons, and there are numerous cases showing the agreement between experimental and calculated values.

20.2. Ionization Potential. In any spectral series the values of the *variable* term gradually decrease, eventually becoming equal to zero. The limit of the series obviously represents the lowest energy level (highest numerical value) to which, for that particular series, the atom always reverts. When there are several different series for a given atom, as there invariably are, then the largest numerical limit must correspond to the normal state of the atom, and hence must be a measure of the work necessary to remove the electron to the zero level, that is, from its normal state entirely away from the attraction of the nucleus. When the electron has been so removed, the atom is ionized, and the work necessary to do so, expressed in equivalent volts, is called the *ionization potential*. Obviously its value may be calculated in the same manner as has been done for radiating potentials. Thus, to consider sodium once more, of the various spectral series for this element, the limit of the principal series has the largest numerical value, namely, 41449. Hence if V is the ionization potential,

$$Ve = h.c.\ 41449,*$$

from which $\qquad\qquad\qquad V = 5.12 \text{ volts.}$

Now there are various ways of observing experimentally the value of V for which colliding electrons ionize a gas or vapor. In the case of sodium, the value observed is 5.13 volts, showing again remarkable agreement between theory and experiment.

20.3. Energy Diagrams. It should now be evident that the special series diagrams, such as those shown in Figs. 19.2 and 19.4, may also be called energy diagrams. Indeed, that is the usual name given to such figures, on which, frequently, excitation potentials are marked. Thus Fig. 20.1, which is identical with a portion of Fig. 19.2, is an energy diagram for the hydrogen atom showing the wave-numbers of a few energy levels, excitation potentials, and wavelengths. Fig. 20.2 shows only a very few of the numerous levels for the sodium atom with the same information as in the case of hydrogen.

---

* Since the value of $\dfrac{hc}{e} = \dfrac{1}{2.42 \times 10^6}$, this and the corresponding similar relation for radiating potentials always reduce to

$$V = \frac{\text{wave-number}}{8.1 \times 10^3} \text{ volts, \quad or} \quad = \frac{1.23 \times 10^4}{\text{wavelength in angstroms}}.$$

20.4. Resonance Radiation. Some years before the advent of Bohr's theory it was known that certain vapors, when illuminated by light of a suitable kind, re-emitted light of the same kind in all directions. To give a concrete illustration, Wood of Johns Hopkins University, showed that, when sodium vapor was illuminated by incident D light, the vapor re-emitted D light in all directions. To such a re-emission he gave the name *resonance radiation*. On Bohr's theory the explanation is not far to seek, for it is evidently just a case of supplying the energy necessary to raise an electron from the normal to the next level, not by colliding electrons but by incident radiant energy. A quantum $h\nu$ is absorbed, (where ν is the frequency of the incident light), the energy is just sufficient to change the level from the innermost to the next, after which the reverse change results in the emission of a quantum of the same frequency. In itself this fact is not necessarily a confirmation of the truth of Bohr's theory, for, on the older views, it may be considered (as has already been done in section 17.5) just a case of the well-known phenomenon of resonance. When, however, one considers the fact that excitation of sodium vapor by light of wavelengths λ 3303 and λ 3302 (second members of the principal sodium series), also causes the emission of the D lines, and when one understands certain facts relating to absorption spectra, it will be seen that the idea of energy levels is strongly supported.

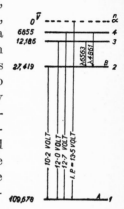

Fig. 20.1. Diagram of a few hydrogen terms with corresponding excitation potentials.

20.5. Absorption Spectra. To understand this additional evidence, suppose a beam of light from a source emitting a wide continuous range of wavelengths traverses a column of sodium vapor in an exhausted tube. When such a beam, on emergence from the tube, is analyzed by a spectroscope or spectrograph, the D lines and other members of the principal series appear as narrow black absorption lines, whereas *there is no absorption of any of the members of the sharp and the diffuse series*. The explanation of the absorption of one series and non-absorption of others can readily be given in terms of energy levels. Since in normal, that is, unexcited sodium atoms, the valency electron is in an orbit corresponding to the innermost level (marked A in Fig. 20.2), it can be displaced as a result of absorption of light, only by those wavelengths which correspond to a transition from some higher level to this normal level. A glance at the energy diagram will show that this is the case for all members of the principal series, such as 5896 and 3303, but not for lines of the other two important series. Thus wavelengths 8195 and 8183, the first pair of the diffuse series, arise from a transition from level C * (Fig. 20.2) to level B.* Hence the absorption of these wavelengths

* In reality, we have two levels close together at B and at C. To keep the diagram as simple as possible only one has been drawn.

could only raise the level from B to C, and, therefore, since in *normal* sodium no level B exists, such absorption is not possible. On the other hand, any of the members of the principal series can raise by absorption the level from A to some higher level and are, therefore, present in the absorption spectrum. For the same reason, absorption by such wavelengths as 3303 and 3302 can put the atom in such a state that it may subsequently radiate the D lines. Thus the absorption of 3303 and 3302 raises the level to D, from which the electron may return to A in stages, the last one being that from level B to level A, which corresponds to the emission of D light.

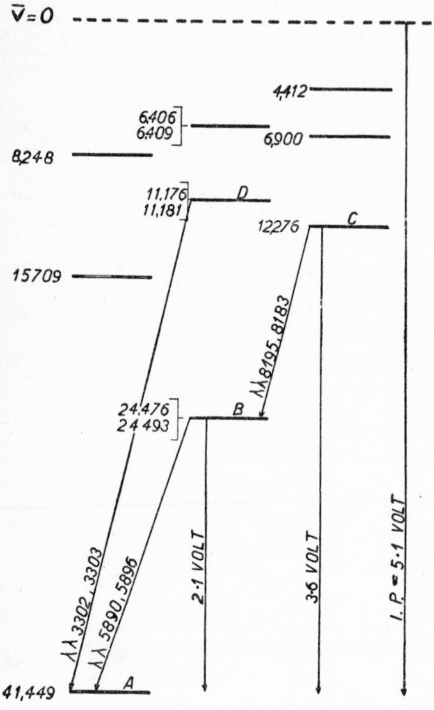

A striking confirmation of the same ideas is provided by experiments on the absorption spectrum of hydrogen. Normal unexcited hydrogen does not absorb the members of the Balmer series, because, before any of such wavelengths can be absorbed, the electron must be in an orbit corresponding to energy level B, Fig. 20.1. In normal atoms, however, the electrons are in orbits corresponding to level A. On the other hand, if, during the absorption experiments, hydrogen is electrically excited (for example, by passing a discharge through it), it was shown by Ladenburg that the Balmer series lines are then absorbed. In this case, as a result of electrical excitation, a large number of hydrogen atoms are in a state where the

Fig. 20.2. Diagram of a few sodium terms with corresponding excitation potentials.

electron has been removed from the normal orbit to that corresponding to level B, and absorption of the members of the Balmer series is then possible. It is interesting to note that this experiment was first performed before the idea of energy levels came into existence.

20.6. Band Spectra. In section 17.3, where a brief reference was made to band spectra, it was pointed out that a single band is characterized by a group of lines so close together that in an instrument of small dispersion the lines fuse together, a whole group of such bands then having a fluted appearance, as shown in Fig. 3, Plate III, facing p. 97. With sufficient dispersion, the individual members of a single band are apparent, frequently separated by intervals which become less and less as an edge, called the band head, is approached. Examine, again, the individual band shown in Fig. 4, Plate III. Before the days of quantum theories, a certain amount of analysis of band spectra had been undertaken, notably by Deslandres (France), and it had been shown, among other things, that the wave-numbers for band heads could be expressed by an empirical relation involving constants and two variable integral numbers. No adequate explanation of the origin of bands was forthcoming, however, until the application of quantum principles was made. The problem, in some respects, is more complex than that of line spectra, for in all cases band spectra result from a luminous substance in the *molecular* state. Remarkable progress has been made, however, by considering radiation as the result of changes in energy values for different states of the molecule, and by quantizing quantities, just as in the case of the atom and line spectra. In the remainder of this chapter a brief summary of the basic ideas will be given.

Consider a diatomic molecule, that is, a union of two atoms, the nuclei and surrounding electrons being so arranged that equilibrium and stability result. An external "exciting" agency may bring about three general changes in such a system: (1) one or more electrons may be displaced from a lower to a higher energy level as in the case of an atom, that is, there may be an electronic change; (2) the two nuclei may be displaced so as subsequently to vibrate with certain amplitudes, that is, with definite amounts of *vibrational* energy; (3) the system may be made to rotate about an axis of symmetry with increased *rotational* energy. A molecule may be excited, therefore, and subsequently radiate because of changes in any or all of these three kinds of energy. In the most general case, when a quantum $h\nu$ is radiated, we may write

$$h\nu = h\nu_e + h\nu_v + h\nu_r, \tag{20.01}$$

when $h\nu_e$ is the energy arising from an electronic change in level, $h\nu_v$ from a vibrational change, $h\nu_r$ from a rotational change.

We shall examine briefly three different kinds of bands.

(1) **Rotation Band.** In quantizing vibrational and rotational changes, the same general ideas as employed for line spectra are utilized. Thus, when considering the rotation of the two atoms of a diatomic molecule about an axis perpendicular to the line joining them, the angular momentum is restricted to integral multiples of $h/2\pi$. Hence, if

I = moment of inertia of the system about the axis of rotation,

ω = angular velocity,

$I\omega$ = angular momentum = $m \cdot \dfrac{h}{2\pi}$, where m has integral values.

From this relation, we may write for W_m, the energy of the mth state,

$$W_m = \tfrac{1}{2}I\omega^2 = \frac{m^2h^2}{8\pi^2 I}. \tag{20.02}$$

According to modern quantum mechanics m^2 is replaced by $J(J + 1)$, where J has integral values 0, 1, 2, 3, etc. We have, therefore, a series of quantized rotational levels defined by this quantum number J. In what is called a *pure rotation band*, radiation (or absorption) takes place solely because of transitions from one of these levels to another. Since in such transitions J changes by 1 only, $\bar{\nu}$, the wave-number of each of the emitted (or absorbed) wavelengths constituting the band is given by

$$\bar{\nu} = \frac{1}{\lambda} = \frac{\text{energy change}}{hc}$$

$$= \frac{1}{hc}\left[(J + 1)(J + 2)\frac{h^2}{8\pi^2 I} - J(J + 1)\frac{h^2}{8\pi^2 I} \right]$$

$$= \frac{2h}{8\pi^2 I c}(J + 1)$$

$$= 2B(J + 1), \quad \text{where } J = 0, 1, 2 \ldots, \tag{20.03}$$

where
$$B = \frac{h}{8\pi^2 I c} = \frac{27.6 \times 10^{-40}}{I}, \tag{20.04}$$

since
$$h = 6.62 \times 10^{-27} \quad \text{and} \quad c = 2.998 \times 10^{10}.$$

In the case of the hydrogen halides HF, HCl, HBr, and HI, bands conforming closely to this law have been observed in absorption in the far infrared region, in a region of wavelengths of the order of 0.1 mm. Their presence in the far infrared where frequencies are so much smaller than in the visible (compare, for example, the frequency for $\lambda = 0.01$ cm with that for $\lambda = 5 \times 10^{-5}$ cm) tells us that rotational energy levels are much closer than those we encounter in line spectra, that is, than electronic levels.

For HCl the *empirical* formula giving the wave-number of each line of the observed rotation band is

$$\bar{\nu} = 20.793(J + 1) - 0.00163(J + 1)^3.$$

If we neglect the small second term on the right-hand side, this expression is of exactly the same form as relation (20.03), $2B$ being equal to 20.793. As a matter of fact, when allowance is made for slight changes in the distance apart of the two rotating nuclei, correcting terms must be added to the simple expression given in (20.03). In presenting the fundamental ideas of band spectra it has been thought wiser to omit such correcting terms, whose magnitudes, as already pointed out in the case of HCl, are small compared with $2B(J + 1)$.

Figure 20.3 gives the levels or term values for an observed rotation band, the first four members of the band being represented by vertical lines. The actual separations of successive levels are (in wave-numbers) 20.79, 41.58, 62.33, and 83.07. Note (1) how small these are compared with the separation of levels encountered in line spectra, such as in Figs. 20.1, 20.2; (2) in conformity with relation (20.03), the increasing separation of the levels, in the ratio $1:2:3:4$ etc.

(2) **Vibration-Rotation Bands.** In addition to the rotation of a diatomic molecule about an axis perpendicular to the internuclear axis, the two nuclei may vibrate about equilibrium positions and so possess also vibrational energy. This energy is quantized in terms of the unit $h\nu_e$ where ν_e is the frequency for vibrations of very small amplitude. In this case the quantum number is represented by the symbol v and, according to quantum mechanics, the vibrational energy for any state v is given by the relation

$$\text{vibrational energy} = (v + \tfrac{1}{2})h\nu_e,^* \quad \text{where}$$
$$v = 0, 1, 2 \ldots . \quad (20.04)$$

To obtain the corresponding *term* values, the energy values as usual must be divided by hc. Thus we have a series of vibrational levels whose values to a first approximation, in wave-numbers, are (if we put $v = 0, 1, 2, 3, \ldots$)

$$\frac{1}{2}\frac{h\nu_e}{hc}, \frac{3}{2}\frac{h\nu_e}{hc}, \frac{5}{2}\frac{h\nu_e}{hc} \ldots .$$

Fig. 20.3. Term values or energy levels for a pure rotation band of HCl. The vertical lines represent individual members of the band.

Associated with *each* of these is a series of rotational levels. In Fig. 20.4, for example, we have represented 3 vibrational levels distinguished by $v = 0, 1$ and 2, and associated with each of these, 4 rotational levels, distinguished by the J values, $0, 1, 2, 3$. A particular rotational level may, therefore, conveniently be referred to as a (v, J) term, where v can have values $0, 1, 2, \ldots$, and J, $0, 1, 2, 3$. Actual experiment shows the existence of wavelengths arising not only from transitions between two successive rotational levels associated with the same vibrational level (that is, a pure rotation band) but also of wavelengths corresponding to transitions from a rotational level of one vibrational group to a rotational level of a different vibrational group. In such transitions values of v may change by 1 or 2 or 3, but changes in J values are restricted to ± 1 or 0. When the transitions are between rotational levels associated with different vibrational levels, the bands are called *vibration-rotation*. All the wavelengths or lines corresponding to the same vibrational change constitute a single vibrational band. Thus, in Fig. 20.4, all the vertical lines joining different rotational levels of the $v = 1$ group to those of the $v = 0$ group represent the wavelengths

---

* Here, again, this is only to a first approximation and correcting terms must be added to take into consideration the fact that the vibrations are anharmonic, not harmonic. The more exact relation is

$$(v + \tfrac{1}{2})h\nu_e - x_e(v + \tfrac{1}{2})^2 h\nu_e + y_e(v + \tfrac{1}{2})^3 h\nu_e + \cdots,$$

where x_e and y_e are very small constants.

which make up the (1, 0) band. Similarly, the (2, 0) band is made up of all the wavelengths arising from transitions between rotational levels of the $v = 2$ group to those of the $v = 0$ group.

The wave-numbers marked in Fig. 20.4 are actual observed values for HCl^{35}.* The fact that the observed spectra, although still in the infrared, are of much shorter wavelength than those for pure rotation tells us that for vibration-rotation bands we are dealing with considerably larger energy values. In the case of HCl (Fig. 20.4) this is at once apparent from the much greater wave-

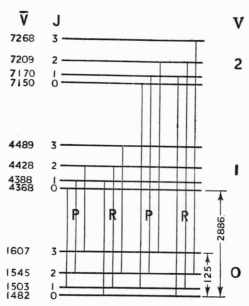

Fig. 20.4. Each group of four horizontal lines represents the four rotational terms or levels associated with each of the three vibrational levels marked v = 0, 1, and 2. The shorter vertical lines marked _P_ and _R_ represent individual members of the (1,0) vibration-rotation band; the longer lines, members of the (2,0) vibration band.

number separation of two vibrational levels as compared with the separation of rotational levels.

It will be noticed in Fig. 20.4 that the lines representing the (1, 0) and the (2, 0) vibration bands are in two groups, marked P and R. The R group or *branch*, as it is usually called, is composed of all lines for which the J value of the lower vibrational level is 1 less than that of the upper level, whereas the P branch is composed of those for which the value is 1 more than that of the upper. In more complicated spectra there is a third branch Q composed of lines for which the change in J is 0.

Isotope Effect. It has been stated before that the wave-numbers in Fig. 20.4

* Chlorine has two isotopes of atomic weight 35 and 37; hence there is HCl^{35} and HCl^{37}.

are those of actual levels for band spectra of HCl^{35}. It is interesting to note that, when a vibration-rotation band of HCl was first discovered in 1919 by Ames (United States), the appearance of each line in the band suggested a doublet. This was later shown by Loomis (United States) and others to be due to two components arising from the two isotopes of chlorine, that is, one component for HCl^{35} and a weaker one for HCl^{37}. The student should see without difficulty that the magnitude of the vibrational frequency, as well as that of I, the moment of inertia (and hence of B, in relation 20.04), varies with the mass of each nucleus.

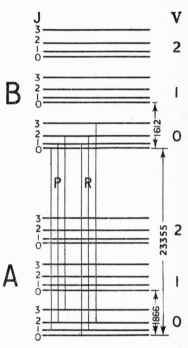

Hence, given known masses, it is possible to predict the isotopic separation between the corresponding members of the two bands, or conversely, from the observed separation, to calculate the ratio of the masses. In the case of HCl^{35} and HCl^{37} good agreement was obtained between observed and predicted values.

After the discovery of heavy hydrogen or deuterium, no difficulty was experienced in obtaining H^2Cl^{35} and H^2Cl^{37}. It then became possible to use the isotopic separation of band spectra in order to compare the mass of the atom of deuterium (that is, of H^2 or D) with that of ordinary hydrogen (H^1). This was done by Hardy, Barker and Dennison (all of United States) by observing the isotopic separation in the case of H^1Cl^{35} and H^2Cl^{35}. A result in excellent agreement with other methods was obtained.

(3) **Electronic Band.** As already pointed out, the energy changes involved in vibration-rotation bands are so small that all the observed lines are in the infrared region. To obtain band spectra in the visible or ultraviolet region much greater energy changes are necessary. Such changes arise when the energy of the molecule is altered by electronic

Fig. 20.5. *A* and *B* represent two sets of 3-vibrational levels, $v = 0, 1,$ and $2,$ with their associated 4 rotational levels. *A* corresponds to one electronic state; *B* to another. *P* and *R* represent individual members of a (0,0) electronic band.

displacements just as in the case of ordinary atomic line spectra. For all the levels shown in Fig. 20.4 the molecule is in the same electronic configuration or *all* the levels there represented correspond to the same electronic state. If increases in energy are brought about by electronic changes, the molecule may be in different quantized electronic states which we shall call A, B, C, etc.

For *each* of these states there is a series of vibrational states distinguished by v values $= 0, 1, 2, 3, \ldots$; and for each vibrational state, a series of rotational levels or states distinguished by J values $= 0, 1, 2, 3, \ldots$. In Fig. 20.5 we have represented two electronic states of a molecule, marked A and B; for each of these, three associated vibrational states; and for each vibrational state, four rotational levels. As a rule the actual levels would be more numerous than those shown in this figure. Some idea of the relative separation of the various levels may be had from the wave-number differences (relating to certain CuH bands) marked on the diagram. Thus the energy of the $v = 0$ vibrational level of electronic state B differs from that of the $v = 0$ vibrational level of state A by about 23355 cm^{-1} (that is, wave-numbers). Compare this with the separation of the two vibrational levels, $v = 1$ and $v = 0$ of state A, which is only 1866 cm^{-1}. The wave-number separation of the $J = 0$ and $J = 1$ rotational levels of the $v = 0$ vibrational state, for electronic state A, is not marked on the diagram but is actually about 16 cm^{-1}.

When, therefore, transitions occur from levels of state A to those of state B the wave-number changes are so great that the emitted (or absorbed) lines are usually in the ordinary visible or ultraviolet region. (The wave-number difference 23355 corresponds to a wavelength of 4282 A.) In such transitions v may change by ± 1, ± 2, $\pm 3 \ldots$, J by ± 1 or 0.

A single band is composed of all lines corresponding to transitions from one vibrational level to another, the band usually being described by giving the value of v, for the upper electronic state, side by side with that of v for the lower. Thus the band $(2, 0)$ refers to the band arising from transitions from the $v = 2$ upper state to the $v = 0$ lower. In Fig. 20.5 lines of the P and R branches for the $(0, 0)$ band are marked with P and R.

Because of the closeness of the rotational levels the individual lines in a band are frequently not separated, unless sufficiently high dispersion is used. With low dispersion a single band has generally the appearance of a sharp edge on one side, where the individual lines are crowded together most closely, with a gradual decrease in intensity (a degrading) to the other side, where sometimes individual lines may be seen. Fig. 3, Plate III, facing p. 97, shows the appearance of a dozen or so unresolved bands. Under very high dispersion the individual lines composing the band are separated. A beautiful example of this (the 2430 band of magnesium hydride), for which the author is indebted to Dr. R. W. B. Pearse of the Imperial College, London, England, is given in Fig. 4, Plate III.

An electronic band *system* is a collection of all the individual bands arising from transitions from one electronic state to another. For example, in the band spectra of nitrogen, there is a *first positive system* arising from transitions from a state B to a state A; a *second positive system*, from state C to state B; and a *fourth positive system*, from state D to state B, as well as other systems.

Sequences and Progressions. Sometimes in the simpler band systems groups are repeated in such a way as to suggest some regularity. On analysis it is found that each group consists of bands for which the numerical difference between the v of the upper electronic state (usually represented by v') and the v of the lower (represented by v'') is the same for each band. Such a group is called a *sequence*. For example, in one of the systems of bands due to CN, there are four sequences corresponding to values of $v' - v'' = +1$, 0, -1, and -2. In a single sequence, such as the -2, there are at least six separate bands corresponding to $v' = 0, 1, 2, 3, 4, 5$ and $v'' = 2, 3, 4, 5, 6$ and 7.

Sometimes bands are also grouped in *progressions*, of which there are two kinds: (1) a v' progression made up of all bands with the same v'' value but different v' values; (2) a v'' progression, in which the v' value is constant and v'' values are variable.

While only the bare elements of the analysis of band spectra has been given, it should be sufficient to enable the reader to understand the fundamental ideas involved. From measurements of wavelengths, the constants occurring in the band spectra relations can be evaluated, and hence a determination can be made of such quantities as the distance between the nuclei of a diatomic molecule or of the amount of work necessary to dissociate such a molecule. Moreover, as already indicated in the case of the two kinds of hydrogen, valuable information regarding isotopic masses can be obtained from an analysis of band spectra.

PROBLEMS

1. (a) Given the value of the Rydberg constant for hydrogen [of mass number 1] $= 109678$, write down approximate numerical values of two diffuse terms for any element with a single valency electron.

(b) If the limit of a sharp series of an element with a single valency electron $= 24475$ work out the *wavelength* of the first number of the associated diffuse series. (Result of part (a) may be used.)

2. Could a wavelength be emitted as a result of a transition from (i) a 4^3D_3 term to a 4^3P_1 term; (ii) a 6^3P_1 term to a 4^3P_1 term?

3. The first (longest) wavelength in a certain series is 6707.9 A and is represented by $\bar{\nu} = 43486$—variable term.

If the Rydberg constant (N) for the element concerned is 109729, calculate the second wavelength in the same series.

4. To excite mercury wavelength 5461 an excitation potential of 7.69 volts is necessary. If the highest term in the spectrum of mercury is 84181 cm^{-1}, find the numerical values of the two terms involved in the emission of 5461.

5. For a certain element, the principal and sharp series of singlets are given by
$$\bar{\nu} = 84178 - m^1P_1 \text{ and } \bar{\nu} = 30113 - m^1So.$$

(a) Find the wavelength of the first member of the P series.

(b) If 10140 A is the first member of the sharp series, find the value of the highest numerical S term.

6. The first member of a diffuse series in an element whose D terms are hydrogen-like is in the visible spectrum. If the limit of the series is 28600, find the wavelength of this member. Take $N = 109678$.

7. Given the Rydberg constant (N) for hydrogen $= 109678$, find: (i) the excitation potential necessary to excite H_α, the first member of the Balmer series; (ii) the ionization potential, for hydrogen.

8. The radiating potential of a certain wavelength is 4.9 volts, and it is emitted as a result of a transition to the ground level 84181 cm^{-1}. Find: (i) the value of the wavelength; (ii) the wave-number of the upper level.

9. Describe the flame spectrum of sodium.

10. *The limit of a spectral series is a term of some other series.* Discuss this statement with reference to the important lithium series.

XXI

The Dilemma

21.1. In the discussion of the relative merits of the corpuscular and the wave theory of light as given in Chapter I, it was pointed out that the discovery of interference not only demanded a wave theory of some kind, but also paved the way for a satisfactory explanation of the outstanding optical problems of the nineteenth century. Moreover, a large portion of this book has been devoted to a study of phenomena which find a ready interpretation on a wave theory, and indeed, some of which can only be explained in such a way. On the other hand, in the chapters immediately preceding this one, irrefutable evidence has been given that there are other optical phenomena, notably those referring to the interaction between radiation and matter, which can be explained only in terms of a quantum theory. Now in some respects, these two theories are contradictory. Consider, again, the outstanding differences.

21.2. According to the wave theory, radiant energy spreads out *continuously*, the amount received per sq cm on any given surface constantly decreasing, the farther the surface is removed from the source. On the other hand, on the quantum theory, radiant energy has an atomicity, the fundamental unit being of magnitude $h\nu$. Moreover, while certain facts can be explained on this theory by restricting the discontinuity to processes of emission and of absorption, the empirical laws of such a phenomenon as photoelectricity seem to require the propagation of light in quanta *which maintain their identity throughout their journey*. The Compton effect (section 21.3) points to the same conclusion. In such cases we have to do with *discontinuous* wave-fronts, and a flight of what are variously called light quanta (after Einstein), light corpuscles, or *photons*. Our position, then, is that apparently certain facts in light can be explained only on a wave theory; certain others, only on a quantum theory which in many respects is similar to the old corpuscular theory of Newton.

It will be recalled also that, in applying quantum ideas, contradictions between old and new views were introduced in regard to dynamics. Classical electromagnetic theory, based on Newtonian dynamics, said that accelerated charges should radiate; quantum theory postulates that this need not be the case. As long as Planck applied to bodies of atomic dimensions Newtonian mechanics, the facts of black body radiation could not be deduced. When a departure from classical conceptions was made, however, a correct interpretation of this problem was given.

Now an introductory text in light is not the place to discuss dynamical principles in detail, but, in general, the student should have no difficulty in realizing that the application of Newtonian laws of mechanics to atoms and molecules does not always account for observed facts. And yet there is no doubt of the amazing accuracy with which such laws apply to large aggregations of molecules, that is, to those masses whose motions are ordinarily considered. (Consider, for example, the exactness with which predictions can be made regarding the motion of astronomical bodies.)

21.3. The physicist is then faced with a dilemma. There seem to be two contradictory theories, one necessary for the interpretation of one group of facts, the other for a second group. Can both be right? Fortunately, such a situation is by no means an unmixed evil, for a scientist usually grasps both horns of a dilemma in his endeavor to wrest from Nature secrets yet denied him. Apparent contradictions sometimes imply the lack of some larger outlook by means of which conflicting views can be shown to be but two different aspects of the same co-ordinating principle. Such a principle has been provided by the theoretical developments of quantum mechanics. This work has shown that, for the interpretation not only of spectra but of all phenomena in all branches of science relating to the interaction of atoms and molecules, we cannot apply the methods applicable to everyday large-scale bodies, but must use more abstract ideas. Although mathematical physicists are largely responsible for the advances made, new ideas have constantly been related to experiment. Before a further reference is made (in section 21.8) to the duality problem in light, a brief discussion is given of experimental investigations which establish the following significant and complementary statements: (1) light corpuscles or photons, in encounters with electrons, may behave like particles of matter; (2) material particles such as electrons, under certain conditions, act like a group of waves.

21.4. The Compton Effect. The idea underlying the first statement was used by A. H. Compton, when Professor of Physics at Chicago University, in connection with the interpretation of results obtained when x-rays are scattered by free electrons. Compton, following the pioneer work of J. A. Gray (Canada), showed that, when a beam of monochromatic x-rays is scattered on passage through certain substances, the scattered radiation is of slightly longer wavelength than the incident. Since a longer wavelength corresponds to a lower frequency, the energy unit $h\nu$ in the original beam must be greater than that of the scattered beam by an amount which can readily be found from observations of the wavelengths concerned. To interpret his observations Compton assumed: (1) in a collision between a quantum and a free electron, energy is communicated to the electron, thus, by the law of conservation of energy, giving rise after the collision to a quantum hv' of less energy; (2) a quantum possesses *momentum* of amount hv/c,* the law of conservation of momentum being applicable to the collision, just as in the case of colliding particles. When the energy and momentum equations are then written down in the usual way, it is easy to derive an expression for the new frequency v' in terms of the original value v, and of the direction in which scattering is observed. The experimental results were found to be in remarkable agreement with the deduced expression.

21.5. Electron Waves. That, under certain circumstances, electrons behave as if they were a group of waves has been shown in two different ways, to each of which a brief reference will be made. In the first method, used by Davisson

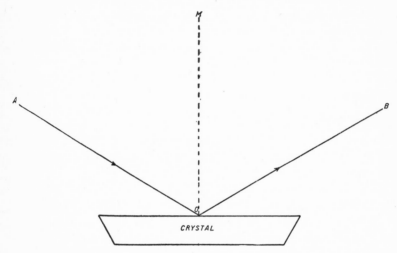

Fig. 21.1. If the velocity of a beam of electrons *AO*, incident on a crystal, is varied, the intensity of the reflected beam along *OB* goes through maximum and minimum values.

and Germer, working in The Bell Telephone Laboratories, New York, a beam of electrons of a known speed was projected obliquely against the face of a nickel crystal and the intensity of the reflected beam was observed in various directions. Two outstanding results were obtained: (1) for electrons of a fixed velocity, the intensity of the reflected beam is a maximum in the direction *OB*, Fig. 21.1, where *OB* makes the same angle with the normal to the face of the crystal

---

* When light is incident on a surface, a pressure p is exerted. In the case of a black body, experiment shows that the pressure is equal to the energy per unit volume in the incident beam. If, therefore, n quanta per second are incident on a surface of 1 sq cm, $p = n \cdot hv/c$, since each quantum possesses hv units of energy and since the velocity of the incident radiant energy is c. Now if particles collide against a surface, the pressure exerted is equal to the rate of change of momentum. Hence, if we compare a quantum to a colliding particle, the change of momentum per second is equal to the pressure and therefore $= n \cdot hv/c$. In other words, each quantum may be thought of as having hv/c units of momentum.

(represented by MO) as does the incident beam in the direction AO; (2) if the velocity of the incident beam is varied, as may readily be done by the method described in (f) of section 17.2, *the intensity of the reflected beam in the direction OB goes through maximum and minimum values. In other words, in the same direction, electrons of some speeds are strongly reflected, of others feebly reflected.*

Now when a beam of x-rays containing many wavelengths is incident on the surface of a crystal in a manner for which Fig. 21.1 will serve as an illustration, certain wavelengths only are reflected in the direction OB. Because of the path difference which exists between the x-ray disturbances reflected from successive parallel layers of atoms, we have to deal with the superposition of beams differing in phase, and hence the resultant reflected beam has a maximum intensity only for certain wavelengths. Thus, if d is the distance between two such successive layers, and $\angle MOB = \theta$, there is a reflected x-ray beam of appreciable intensity *only* for wavelengths which satisfy the relation

$$n\lambda = 2d \cos \theta,^* \text{ (where } n \text{ is integral).} \qquad (21.01)$$

If then d is known and θ is observed, the corresponding wavelengths may readily be calculated.

Hence, Davisson and Germer, making the assumption that electrons were waves, or were associated with a group of waves, reasoned that such a relation should hold for the reflection of electrons also. The fact that electrons of some velocities are strongly reflected, whereas others are not, follows at once *if the wavelengths of such waves depend on the velocity of the electron.* On this hypothesis, then, the wavelength associated with a velocity which gave intense reflection can be calculated from the relation (21.01). As an example of the results obtained by such calculations, these experimenters found for 54-volt electrons, $\lambda = 1.67$ A, and for 65 volts, $\lambda = 1.52$ A. If this were the whole story, no one could be blamed for being skeptical about the existence of electron waves. Fortunately, it is not, for, as a matter of fact, these results are a confirmation of results predicted by what is known as *wave mechanics,* one of the approaches to quantum mechanics.

21.6. Wave Mechanics. Wave mechanics is the name given to a method of interpreting physical phenomena which has provided a fundamental principle that reconciles the conflicting views we have been considering. To explain the connection between the experimental work of Davisson and Germer and this theory, a brief digression is necessary. In Chapter XIX, dealing with the rise of the quantum theory, attention was directed to the initial successes of Bohr's theory of the origin of spectra and to his manner of quantizing the atom. Bohr's pioneer work was the basis of a tremendous amount of subsequent work on the part of mathematical physicists. When the theory was generalized, many prob-

---

* The path difference in question $= 2d \cos \theta$. Compare the expression for path difference in the case of a Fabry-Perot étalon.

lems such as the complex Zeeman effect, the Stark effect, and the fine structure of individual hydrogen lines were satisfactorily explained. There were many other problems, however, such as those dealing with intensities of spectral lines and with the spectra of atoms more complicated than hydrogen, for which adequate solutions were not forthcoming. Moreover, from the outset Bohr's theory had nothing whatever to say about the actual process of emission when an electron passes from one orbit to another. So many difficulties presented themselves to theoretical physicists that revisions in theories were constantly being made, and new concepts were introduced. As one example, we may mention the use of the spinning electron in order to interpret the meaning of multiple energy levels. Such work culminated in the introduction of systems of quantum mechanics in which men no longer made the picture of an atom model (such as the planetary atom of Bohr) the starting point for their theories, but rather certain abstract ideas. The most outstanding of such theories is known as wave mechanics, the foundation of which was laid by Louis de Broglie (France). In its subsequent development the name of Schrödinger* (Germany) is outstanding.

While a detailed consideration of this work is much beyond the scope of this book, it may be stated that de Broglie, accepting the modern idea of the equivalence between mass and energy, postulated that, in every mechanical system, waves are associated with mass particles. The development of de Broglie's basic idea leads to the view that, just as optical problems relating to large openings may be solved by using the rectilinear propagation of rays of light, whereas, for small openings, the spreading out of waves is essential for a correct solution, so wave mechanics replaces ordinary mechanics when we have to deal with bodies of atomic dimensions rather than those usually encountered. Stated otherwise and perhaps more correctly, just as the wave theory leads to laws of geometrical optics for big openings but is necessary to explain diffraction effects, so the more general wave mechanics is equivalent to ordinary mechanics for bodies of large dimensions but is necessary for the correct solution of problems dealing with masses of atomic and sub-atomic dimensions. Now an essential feature of wave mechanics is that the waves associated with a particle of mass m and velocity v have a wavelength given by the relation

$$\lambda = \frac{h}{mv}. \tag{21.02}$$

Here then is a prediction of associated waves which may be tested experimentally. Let us apply it to the work of Davisson and Germer. An electron with charge of e statcoulombs which has fallen through a potential difference of V volts has acquired energy $= Ve/300$ ergs, and hence we may write,

$$\tfrac{1}{2}mv^2 = \frac{Ve}{300}, \tag{21.03}$$

---

* Using an entirely different method of approach Heisenberg developed a system of quantum mechanics which proved to be essentially the same as wave mechanics.

where m is the mass and v the velocity of the electron. If now we eliminate v between relations (21.02) and (21.03), we obtain

$$\lambda = h\sqrt{\frac{150}{mVe}}. \tag{21.04}$$

Substituting the standard values $e = 4.80 \times 10^{-10}$; $h = 6.62 \times 10^{-27}$; $m = 9.11 \times 10^{-28}$ g, we have

$$\lambda = \frac{12.26}{\sqrt{V}}. \tag{21.05}$$

Hence for 54-volt electrons, $\lambda = 1.67$ A, for 64-volt electrons, $\lambda = 1.52$ A, results in excellent agreement with the values (1.65 and 1.52) obtained experimentally on the supposition that the reflection of electron waves follows x-ray laws. It would seem, then, that good evidence has been obtained that at least sometimes electrons behave as if they were a group of waves.

21.7. Further confirmation of the truth of this result is provided by the work of G. P. Thomson (Great Britain), who used a method which involved the passage of a beam of high-speed electrons through thin layers of matter. Here again the experimental test made use of a standard means of measuring x-ray wavelengths. Indeed the method was essentially the same as that used by Laue and his co-workers when they proved the wave nature of x-rays by the passage of a narrow beam of these rays directly through a crystal. Because of diffraction, with such an arrangement, a number of well-defined spots are obtained on a photographic plate receiving the emergent beam. If the crystal is replaced by a powder in which a number of small crystals are arranged at random, the spots coalesce to form a series of concentric rings, whose radii depend on the wavelength and on the crystal arrangement. If, then, electrons are accompanied by waves it is reasonable to argue that a similar result might be detained with suitable wavelengths.

That this is actually the case Thomson showed by the use of extremely thin layers of metal (with thickness of the order of 10^{-6} mm). By using potentials ranging from 10,000 to 60,000 volts, wavelengths much shorter than those of Davisson and Germer were obtained [see relation (21.05)]. When a narrow beam of such high-speed electrons was incident normally on one of these films, a photographic plate some 30 cm away showed the presence of well-defined rings. An actual photograph of the ring system for a very thin layer of gold is given in Fig. 2, Plate IX, facing p. 352.* Moreover, since the radii of the rings depend on the wavelength (and therefore on the voltage employed), as well as on the spacing of the atoms in the material, quantitative tests could be made. When calculations were made using the measured diameter of the rings, even more striking agreement was obtained between experimental results and the pre-

*For this photograph the author is greatly indebted to Sir George Thomson.

dictions of wave mechanics than in the work of Davisson and Germer. Again, it seems impossible not to conclude that, under certain circumstances, electrons behave like a group of waves whose wavelength is given by relation (21.02). On the other hand, it should be stated that these waves are not of the same nature as x-rays of the same wavelengths. That this is the case will be evident at once from the following facts: (1) electron waves, as shown by Thomson, are deflected by a magnetic field; (2) the penetrating power of electron waves (which penetrate only extremely thin layers of matter) is much less than that of x-rays of equal wavelength.

Schrödinger's development of de Broglie's ideas led to the establishment of a differential wave equation which is fundamental in quantum mechanics. In this equation there appears a symbol ψ representing the amplitude of the waves associated with a particle. When this equation is applied to the case of an electron revolving about a nucleus, as in the hydrogen atom, only certain characteristic solutions are possible. These solutions correspond to discrete energy states and lead to exactly the same expression for the energy values as that given by the Bohr-Sommerfeld theory (relation 19.15). Moreover, in the course of the solution of the equation, quantum numbers n and l appear quite naturally, that is, they are not introduced in the arbitrary manner of the earlier theories. Altogether, with the application of quantum mechanics to atomic systems, it has been possible to interpret correctly the radiation problems which could not previously be solved by the early quantum ideas.

Although the waves associated with a particle of matter are sometimes called "material," the student should not think of them as "common-sense" waves, that is, waves which can be visualized in space and in time. That they have a reality of some kind is obvious from such experimental work as that of Thomson and Davisson and Germer. But, as we have already pointed out, they must not be considered to have the same nature as electromagnetic waves. Indeed they are best described as mathematical waves governed by an equation by means of which correct predictions can be made about the behavior of atomic systems.

21.8. Let us sum up, now, what we have found. (1) As far as interchanges of energy are concerned, light is a quantum or corpuscular phenomenon, whereas its laws of propagation, as well as the facts of interference and diffraction, are accurately represented by Maxwell's equations of the electromagnetic field, which postulate a continuous wave-front. Light then seems to have a dual aspect. (2) Particles such as electrons, which in a host of phenomena can be treated as mass-particles subject to ordinary dynamical laws, have been shown to act in certain circumstances as a group of waves. Particles, then, when of atomic or sub-atomic dimensions, can also exhibit a dual aspect. It is not amiss to think of the wave theory as an accurate representation of facts when we have to deal with the operation of a large number of photons, whereas in processes involving interchanges of energy where a single quantum is concerned, the particle aspect or quantum mechanics is necessary.   Here, in fact, is the clue to the duality problem.   Waves tell us nothing about the behavior of individual photons, but, when we are dealing with a large aggregate (as in ordinary sources of light), the wave theory gives us the probability of where the energy will be concentrated.   According to either wave theory or quantum mechanics, at a dark fringe of zero intensity, the probability of photons reaching there is negligibly small.

XXII

Can the Existence of an Ether
Be Detected?

22.1. In Chapter XVI it was pointed out in some detail how the electromagnetic theory replaced the elastic solid theory. The resulting change in outlook did not overthrow the conception of an ether. The difficulty of imagining a medium with an elasticity sufficiently great to transmit vibrations with the speed of light, and yet so rarefied as to permit apparently unrestricted motion of material bodies through it, was, of course, removed. But an ether was still considered necessary as the vehicle for the transmission of electromagnetic waves. Indeed, although the propagation of light was represented by differential equations, underlying Maxwell's work was the Faraday conception of electric tubes representing stresses in an all-pervading ether. Throughout the nineteenth century, therefore, both before and after the advent of the electromagnetic theory, it was natural that scientists should be concerned with questions relating to the relative motion of ether and terrestrial objects. Is there any experimental evidence that the earth and all objects on it are moving through an invisible medium, the carrier of light and all electromagnetic disturbances? That is the question we wish to examine in this concluding chapter.

22.2. Aberration of Light. Early in the eighteenth century, an Englishman, Bradley by name, discovered a phenomenon which showed that the *direction* in which light is received from a star is altered by the motion of an observer on the earth, thus giving rise to an erroneous result in fixing the position of the star. Bradley considered his observation a proof that light has a finite velocity, and he was able to calculate a value for this constant in fair agreement with the results of later and more accurate methods. Let us examine somewhat carefully this so-called *aberration of light*. To make our ideas concrete, consider a *stationary* observer holding a long cylindrical tube with its axis AB, Fig. 22.1(a), in such a direction that a line of falling particles (raindrops, for example), traveling in the direction DA pass straight down the center of the tube. Obviously, in such a case, the direction of the axis of the tube gives the direction in which the particles are traveling. If the particles are replaced by a wave disturbance in the direction

DA, originating in some source along AD produced, the same result holds; that is, the axis of the tube gives the true direction in which the source lies.

Suppose, however, that the observer is *moving* with the tube in the direction of the arrow as in Fig. 22.1(b), with velocity v. In such a case, if we wish a particle entering the upper end of the tube at the point A, the center of the opening, to emerge from the lower end at the center, evidently the tube must be slanted so that, when the center of the upper end is at A, that of the lower end is at B', where BB' is the distance the tube is carried along during the time that the particle travels from A to B. For, with such a slant, the center of the lower end of the tube reaches B at the same instant as the particle. If the falling

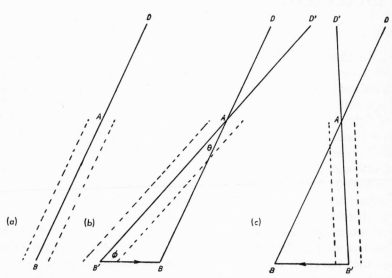

Fig. 22.1. In order to view a source of light sending waves in the direction DA, the axis of a telescope moving in the direction B' to B must be directed along AD'. DAD' is called the angle of aberration.

particles are replaced by a wave motion or by quanta coming from a source along AD produced, the direction of the axis of the tube no longer gives the direction from which the waves or quanta are coming, nor does the tube point to the true position of the source. The angle DAD' or $B'AB$, between the true direction and the axis of the tube (or the apparent direction), is called the *angle of aberration.*

If the cylindrical tube is replaced by a telescope receiving light from a stationary non-terrestrial source such as a star, it follows that, because of the translatory motion of the earth, the axis of the telescope does not indicate the true position of the star. Moreover, because the direction of the earth's motion continually changes throughout a year, the angle of aberration must continually change also. Thus some months after the time represented by Fig. 22.1(b), conditions might be represented by Fig. 22.1(c), where it will be noted the apparent position of the star is on the other side of the true position. Now it was just this apparent change in the position of a star which Bradley discovered, and by means of which he worked out a value for the velocity of light. Let us see how that can be done.

Let θ = angle of aberration, that is, $\angle DAD'$ or $\angle BAB'$, in Fig. 22.1(b), and let $\phi = \angle AB'B$, that is, the angle between the direction in which the observer is moving, and that of the axis of the telescope.

We have then,
$$\frac{\sin \theta}{BB'} = \frac{\sin \phi}{AB},$$

from which
$$\sin \theta = \frac{BB'}{AB} \cdot \sin \phi$$

$$= \frac{v}{V} \cdot \sin \phi,$$

where v is the velocity of the observer, and V that of the light.

Since θ is a small angle, we may write

$$\theta = \frac{v}{V} \sin \phi. \tag{22.01}$$

The maximum value of the angle of aberration is, therefore, given by

$$\theta \text{ maximum} = \frac{v}{V}.$$

Now observation gives the maximum value of θ about $20''$; hence, taking $v = 19$ miles per sec, we find V to be of the order of 180,000 miles per sec.

But, it is asked, where does the ether come in, in all this work? The answer should now be clear. *Either it does not enter into the problem at all, that is, we may ignore its existence altogether; or, if it does, it must be at rest with respect to the telescope.* For if the ether were carried along with the telescope, so too would the wave disturbance be carried along, and hence light would not continue to travel in the direction AB.

22.3. Airy's Experiment. In 1871 an important variation in the aberration experiment was performed by Airy, then Astronomer Royal in England. From the explanation given previously, it follows at once that the smaller V, the greater the angle of aberration. If, therefore, the air inside a telescope is replaced by water in which light travels more slowly than in air, the angle of aberration for any observed star ought to be greater. Airy tried this experiment and *found the angle exactly the same as for air*. Now, that the velocity of light in water is less than in air, there could be no doubt—experiment had shown that to be the case. There must then, it was argued, be some factor or factors which alter the velocity in the case we are considering. Moreover, since the angle of aberration remains the same, then if DA, Fig. 22.2, represents the direction of the light incident on the telescope, the axis of the instrument must (as before) point in the direction BAD', where $\angle DAD' = \angle BAN$ is θ, the angle of aberration. Hence if BM (equal to BB' of Fig. 22.1(b)) represents v the velocity of translation of the telescope, AM must represent the resultant velocity of the light in the water inside the moving telescope. What, then, can bring about such a change in the velocity inside the telescope? In the first place, it is well to note that because the incident beam of light does not strike the telescope objective

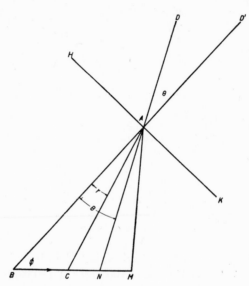

Fig. 22.2. Diagram used in determining the expression for velocity of ether drift.

normally, there will be refraction. For this reason alone, the light inside the tube would travel in the direction AC with a velocity equal to V/n, the exact direction being given by the ordinary sine law,

$$\frac{\sin \angle DAD'}{\sin \angle BAC} = n \text{ (since } D'A \text{ is normal to } HK,$$
$$\text{the telescope objective)}$$

or
$$\frac{\sin \theta}{\sin r} = n,$$

from which, since these angles are both small, we have

$$r = \frac{\theta}{n}, \quad \text{where} \quad r = \angle BAC.$$

The actual direction of the light in the tube, however, is along AM. An alteration in direction from AC to AM would take place if the medium carrying the light disturbance, that is, the ether, was not at rest with respect to the telescope but was carried along by it with just the necessary velocity to allow us to represent the resultant velocity by the line AM. For this to be the case, the necessary velocity of the ether with respect to the telescope, the ether *drift* we shall call it, would necessarily be represented by CM.

Let us now find the magnitude of the ether drift, bearing in mind that BM represents a velocity v; AC a velocity V/n; CM the velocity of the ether drift; that the angle $BAC = r = \theta/n$. Let also the angle $ABM = \phi$. For $\triangle BAC$ (Fig. 22.2), we can write

$$\frac{\sin r}{\sin \phi} = \frac{BC}{AC} = \frac{nBC}{V}.$$

$$\therefore \quad \frac{\theta}{n \sin \phi} = \frac{nBC}{V}$$

$$\frac{\theta}{\sin \phi} = \frac{n^2 BC}{V}. \tag{22.02}$$

For $\triangle BAB'$, Fig. 22.1(b),

$$\frac{\sin \theta}{\sin \phi} = \frac{BB'}{AB} = \frac{v}{V}$$

$$\therefore \quad \frac{\theta}{\sin \phi} = \frac{v}{V}. \tag{22.03}$$

Hence, combining relations (22.02) and (22.03), we have

$$\frac{n^2 BC}{V} = \frac{v}{V}$$

or

$$BC = \frac{v}{n^2}.$$

But

$$BC = BM - CM$$

$$= v - \text{ether drift},$$

$$\therefore \quad \text{velocity of ether drift} = v - BC$$

$$= v - \frac{v}{n^2}$$

$$= \left(1 - \frac{1}{n^2}\right) v. \tag{22.04}$$

Note what has been proved. The observed result that there is no change in the angle of aberration when air is replaced by water, would follow if the ether were dragged along with the water of the telescope by $[1 - (1/n^2)]$ of the velocity of the instrument. Taking $n = 1.33$, we find this fraction has the value 0.44. For air, where $n = 1$ (approximately) this result implies no ether drift, in line with the conclusion already noted. Now the remarkable feature about all this is that an ether drift of exactly this magnitude had been deduced years before by Fresnel on the supposition that the density of the ether varies with the material body in which it is found. Moreover, over a decade before the work of Airy, Fizeau (France, 1819–1896) had performed another celebrated experiment in which he showed that the interference fringes obtained by superimposing two beams traveling equal paths through columns of moving water, one beam with the stream, the other against, were shifted from the position of such fringes when the water was stationary. Granted an ether drift, this result at once follows. From the fringe shift observed with a given velocity of water, it is not difficult to calculate the magnitude of the ether drift. The results obtained not only by Fizeau, but over thirty years later, with more refined apparatus, by Michelson and Morley, verified Fresnel's formula. It would seem, then, *as if* evidence had been obtained that ether is dragged along by moving matter. To this point reference will again be made. Before leaving it, it is well to note the following:

22.4. (1) In both the aberration experiment and in that of Fizeau, there is *relative* motion between the instrument and some other material object. Thus the telescope moves with respect to the star, and, in Fizeau's experiment, the water moves with respect to the instrument receiving the light.

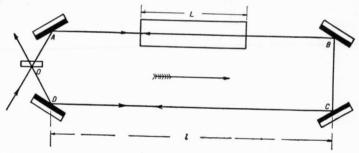

Fig. 22.3. Arrangement of mirrors A, B, C, D and glass block L to test for any difference in the times between clockwise and contra-clockwise passage of light.

(2) If we accept as established the existence of the ether drift of an amount given by Fresnel's coefficient, it follows that, *as far as first order effects are concerned*, it is impossible to detect any relative motion between the *earth* and the ether. The reason should be clear from a consideration of the following experiment. Suppose a set of mirrors A, B, C, D, is arranged as in Fig. 22.3, so that interference fringes are obtained between rays which have been reflected from mirror to mirror in a clockwise direction and those reflected in a contraclockwise direction. Let L represent the length of a glass block in the path of one arm, of total length l, of such an interferometer, and suppose the apparatus so placed that the earth has a velocity v in the direction of the arrow. Inside the glass block the ether then has a velocity $[1 - (1/n^2)] \cdot v$ or ζv, we shall write it for short, where $\zeta = 1 - (1/n^2)$.

In finding the difference in the times taken by the clockwise and the contra-clockwise beams to cover the complete path $OABCDO$, we shall make use of the fact that the motion of an object through a stationary ether is exactly the same as if the object were stationary and the ether streaming with equal speed in the opposite direction—a virtual ether stream we shall call it. In other words, we may superimpose on the whole system a velocity equal and opposite to v. Hence if $T_1 =$ the time taken by the clockwise beam, we may write

$$T_1 = \frac{l - L}{V - v} + \frac{L}{\dfrac{V}{n} - (1 - \zeta)v} + \frac{l}{V + v}$$

$$= \frac{l - L}{V - v} + \frac{L}{\dfrac{V}{n} - \dfrac{v}{n^2}} + \frac{l}{V + v}, \qquad (22.05)$$

since $V =$ velocity in air for a stationary ether,

$V - v =$ velocity against the virtual ether stream,

$\dfrac{V}{n} =$ velocity in glass for a stationary ether, and

$(1 - \zeta)v =$ the virtual ether stream in the glass (v and ζv in opposite directions).

Similarly T_2, the time taken by the contraclockwise beam is given by

$$T_2 = \frac{l - L}{V + v} + \frac{L}{\dfrac{V}{n} - \dfrac{v}{n^2}} + \frac{l}{V - v}. \qquad (22.06)$$

Now if these two times are subtracted, it can easily be shown by elementary algebra that, when the ratio v^2/V^2 is neglected in comparison with unity, the difference is zero. In other words, if it were sought to detect a shift in the inter-ference fringes observed with such an arrangement when the apparatus was rotated through 180°, a negative result should be obtained. *Such is actually the case.*

If, however, the factor v^2/V^2 is retained, T_2 is not exactly equal to T_1. Hence, if fringes were observed for the position indicated by Fig. 22.3, and the apparatus were then rotated through 180°, at any given place in the field of view where the two beams meet, there would be a phase difference introduced corresponding to a time difference of $2(T_2 - T_1)$. Theoretically, therefore, there ought to be an observed shift; but whether it could be observed or not, would depend on its magnitude. With the apparatus we have been discussing, as already noted, actually no shift can be detected. Is it possible to do so with any arrangement? If so, the apparatus must be sufficiently sensitive to detect a difference of about 1 part in 100,000,000.* Because of the shortness of light waves such an ap-

* Taking $v = 19$ miles per sec.; $V = 186,000$ miles per sec; $v/V = 10^{-4}$ approximately. Hence $v^2/V^2 = 10^{-8}$.

paratus can be designed, and hence a test made to see if relative motion between the earth and the ether can be detected even when second-order quantities are taken into consideration.

22.5. The Michelson and Morley Experiment. Probably the most famous of such tests was the pioneer one made by Michelson and Morley in 1881. The arrangement utilized was essentially a Michelson's interferometer, with each optical path lengthened by the use of several mirrors reflecting the light back and

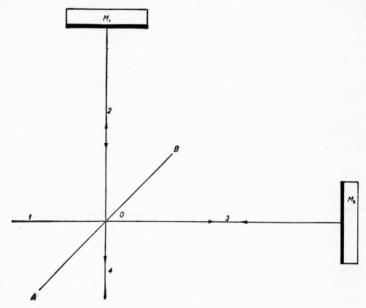

Fig. 22.4.   Michelson-Morley experiment.   Diagram used in deriving an expression for the difference in the times taken by light to travel the paths OM_1 and back again and OM_2 and back again, if relative motion between the earth and the ether can be detected.

forward, while the test consisted in watching for the second-order shift in interference fringes which should be observable *if* relative motion of the earth and the ether could be detected.   To understand the nature of the test, consider a simple interferometer arrangement such as represented in Fig. 22.4, where ray 1 is partly reflected, partly transmitted at the half-silvered surface AB, thus giving rise to rays 2 and 3, which after reflection at mirrors M_1 and M_2 subsequently come together in direction 4.   Suppose that the optical paths of rays 2 and 3 are each equal to l, and that the interferometer is so placed that ray 3 is parallel to the orbital motion of the earth.   As has already been pointed out, if the instrument is moving through a stationary ether with velocity v, the problem is the same as if the instrument were stationary, while an ether streamed past with velocity v in the opposite direction.

If, then, V = the velocity of light in a stagnant ether,
   $V + v$ = the velocity with such an ether stream,
   $V - v$ = the velocity against such a stream.

Hence, the time required for light to go from O to M_2 and back to O

$$= \frac{l}{V - v} + \frac{l}{V + v} = \frac{2lV}{V^2 - v^2}$$

$$= \frac{2l}{V\left(1 - \dfrac{v^2}{V^2}\right)} = \frac{2l}{V} \cdot \left(1 + \frac{v^2}{V^2}\right), \qquad (22.07)$$

if we neglect the fourth and higher powers of v^2/V^2.

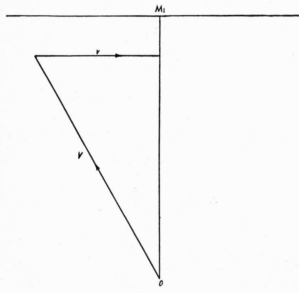

Fig. 22.5.   The resultant velocity in the direction OM_1 of the components V and v is $\sqrt{V^2 - v^2}$.

To find the time required to travel from O to the mirror M_1 and back again, it is well to realize that the problem is essentially the same as that of a boat crossing a flowing stream.   In such a case it is necessary to know the resultant velocity in the direction of the path.   In the direction OM_1 we see at once from the vector diagram of Fig. 22.5, that the velocity has the magnitude $\sqrt{V^2 - v^2}$. Hence the time to travel the path OM_1

$$= \frac{l}{\sqrt{V^2 - v^2}}.$$

Since an equal time is taken to cover the path M_1O, the total time

$$= \frac{2l}{\sqrt{V^2 - v^2}} = \frac{2l}{V\left(1 - \dfrac{v^2}{V^2}\right)^{1/2}}$$

$$= \frac{2l}{V}\left(1 + \frac{v^2}{2V^2}\right), \tag{22.08}$$

again neglecting the fourth and higher powers of v^2/V^2.

Hence ΔT, the *difference* in the times for the two paths is given by

$$\Delta T = \frac{2l}{V}\cdot\left(1 + \frac{v^2}{V^2}\right) - \frac{2l}{V}\cdot\left(1 + \frac{v^2}{2V^2}\right)$$

$$= \frac{lv^2}{V^3}. \tag{22.09}$$

Suppose, now, that the whole apparatus is carefully rotated through 90° so that the path OM_1 becomes parallel to the direction of the earth's motion. Such a rotation then introduces a difference in time $= 2lv^2/V^3$. That is, at any given place in the field of view where fringes are observed, a difference of phase is introduced of an amount corresponding to this time difference, hence a fringe shift should be observed provided the magnitude is great enough. Let us see what shift is to be expected in the Michelson and Morley arrangement.

If f = the fringe shift, λ = the wavelength of light used, then the time

difference $\qquad\qquad\qquad\qquad = f\cdot\dfrac{\lambda}{V}.$

$$\therefore\quad f\cdot\frac{\lambda}{V} = \frac{2lv^2}{V^3}$$

or $\qquad\qquad\qquad\qquad f = \dfrac{2l}{\lambda}\cdot\dfrac{v^2}{V^2}.$

In one actual arrangement, l was about 1100 cm, while v/V, as has been already pointed out, $= 10^{-4}$ approximately. Therefore, for $\lambda = 6 \times 10^{-5}$ cm, we have

$$f = \frac{2 \times 1100}{6 \times 10^{-5}} \times 10^{-8} = 0.4.$$

If, therefore, such an instrument is moving through a stationary ether, on rotation through 90° a shift of about 0.4 of a fringe, *one readily discernible*, should be observed. "In order to minimize the displacements due to external factors . . . the interferometer was mounted on a block of stone 1.5 m square and .25 m thick resting on an annular wooden ring which floated the whole apparatus on mercury" (Michelson). But in spite of the most elaborate precautions, *no shift was observed*.

In 1905 the Michelson and Morley experiment was repeated by Morley and Miller, with more sensitive apparatus, and the same negative result was obtained.

Moreover, other methods of detecting a relative motion of the earth and the ether were tried, and these, too, led to the same conclusion. Into the details of other methods we shall not enter, except to indicate that in one well known experiment use was made of the fact that, if this relative motion existed, a couple should act on a parallel plate electric condenser delicately suspended. In 1902 Trouton and Noble (Great Britain) made a test of this sort with a negative result, a conclusion supported by the repetition of their work with greater refinement by Tomaschek (Germany), in 1925, and by Chase (United States), in 1926.

During the years 1921 to 1925, an elaborate series of observations was carried out by Miller, the result of which seems to indicate an ether drift with a velocity about one-third of the orbital motion of the earth. This drift, however, is not the result of the earth's orbital motion but rather is considered (if a real effect) to be due to "a velocity of the solar system relative to stellar space" (Michelson) or, to quote Miller himself, to be "a systematic cosmical effect as of a true ether drift." But even if Miller's recent experiments (together with all others of its kind) indicate no ether drift as a result of the earth's orbital motion, his work has consequences which cannot be ignored, for it affects the whole basis of the theory of relativity. (See section 22.7.) For that reason, other repetitions of the ether drift experiments were subsequently made, the utmost care being taken to make such tests as refined as possible.

Of these, reference has already been made to that due to Tomaschek and that to Chase. Another important test was made by Kennedy at the California Institute of Technology with an apparatus capable of detecting a shift one-quarter of that observed by Miller. The result was negative. Michelson himself, assisted by Pearse and Pearson, repeated the original Michelson and Morley experiment under somewhat different conditions, and with the most elaborate precautions, and once again the original negative result was obtained. In Germany Joos also repeated the Michelson-Morley experiment and again a negative result was obtained. *The weight of the evidence is then decidedly in favor of the view that the existence of an ether cannot be proved by such experiments.* In the following sections, particularly section 22.8, further information is given about the possible existence of an ether.

22.6. For years before Miller's disquieting results were announced, many physicists had concluded that *it is not possible to detect a motion of the earth with respect to an all-pervading ether.* On the other hand, the ether drag experiments discussed in section 22.3 give positive evidence of an ether being dragged along by moving matter. Do scientists, then, still believe in an ether, and if there is an ether through which the earth is moving, why then the failure to detect a fringe shift which could readily have been observed? The answer to the second question was much debated after the original Michelson and Morley experiment. To it three answers may be given. (1) The premise is wrong, an ether does not exist. It will be pointed out presently that the theory of relativity explains *all* the phenomena discussed in this chapter without postulating an ether, so that this is indeed a possible solution. To this point we shall return.

(2) The ether is of such a nature that in the neighborhood of the earth's surface it is dragged along with the earth, there thus being no relative motion of the two. For a time this idea was given serious consideration, although it led to difficulties concerning the nature of the ether. It was abandoned, however, because an apparently satisfactory explanation was provided by the third answer to our question—one, moreover, which involved ideas ultimately shown to agree with other facts not related to the particular problem we are discussing.

(3) **The Fitzgerald-Lorentz Contraction.** An *ad hoc* explanation (that is, one especially devised to fit the case) which proved to have a wider scope than its author realized was suggested by Fitzgerald (Great Britain). According to his hypothesis, the earth moves through a stagnant ether, but all bodies on its surface suffer a contraction in the direction of their motion relative to the ether, none at all in a direction at right angles. If this change in length is in the ratio $1 : \sqrt{1 - (v^2/V^2)}$, it is not difficult to show that the dimensions of the Michelson and Morley apparatus would be so altered that no phase difference is introduced on rotation through 90°, hence no fringe shift. By actual measurement, any such change in dimension could never be demonstrated, for the dimensions of rulers and all measuring instruments would always alter in the same ratio as those of the bodies to which they were applied. The Fitzgerald hypothesis, therefore, being of the *ad hoc* variety, and, indeed, being one which raised certain serious difficulties which need not here be considered, could not by itself be considered a highly satisfactory solution of the problem.

By means of an extension due to Lorentz (Holland), however, the same contraction formula was deduced on a more fundamental basis. Moreover, the hypothesis of Lorentz led to results confirmed by experiment. In brief, by utilizing standard electromagnetic theory, Lorentz showed that, *granted a contraction of individual moving electrons*, the bulk contraction of Fitzgerald followed. Stated thus, there may seem little difference in the two theories, but, when it is realized, not only that Lorentz' work did not give rise to the difficulties encountered in the original proposal, but also that it led to a conclusion verified by direct experiment, it will be realized how much more fundamental was this new viewpoint. According to the Lorentz theory, the *mass* of an electron should increase with its speed in the ratio $1 : \sqrt{1 - (v^2/V^2)}$. Subsequent experiments on high speed electrons amply verified this conclusion. It would seem, then, as if a satisfactory explanation of the negative result of the Michelson and Morley experiment had been provided—one, moreover, *which accepted the idea of an ether* with reference to which the absolute motion of bodies could be expressed.

22.7. But the negative result was to have consequences that were much more far-reaching than those of the Fitzgerald-Lorentz contraction hypothesis, for it led to the theory of relativity, one of the most remarkable developments of modern physics. While the author feels it is wise to conclude this book by leaving the reader at the entrance to this fascinating field, and therefore has no intension of going into the details of relativity, one or two general remarks are not amiss. As most people know, the foundation of this theory was laid by Einstein (Germany), who, as a basis on which to build his structure, postulated two things.

(1) The velocity of light is independent of the velocity of the source and of the observer. About this there was nothing new, for it is confirmed by observation, and, indeed, for that reason, it is a fact rather than a postulate.

(2) It is impossible to detect a uniform motion of the earth or any system through space by observations made on that system. In effect this says, there is no such thing as absolute motion relative to an all-pervading ether. No experiments have ever shown the existence of such a motion and none ever will. Accepting this postulate, further experiments such as the Michelson and Miller are, of course, useless.

With these postulates as a basis, the (special) theory of relativity shows that the dimensions of moving bodies vary with their velocities in accordance with the law exemplified by that governing the Fitzgerald-Lorentz contraction; that the mass of a moving body depends on its velocity subject to the law given by Lorentz; and, in fact, that all the phenomena discussed in this chapter find a ready interpretation. For all the work on relativity, the ether concept is superfluous. Is, then, the ether to be discarded?

22.8. Is There an Ether? In concluding this book with a section dealing with this question, a brief summing up of the work of this chapter is desirable. Note the following. (1) Positive evidence of the existence of an ether is provided by the experiments relating to ether drag and the Fresnel coefficient $[1 - (1/n^2)]$. On the other hand, as Leon Blitzer (United States) has pointed out, by making use of the Lorentz transformation equations in relativity, it is easy to interpret this coefficient as "the fractional relative velocity that enters because of the relative motion of the medium and the observer, without any assumptions as to the properties or even existence of an ether." (2) As we have noted previously, according to the theory of relativity, which is based on the negative result of the Michelson-Morley experiment, an ether is unnecessary—and the theory of relativity represents a body of knowledge leading to important conclusions confirmed by experiment. (3) It would seem then that the ether should be disregarded, as indeed it has been by many physicists in the last few decades. Not, however, by all. Some years ago, Eddington (Great Britain), a well-known relativist, wrote: "We postulate ether to bear the characters of the interspace, as we postulate matter or electricity to bear the characters of the particles." Sir Edmund Whittaker (Great Britain), in his preface to a 1951 edition of his book *History of the Theories of Ether and Electricity*, writes: "It seems absurd to retain the name 'vacuum' for an entity so rich in physical properties, and the historical word 'ether' may fitly be retained." In November 1951, Dirac (Great Britain), the world-famous theoretical physicist in a letter to *Nature*, gives reasons, based on a new theory of electrodynamics, for concluding that "the ether is no longer ruled out by relativity," that "good reason can now be advanced for postulating an ether," and "with the new theory of electrodynamics we are rather forced to have an ether."

The student may be forgiven for having a feeling of dissatisfaction and for being inclined to agree with the accusation sometimes made against the scientist that he is always changing his mind. Let him remember, however, that the true scientist gladly pleads guilty to that charge, for it is a foundation stone of his faith that he must keep an open mind about all questions and, if necessary, alter his theories in the light of increasing knowledge. Progress in every sphere is made by searching for truth, not by looking for arguments to support a theory. As far as the ether is concerned, the student may wish to accept the view of the author and think of it as the vehicle necessary for the transmission of electromagnetic energy.

Table XX. Some Useful Wavelengths in the Laboratory

Source	Wavelength
Hydrogen vacuum tube	6562.79(H_α) 4861.33(H_β) 4340.47(H_γ) 4101.74(H_δ)
Helium vacuum tube	7065.19 6678.15 5875.62 — (d_3) 5015.67 4921.93 4713.14 4471.14 4387.93 4026.19 3888.65
Mercury vapor lamp (glass)	5790 5770 5460.7 4358.3 4046.5
(quartz)	3662.9 3654.8 3650.1 3131.5 3125.7 2967.3 2536.5
Sodium flame	5895.93 — (D_1). 5889.96 — (D_2).

Table XXI.   A Few Members of the Principal, Sharp and Diffuse Series of Lithium
(Wavelengths from Fowler's Report on Series in Line Spectra.)

Principal $1S - mP$.			Sharp $1P - mS$		
$1S = 43486.3$			$1P = 28582.5$		
λ	m	mP	λ	m	mS
6708.85	1	28582.5			
3232.61	2	12560.4	8126.52	2	16280.5
2741.31	3	7018.2	4971.93	3	8475.2
2562.50	4	4473.6	4273.28	4	5187.8
2475.29	5	3099.2	3985.79	5	3500.4

Diffuse $1P - mD$

	m	mD
$1P = 28582.5$		
6103.53	2	12203.1
4602.99	3	6863.5
4132.29	4	4389.6
3915.0	5	3047.0

Answers to Problems

Chapter II

1. (a) 2.988×10^8 m per sec. (b) 2250 rpm. **2.** 305.5, 458.2, 763.7 rpm. **3.** 3.00 $\times 10^8$ m per sec. **4.** 353.3 and 265 rps. **5.** 2.999×10^8 m per sec.

Chapter III

1. 3.00 ft. **2.** 8 ft. **3.** 1.58. **4.** 78°. **6.** 11.2 cm. **7.** (c) $2 \sin^{-1} \dfrac{V}{v}$. **8.** (b) 48°35′.
9. 38°. **10.** At 34°49′ with AC. **13.** 1.6 cm. **14.** 31.25 cm from surface. **15.** 31.8 cm in front of surface. **16.** 51.3 cm from surface. **17.** 30.1 cm beyond plane window. **18.** 13.2 cm from lens in air. **19.** 80.1 cm from window. **20.** 50.5 cm from lens. **21.** 23.0 cm from lens. **22.** 12.4 cm from lens. **23.** 40.1 cm from lens in second liquid. **24.** (a) +19.1 cm. (b) +38.2 cm. (c) −38.2 cm. (d) +343.5 cm. (e) −343.5 cm. **25.** +91.6 cm. **27.** −131 cm. **28.** (a) 0.656; (b) 8.3 cm. **29.** 0.393. **30.** 2.0. **31.** 2.68.

Chapter IV

1. (a) 24 cm, 36, 10. **2.** 11 in. **3.** (a) 6.67 cm. (b) 10.67 cm. **4.** 8.67 cm. **5.** 4 cm. **6.** 2.67 cm. **7.** 5.3 cm in front of diverging lens. **8.** 18 cm beyond converging lens. **9.** 36 cm on object side of second lens. **10.** Image 6.67 cm beyond second lens, 0.33 cm long. **11.** (a) 24 cm in front of second lens; (b) 8 cm. **12.** (a) 20 cm in front of diverging lens; (b) 0.67 cm. **13.** (a) 26.7 cm beyond second lens. (b) 2.33 cm. **14.** 10.44 cm. **15.** (a) 16 cm. (b) 2.4 cm. **16.** 18 cm. **18.** 40 cm beyond second face. **20.** (a) $\alpha = +0.53$ cm; $\beta = -0.80$ cm. (b) 87.7 cm from second face; (c) 82.3 cm from second face. **21.** 39.8 cm from second face.

Chapter V

1. 30 cm, 6 cm. **2.** 6 cm to 4.84 cm. **4.** 24°. **5.** (a) 64.2 cm. (b) 12.6 cm. **6.** (a) 4.67 cm beyond eye lens. (b) 0.33 cm. (c) 61 min. **7.** 1.4 cm. **8.** 6.48 meters. **9.** (a) (i) M.P., 6.25 and 7.14; L.M., infinity and 8; M.P., 6.9, L.M., 10. **11.** (a) 34.45 cm. (c) 6.75. **12.** 4.5 mm. **13.** 5.56. **14.** 7.4. **18.** (a) 6.25 mm. (b) 1.64 cm from eye lens. **20.** 1.26 mm. **21.** (a) 5. (b) 5 cm from magnifier. (c) 6. **22.** 7.2. **24.** 160. **25.** (a) 150. (b) 66.7. **26.** (a) 1.6 mm. (b) 154. **27.** 1.95 mm. **28.** (a) at infinity; (b) 39 cm in front of lens next eye.

Chapter VI

1. (a) 31°12′; (b) 22°24′; (c) 21°54′. **2.** 50°19′. **3.** -1.47×10^3 cm^{-1}. **5.** (b)(i)10°; (ii) 6.98 mm. **7.** 23.3 mm. **8.** (a) 0.314 mm; (b) 27 min. **9.** 4°54′. **10.** 33°28′. **11.** 1.5 mm. **12.** 10.5°; 2.24°. **13.** (a) 3.86°; (b) 3.80°. **14.** (a) 1.6244, 1.5106; (b) 7.34°; (c) 0.042°. **15.** 6.91°; 14.3°. **17.** (a) −30 cm; (b) 1.5. **18.** −38.4 cm. **19.** C light, 24.82, 42.33; for F, 24.43, 41.19. **20.** 58.03 cm. **21.** $r_1 = +21.6$ cm, $r_4 = +197.6$ cm. **22.** $r_1 = +32.3$ cm, $r_2 = -34.6$ cm. **23.** 20.34 cm. **24.** crown 0.0161, flint 0.0274. **25.** 0.0164. **26.** 20.16 cm, 19.61 cm. **27.** 3.5 mm. **30.** 5.1 mm.

Chapter VII

1. (a) 1825. (b) 45°. **2.** 3.80. **3.** (b) 335°, 270°, 225°, 180°, 162°. (c) −7.07, −10.0, −7.07, 0, +3.09. **4.** (a) 120°, 0°, 300°. (b) +8.66, 0, −8.66. **5.** (a) 160°, 30°, 340°. (b) 36 cm. (c) 5 cm. (d) DA = 2 cm, BE = 3 cm; order of particles, D, A, B, E, C. **6.** (a) 0.06 sec. (b) 10 cm. **7.** (a) 5000 cm per sec. (b) 60°. **8.** 0.0075 sec. **9.** (a) +3.0, +5.2. (b) 36.7 cm. **10.** (a) 156°25′. (b) 180 cm. **11.** (a) (i) 72 cm, (ii) 1440 cm per sec. (b) 1.74 units. **12.** 23.7 cm, 83.7 cm. **13.** (a) 1.41 a. (b) 0. (c) $2a$. **14.** 10.1. **15.** (a) $y = 13.5 \sin\left(\dfrac{2\pi t}{T} - 17°12'\right)$. (b) $y = 12.2 \sin\left(\dfrac{2\pi t}{T} + 4°43'\right)$. (c) $y = 8.2 \sin\left(\dfrac{2\pi t}{T} - 16°50'\right)$. **17.** (a) 11.9. (b) $y = 11.9 \sin\left(\dfrac{2\pi t}{T} - 42°20'\right)$. **18.** 60°. **21.** 5 units. **24.** $y = 12 \sin\left(\dfrac{\pi x}{50} - \dfrac{\pi}{2}\right)$. **25.** (a) $y = 10 \sin\pi\left(\dfrac{x}{100} + \dfrac{5}{6}\right)$. (b) $y = 10 \sin\left(\dfrac{\pi x}{100} + \dfrac{\pi}{6}\right)$. **26.** (a) $y = 2 \sin\left(\pi + \dfrac{2\pi x}{40}\right)$. (b) $y = 2 \sin\left(\dfrac{\pi}{2} + \dfrac{2\pi x}{40}\right)$. **27.** (a) 21 sec. (b) 400 cm; 100 cm per sec. (c) 2.3.

Chapter IX

1. 0.75. **3.** 2.0. **4.** 0.853. **5.** (a) 0.8 mm; (b) 45°; (c) 0.85. **6.** 14.9. **7.** 0.376 mm. **8.** 90°. **9.** 6.4×10^{-5} cm. **10.** 3.75 min. **11.** 41.1. **12.** 1.00029. **13.** 1.000268. **14.** 1.000322. **15.** 1.000335. **16.** 4.7 mm. **17.** 0.1 sec. **18.** 0.364 mm. **19.** 6.2×10^{-5} cm. **20.** 0.144 mm. **21.** 1.606. **22.** 0.0624 mm. **23.** 30 sec. **24.** 5.63×10^{-5} cm. **25.** (a) 2.29×10^{-2} mm; (b) 27.3 cm. **26.** 1.42 mm. **27.** 1.06 mm. **28.** (a) (i) 2.59×10^{-3} mm; (ii) 2.05×10^{-3} mm. (b) 3.23 mm, 2.96 mm; (c) 2.80 mm, 2.57 mm. **30.** $D_n{}^2 = 2(2n - 1)\lambda R$. **31.** 0.79. **32.** 0.998, 0.4. **34.** (a) 60°; (b) 40°. **35.** 270°. **36.** 288°. **37.** 4667 A, 5600 A, 7000 A. **38.** Violet end. **39.** 0.29 mm.

Chapter XI

1. (a) 3; (b) 300. **4.** (a) 5.9×10^{-4} mm; (b) 108.6 cm. **5.** 5.34×10^{-4} mm. **6.** 0.126 mm. **8.** To 0.25 of original value. **9.** (b) 0.5. **10.** 4.9 mm. **11.** 75°. **12.** 2.47. **13.** (a) (i) 0.18 mm. (ii) 0.12 mm. (b) $\dfrac{2\sqrt{2}}{\pi}, \dfrac{3}{\pi}$. **14.** 0.135 sec. **16.** 0.39 mm. **17.** 0.98 mm. **18.** 1.84 mm. **19.** 15.5 mm. **20.** 661. **21.** (a) 0.157; (b) 332. **22.** 3.785 $\times 10^4$, 5.21×10^4. **24.** 222. **25.** 5.9×10^{-5} cm. **26.** 4.08 mm. **27.** 0.208 mm. **28.** 6510 A. **30.** (a) 2°59′; (b) 25. **32.** 60,000. **33.** (a) 1.46×10^4 radian per cm; (b) 14,636; (c) 17.7×10^3. **34.** 1.17 mm. **35.** 31.7. **37.** 36.6 cm.

Chapter XV

5. 4 images, with intensities in ratio 1, 1.42, 1, 1.42. **6.** (a) 45°; (b) 54°44′. **7.** (a) 15 per cent; (b) 74 per cent. **8.** 1 to 1.46. **10.** By 41.3 per cent. **12.** 1.540. **13.** 1.732. **15.** Vibration plane of light incident on crystal must make angle of 35°16′ with principal plane of crystal. **16.** (a) 90°; (b) 0.528; (c) elliptical. **17.** (a) linear; (c) 0.030 mm. **18.** 4.94 mm. **19.** 0.0156 mm. **20.** 6.2 mm. **22.** 1 to 0.094. **23.** 2.085 mm. **30.** 3.6 mm.

Chapter XX

1. (a) 12,186 cm^{-1}; 6,855 cm^{-1}. (b) 8137 A. **3.** 3231 A. **4.** 40,205 cm^{-1}; 21,891 cm^{-1}. **5.** (a) 1849 A; (b) 20,251 cm^{-1}. **6.** 6092 A. **7.** (i) 12.0 volts; (ii) 13.5 volts. **8.** (i) 2520 A; (ii) 44,491 cm^{-1}.

Index

Aberration
astigmatism, 50
coma, 49
chromatic, 51, 59, 106
curvature of field, 51
distortion, 51
of light, 12, 387, 389
spherical, 48, 79, 82
Absorption
band, 307
coefficient, 136
explanation of, 307, 369
selective, 316
spectrum, 316, 366, 369, 370
Acceleration of electric charge, 323, 350, 379
Accommodation, 72
Achromat, 88
Achromatic:
combination, 80, 108
lens, 107, 109
Achromatism, 106
Airy, 389, 392
Airy's experiment, 389
Amplitude:
and intensity, 136
and law of Malus, 266
and obliquity, 193
decrease with distance, 135
definition of, 118
resultant for several S.H.M., 128
resultant for two S.H.M., 127
Analysis:
of optically active substances, 289
of polarized light, 278
spectrum, 321
Analyzer, 264, 265, 273, 275
Anastigmat, 51
Anderson, 17
Angstrom, International, 101, 180
Angular momentum quantized, 351, 359, 362, 363
Anomalous:
dispersion, 308
Zeeman effect, 327

Anti-nodes, 138, 306
Apatite, 249
Apochromat, 88
Arago, 14, 285
Aragonite, 249
Aslakson, 19
Astigmatism, 50
Atomic:
nucleus, 312
number, 313
Avogadro's number, 336
Axis, optic, definition of, 247
Azimuthal quantum number, 359, 362

Babinet compensator, 280
Balmer, 340, 341
Balmer series and helium, 358
Balmer series of hydrogen, 341, 350, 353, 354, 370
Band:
electronic, 375
head, 315
isotope effect, 374
progressions, 376
rotation, 371
sequence, 376
single, 370, 376
spectrum, 315, 370
system, 376
vibration-rotation, 373
Barker, 375
Barrell, 177, 181
Bartholinus, 247
Bearden, 20
Benoît, 180
Bergstrand, 18
Biaxial crystal, 249
Biprism, 149
Biquartz, 288
Birge, 20, 356
Black body, 330, 332
Blitzer, 399
Blue of the sky, 241
Bohr, 350

Bohr's:
  frequency condition, 350
  quantum condition, 352
  theory, 350, 383, 385
  theory and heavy hydrogen, 356
  theory and ionized helium, 357
Bol, 19
Boltzmann, 301
Borax, 249
Brackett, 342
Bradley, 12, 387, 389
Brewster, 264
Brickwedde, 356, 357
Buckley, 284
Bullard, 177
Burch, 218

Cadmium red line, 101, 180
Cadmium series, 347
Canada Balsam, 256
Candela, 331
Cauchy, 103
  dispersion formula, 103, 308
Caustic curve, 36
Chase, 397
  ether test, 397
Chromatic aberration, 51, 79, 106
Chromatism:
  axial, 107
  lateral, 51, 107
  longitudinal, 51
Circular:
  motion, 132, 278
  polariscope, 281
  vibrations, composition of, 371
Circularly:
  doubly refracting, 293
  polarized light, 132, 277, 279, 281
Cohen, 20
Coherent sources, 148
Collier, 333
Collimator of spectrometer, 97
Color temperature, 333
Coma, 49
Combination law, 344
Compensator, Babinet, 280
Complementary colors, 274
Compton, 380
  effect, 379, 380
Concave grating, 237
Condenser, microscope, 219
Congruent rays, 170
Continuous:
  spectrum, 314, 326, 329
  wave-front, 11, 9, 337
Convention for signs, 39, 44
Cornu, 13
Cornu-Jellett Nicol, 289

Cornu's spiral, 201
Corpuscular theory, 3, 4, 8, 379
  and reflection, 4
  and refraction, 4
Critical angle, 29
Crossed position of polariscope, 273
Crosshair lines, 86
Crystal reflection:
  of electrons, 381
  of x-rays, 382
Curvature:
  measure of, 33
  of field, 51

Davisson, 381, 382, 383, 384, 385
Delaup, 161
De Broglie, 383, 385
De Groot, 333
De Lury, 317
Dennison, 375
Descartes, 1, 3, 26
Deslandres, 371
Deuterium, *see* Heavy hydrogen
Deviation:
  by prism, 96
  minimum, 96
  without dispersion, 108
Dextro-rotatory, 286, 293
Dichroism, 257
Dielectric:
  constant, 301
  index of refraction of, 301
Diffraction:
  and interference, 187, 190
  circular aperture, 194
  circular obstacle, 188, 195
  Cornu's spiral, 201
  double slit, 221
  Fraunhofer, 205
  Fresnel, 205
  general treatment of, 198
  grating, concave, 237
  grating, reflection, 235
  grating, transmission, 224
  half-period elements, 190, 201
  half-period zones, 190
  Huygens' Principle, 187
  large aperture, 195
  large obstacle, 195
  limit of resolution, 211
  many apertures, 224
  measurement of wave-length, 227
  narrow aperture, 188, 189, 201, 207
  narrow wire, 201
  orders, 227
  rectangular aperture, 188, 189, 201, 207

rectilinear propagation, 22, 187, 197, 211
resolving power, 211
straight edge, 203
two apertures, 221
zone plate, 197
Diffuse series, 343, 345
Dilemma in light, 379
Dirac, 400
Direct vision spectroscope, 111
Dispersion, 99, 101, 306
  and resolving power, 232
  anomalous, 308
  Cauchy formula, 103
  curve, 102
  formulae, 103
  Hartmann formula, 104
  irrational, 104, 108
  normal, 103
  of grating, 232
  of instrument, 106, 232
  theory of, 306
Dispersive power, 110
Displacement currents, 299
Distortion, 51
Doppler effect, 318, 322
Dorsey, 20
Double-image prism, 262
Double refraction, 247
  apatite, 249
  aragonite, 249
  biaxial crystal, 249
  borax, 249
  dichroism, 257
  double-image prism, 262
  E image, 248
  extraordinary index, 254
  Foucault prism, 257
  Huygens' construction of wave surfaces, 250
  Huygens' explanation of, 249
  ice, 249, 255
  Iceland spar, 247, 255
  in strained glass, 281
  mica, 249
  negative crystal, 255
  Nicol prism, 255
  nitrate of soda, 249, 255
  O image, 248
  optic axis, 247
  Polaroid, 257
  polarization of beams, 262
  positive crystal, 255
  principal plane, definition of, 257
  quartz, 249, 255
  tourmaline, 249, 255, 257
  uniaxial crystal, 249
Double slit, 7, 148, 221

Doublet fine structure, 361
Doublet series, 345
Doublets, 345
Doubly refracting, circularly, 293
Drag of ether, 391
Drift of ether, 391
Du Mond, 20
Dynamics, Newtonian, 454

Echelle grating, 236
Echelette grating, 236
Echelon, 236
Eddington, 399
Einstein, 336, 379, 399
  and relativity, 399
  law of, 337
Elastic modulus, 298
Elastic solid, 298
  ether, 8, 298, 387
Elasticity, coefficient of, 298
Electric:
  displacement currents, 299
  field, Stark effect, 320
  nodes, 306
  vector, 305
  waves, 302, 304, 305
Electrical source of spectra, 323
Electrodeless discharge, 314
Electromagnetic:
  constant, 300
  theory, 8, 298, 299, 385
  theory and dispersion, 306
  waves, 298, 299, 303, 306
  waves, range of, 304
Electron microscope, 220
Electron orbits, 361
Electron spin, 361
Electron waves, 381
  measurement of wavelength, 383
Electronic:
  band, 375
  bombardment, 312
  energy change, 371
  energy level, 376
Electrons:
  and waves, 381, 384
  collisions with quanta, 379
  contraction of, 398
  emission of, 313
  reflection of, 382
  variation of mass with speed, 398
Element, grating, 225
Elements, half-period, 190
Elliptic polarization, 277, 279
  analysis of, 278
Emission:
  of electrons, 313

of single spectral line, 314
spectra, 314
Energy:
    and spherical waves, 135
    change, electronic, 371
    change, rotational, 371
    change, vibrational, 371
    diagrams, 368, 369, 370
    distribution of, in spectrum, 329
    levels, 351, 358, 370, 373, 374, 375
    quantum of, 335
    unit, Planck's, 9, 335
Epoch, 122
Equivalent focal length, 66
Essen, 19
Étalon, Fabry-Perot, 172, 176, 364
Ether, 4, 6, 8, 298, 387, 399
    and absolute motion, 398
    and theory of relativity, 399
    contractile, 299
    dragged by matter, 391, 399
    drift, 391
    elastic solid, 8, 298
    existence of, 387, 397, 399
    stream, virtual, 393
    test, first order effect, 392
    test, Fizeau's experiment, 392
    test, second order effect, 393, 394
Euler, 3
Excitation potential, 367
Exit pupil, 77, 91, 220
Extraordinary:
    image, 248
    image, polarized, 262
    index, definition of, 254
Eye, 71
    limit of resolution of, 214
Eyepiece:
    and double-image prism, 263
    equivalent focal length, 83
    Huygens, 85
    magnifying power of, 84
    of microscope, 87
    of telescope, 79, 80
    Ramsden, 80
Eye point, 77, 78
Eye ring, 77, 214

Fabry-Perot:
    étalon, 172, 176, 364
    interferometer, 172
Faraday, 291, 387
    tubes, 299, 302, 387
Field of view, 79
Filter, interference, 175
Finch, 221
Fine structure:
    doublet, 361

hydrogen, 177, 362
    ionized helium, 363
Fitzgerald, 398
Fitzgerald-Lorentz contraction, 398
Fizeau, 12, 14, 166, 392
Fizeau's experiment, 392
Fizeau fringes, 166
Flame spectrum, 311
Focal length:
    equivalent, 66
    of lens, 46
    of spherical mirror, 36
Foote, 314
Foster, 321
Foucault, 2, 8, 14
Foucault prism, 257
Fourier's theorem, 132
Fowler, 358
Franck, 338
Fraunhofer, 229
    diffraction, 205
    lines, 316, 317, 318
Fraunhofer's gratings, 229
Frequency:
    condition of Bohr, 450
    natural, 307
    orbital, 326
Fresnel, 6, 187, 294, 392
    diffraction, 205
    mirrors, 150
Fresnel's coefficient, ether drift, 391
Fringes, interference:
    biprism, 149
    double slit, 6, 148, 152, 156, 221
    Fabry-Perot, 172, 176
    Fizeau, 166
    Fresnel mirrors, 150
    Haidinger, 172
    Hooke's explanation of, 170
    intensity distribution of, 147, 173
    Lloyd's single mirror, 150
    Newton's Rings, 168, 174
    of equal inclination, 170
    of equal thickness, 165
    quartz wedge, 274
    shift of, 159, 393, 396
    soap film, 162
    thin film, 162
    white light, 152, 162
    width of, 147, 173
Fuchsine, 309

Galileo, 10
Gamma rays, 305
Germer, 381, 382, 383, 384, 385
Grating, diffraction:
    concave, 237
    dispersion of, 232

echelle, 236
echelette, 236
echelon, 236
element, 225
rational spectrum, 227
reflection, 235, 238, 239
resolving power of, 232, 236
spectra, 227, 228
transmission, 224
used by Fraunhofer, 229
width of maxima, 225
wire, 229
Gray, 380
Green, 299
Grimaldi, 2, 6, 187, 188

Haidinger fringes, 172
Half-period:
  elements, 190
  zones, 190
Hansen, 19
Hardy, 375
Harrison, 237
Hartmann dispersion formula, 104
Heavy hydrogen:
  and Bohr theory, 356
  discovery of, 356
Heisenberg, 383
Helium:
  ionized, 357, 363
  spectrum, 315, 357
  wavelengths, 400
Herapath, 258
Herapathite, 258
Hertz, 8, 9, 301, 302, 304, 336, 338
Hertzian waves, 302
Hooke, 3, 6, 170
Hooke's law, 298
Houston, 19
Hughes, 336
Huygens, 3, 21, 22, 249
  construction, 21
  explanation of double refraction, 249
  eyepiece, 85
  Principle, 21, 22
Hydrogen:
  absorption spectrum of, 370
  energy diagram, 369
  fine structure, 177, 362
  heavy, 177, 356
  isotopes, 356
  series, 340, 353
  spectrum, 315, 359
  terms, 361
  wavelengths, 400
Hyperfine structure, 364

Ice, 249, 255
Iceland spar, 247, 255

Illumination, 334
Image:
  extraordinary, 248
  ordinary, 248
Inconel deposit, 232
Index of refraction:
  and electromagnetic theory, 301
  definition of, 26
  determination of, 27, 158, 161, 254
  of gas, 158, 161, 302
  tables of, 98, 102, 255, 302
Initial magnification of microscope, 87, 216
Inner quantum number, 362
Integrating sphere, 334
Intensity:
  and amplitude, 136
  distribution in fringes, 147, 173
  luminous, 331
  of diffraction pattern, 210, 222, 223
Interference, *see also* Fringes
  and light theories, 67, 187
  and scattering, 275
  coherent sources, 148
  congruent rays, 170
  étalon, 172
  filter, 175
  Lummer plate, 178
  measurement of
    angular separation of two stars, 157
    angular width of star, 157
    distance, 179
    index of refraction, 158, 161
  of polarized light, 271, 282, 284
  principle of, 7
  realization of, 148
  standard meter, 179, 181
  with multiple reflections, 172, 174, 177
  with two sources, 146, 151, 173
Interferometer:
  Fabry-Perot, 172
  Michelson, 178
  Rayleigh, 155, 158
International angstrom, 101
Inverse square law, 135
Ionization potential, 368
Ionized helium, 357, 363
Irrational dispersion, 104, 108
Isotopes:
  band spectra, 374
  of hydrogen, 356
  of mercury, 356
  shifts, 365

Johnson, 217, 218
Jones, 177
Joos, 397

Kelvin, 299
Kennedy, 397
Kerker, 240
Kinetic theory and Doppler effect, 322
Kirchhoff, 23
Kirchhoff's law, 317
Krypton, 84, 182

Ladenburg, 370
Laevo-rotatory, 286, 293
Lagrange's theorem, 42
Land, 258
Laplace, 3
La Mer, 240
Lenard, 336
Lens:
    aberrations, 48, 49, 50, 51
    achromatic, 107, 109
    and plane waves, 46
    and spherical waves, 48
    sign convention, 39, 44
    thick, 61
Lenses, combinations of, 59, 66
Level:
    electronic, 376
    energy, 358, 366, 368, 369, 370
    normal, 368
    rotational, 373
    vibrational, 375
Lightwatt, 332
Limit of resolution, 211
Limit of series, 343
Line spectra, 315 (*see also* Spectrum)
Line, spectral, analysis of, 176
Linear magnification, 68
Lissajous figures, 131
Lithium:
    series, 343
    terms, 401
    wavelengths, 401
Lloyd's single mirror, 150
Lodge, 323
Longitudinal vibrations, 247, 299
Loops, 138
Lorentz, 323, 326, 327
    Fitzgerald-Lorentz contraction, 398
Lumen, 330, 332
Luminance, 334
Luminosity curve, 330
Luminous emittance, 334
Luminous flux, 330
Luminous intensity, 331
Lummer plate, 178
Lux, 334
Lyman, 342
    series, 342, 354

Magnesium spectrum, 316, 338
Magnetic field:
    and electromagnetic theory, 300
    rotation by, 291
    Zeeman effect, 320, 323
Magnification:
    initial, 87, 216
    linear, 68
    normal, 90, 220
    of electron microscope, 221
Magnifier, 73, 86
Magnifying glass, 73
Magnifying power, 72, 73
    and resolving power, 214, 217, 219
    normal, 90, 220
    of eyepiece, 73, 75
    of magnifier, 86
    of microscope, 87, 219
    of Ramsden eyepiece, 83
    of telescope, 77, 82
Malus, 263, 265
    law of, 265
Mass of electron, variation with velocity, 398
Maxwell, 8, 299, 300, 301, 304, 387
    displacement currents, 299
    electromagnetic theory, 9, 299, 385
Mechanical equivalent of light, 332
Mechanics:
    Newtonian, 335, 379, 380
    quantum, 362, 363, 382
    wave, 382
Meggers, 181, 314
Menzel, 356
Mercury:
    isotope, 198, 182
    isotopes, 356
    spectrum of, 315
    wavelengths, 400
Meter, measurement of, 179, 181
Mica, 255
Michelson, 2, 8, 15, 16, 157, 178, 180, 182, 236, 392, 394, 396, 399
    and Morley experiment, 394, 396, 399
    interferometer, 178
    measurement of meter, 179
Microscope, 86
    condenser, 219
    electron, 220
    exit pupil, 91
    initial magnification, 87, 216
    magnifying power, 88, 219
    normal magnification, 90
    numerical aperture, 89, 217, 219
    objective, 86, 88, 216
    phase contrast, 229
    reflecting, 218

resolving power, 215, 217, 219
  simple, 75
Miller, 396, 397, 399
Millikan, 336, 338
Minimum deviation, 96
Mirrors, Fresnel, 150
Modulus, elastic, 298
Mohler, 315
Moment of inertia:
  and band spectra, 371
Momentum:
  angular, 351, 352, 362
  of quantum, 381
  spin, 362
Morley, 392, 394
  and Michelson experiment, 394, 396, 399
Multiplet series, 345
Murphy, 356, 357

Negative:
  contrast, 232
  crystal, 255
Newcomb, 15
Newton, 3, 4, 5, 6, 100, 170, 187, 188, 379
Newtonian:
  dynamics, 379
  mechanics, 335, 379, 380
Newton's Rings, 168, 174
Nichols, 305
Nicol prism, 255
Nitrate of soda, 249, 255
Noble, 397
  and Trouton experiment, 397
Nodal points, 65
Nodes, 138, 306
Non-radiating orbit, 350
Nonreflecting glass, 166
Normal dispersion, 103
Nuclear spin, 365
Numerical aperture:
  and magnifying power, 90, 217
  and resolving power, 217, 219
  of microscope, 89

Objective:
  achromat, 88
  apochromat, 88
  oil-immersion, 88, 217
  of microscope, 88, 216
  of telescope, 76, 155, 171, 207, 211, 214
Optic axis, 247
Optically active substance, 286, 289
Orbit:
  circular, 351, 360
  electron, 361
  elliptical, 359, 360
  non-radiating, 350
  stable, 350

Orbital frequency, 326
Orbits and energy levels, 354
Orders:
  number of, in grating, 227
  spectral, 227
  width of, 225
Ordinary image, 248
  polarization of, 262
Origin of spectra, 311
Oscillator, electronic, 335

Paraxial:
  equation, 42
  ray, 42
Particle and waves, 383
Paschen, 342
  series, 342, 354
Path difference:
  and phase difference, 133
  for thin film, 165
Pearse, 357, 376
Pearson, 16, 397
Pease, 16, 397
Periodic time, 26
Perot, see Fabry
Pfund, 342
Phase:
  angle, 122
  change of, on reflection, 166
  contrast microscope, 229
  difference, 133
  plate, 231
Photoelasticity, 281
Photoelectricity, 9, 336
Photometry, 330
Photomicrography, 217
Photon, 9, 12, 379
Pile of plates, and polarization, 263
Planck, 335, 350, 379
  constant, 335
  energy, unit, 335
  radiation law, 336
Plane of polarization, 264
Plane parallel surfaces, 171
Plane polarized light, see Polarization
Plane wave:
  equation of, 133
  oblique reflection of, 24
  refraction of, 26
Plane wave-front, 22, 135
Plurality of spectra, 315
Polarization:
  analysis of, 278
  analyzer, 264, 265, 273
  and interference, 27, 282, 284
  Babinet compensator, 280
  biquartz, 288

by reflection, 263
by scattering, 260, 275
circular, 277, 279, 281
complementary colors, 274
Cornu-Jellett Nicol, 289
detection of strain, 281
double-image prism, 262
elliptical, 277, 279
extraordinary beam, 262
Law of Malus, 265
meaning of, 259
Nicol prism, 255
of skylight, 262
ordinary beam, 262
plane polarized light, 259
polarimeter, 289
polariscope, 265, 281
polarizer, 265, 273
quarter-wave plate, 278, 279, 281, 282
removal of glare, 268, 282
rotatory, 285, 292
saccharimeter, 289
sensitive tint, 288
specific rotation, 291
test of strain, 281
tint of passage, 287
tourmaline, 249, 255, 257
vibration plane, 260, 261, 264
Zeeman effect, 263
Polarizer, 265, 273
Polaroid, 257
advantages of, 268
disadvantages of, 268
Vectograph, 269
Positive:
contrast, 232
crystal, 255
Potential:
excitation, 367
ionization, 368
radiating, 366, 367
radiation, 366
Power:
dispersive, 110
resolving, 211, 214, 215, 217, 219, 232, 236
Pressure, and width of spectral line, 321
Principal plane, definition of, 257
Principal planes:
of eyepiece, 83, 84
thick lens, 64
two thin lenses, 66
Principal points, 64, 66
Principal series, 343, 345
Prism:
achromatic combination, 108
deviation, 96
double-image, 262

sodium vapor, 310
spectrograph, 104
Progression, band spectra, 376
Propagation:
of light, 1
rectilinear, 2, 6, 22, 187, 197, 211
Ptolemy, 1

Quantum, 9, 329
collision with electron, 380
condition, 351
defect, 349
mechanics, 362, 363, 382
momentum of, 381
number, azimuthal, 359, 362
number, inner, 362
number, total, 359
of energy, 9, 335
Quantum theory, 9, 329, 335, 338
and photoelectric effect, 336
birth of, 329
Quarter-wave plate, 278, 279, 281, 282
Quartz:
Babinet compensator, 280
doubly refracting, 249, 255
rotatory polarization, 285
sensitive tint, 287
tint of passage, 287
wedge, 274

Radiating potential, 366
Radiation:
black body, 330, 332
electromagnetic, 299
from accelerated charges, 323, 350, 379
laws, 335
on Bohr's theory, 350
Planck's law, 336
potential, 366, 367
Rayleigh's law, 335, 336
resonance, 369
Wien's law, 335, 336
Ramsden eyepiece, 80, 83, 84
Rational spectrum, 227
Ray, definition of, 23
Rayleigh, 242, 299, 327
and scattering, 242
criterion, 213
radiation law, 335, 336
refractometer, 155
Rays:
congruent, 170
paraxial, 42
Rectilinear propagation, 2, 6, 22, 187, 197, 211
Reflecting telescope, 215
Reflecting microscope, 218

Reflection:
  and phase change, 166
  and polarization, 263
  fits of, 5
  grating, 235, 238, 239
  of electrons, 382
  of plane waves, 24, 35
  of spherical waves, 30, 37, 38
  on corpuscular theory, 5
  on Huygens' Principle, 24
  regular, 1
  total, 4, 27
Refraction:
  by prism, 95
  double, 247
  index of, 26, 27, 158, 161, 254, 302
  of plane waves, 26, 40
  of spherical waves, 31
  on corpuscular theory, 4
  on Huygens' Principle, 26
  sine law, 1, 26
Refractometer, Rayleigh, 155
Relative luminosity curve, 331
Relative luminous efficiency, 331
Relativity, theory of, 399
Resolution, limit of, 211
  of eye, 214
Resolving power, 211
  and dispersion, 232
  and magnifying power, 214, 217, 219
  and numerical aperture, 217
  of grating, 232, 236
  of microscope, 215, 217
  of telescope, 211, 214
Resonance, 307, 317
  radiation, 369
Reversal of spectral line, 318
Ritz combination law, 344, 347
Roemer, 10, 11
Rotation:
  band, 371
  by magnetic field, 291
  of vibration plane, 285, 292
  specific, 291
Rotational energy level, 371
Rotatory polarization, 285
  Fresnel's explanation of, 292
Rowland, 238
Rutherford, 350
Rydberg, 343, 358
  constant, 343, 353

Saccharimeter, 289
Sargent, 181
Scattering:
  and polarization, 260, 275, 287
  of light, 239
Schmidt, 215

Schmidt camera, 215
Schrödinger, 383, 385
Sears, 181
Selection Principle:
  first, 361
  second, 362
Selective absorption, 316
Self-reversal, 318
Sensitive tint, 288
Sequence, band spectra, 376
Sequence number, 343
Series:
  Balmer, 340, 341, 350, 354
  Brackett, 342
  cadmium, 347
  combination law, 344
  designation of terms, 349
  diffuse, 343, 345
  doublet, 345
  general relations, 342
  graphical representation, 342
  helium, 357
  hydrogen, 340, 353
  interpretation of, 359, 363
  limit of, 343
  lithium, 343
  Lyman, 342, 354
  multiplet, 345
  Paschen, 342, 354
  Pfund, 342
  principal, 343, 345
  Ritz combination law, 344, 347
  Rydberg constant, 343
  sequence number, 343
  sharp, 343, 345
  singlet, 349, 363
  sodium, 346, 348
  spectral, 340
  triplet, 347, 363
  variable term, 343
  wave number, 341
Sharp series, 343, 345
Shear, 298
Shift of fringes, 159, 393, 396
S.H.M.:
  at right angles, 129, 132
  composition of, 123, 129
  definition of, 118
  equation of resultant, 128
  general equation of, 121
  graphical representation of, 119
  resolution of, 267
Sign convention, 39, 44
Sinclair, 240
Sine condition, 42, 89, 91, 216
Sine law of refraction, 1, 26
Singlet series, 349, 363
Skinner, 289

Sky:
  color of, 241
  polarization of light from, 262
Slope angle, 43
Snell, 1, 26
Snell's Law, 1
Sodium:
  absorption spectrum, 317, 369
  energy diagram, 370
  ionization potential, 368
  resonance radiation, 369
  series, 346, 348
  spectrum, 315, 317
  term values, 361
Sommerfeld, 359, 362, 385
Source of light:
  and electron, 323
  atomic, 321
  electrical, 323
Sources, light, 311
Spark spectrum, 316
Specific rotation, 291
Spectra, *see also* Spectrum
  band, 315, 370
  grating, 227
  line, 315
  origin of, 311, 321
  plurality of, 315
  series, 340
  triplet, 345
Spectral:
  line, 315, 322, 338
  line, analysis of, 176
  line, reversal of, 318
  line, single, 314
  line, width of, 322
  orders, 227
  series, 340
  terms, 343, 361, 401
  terms and energy levels, 358, 366, 368, 369, 370
Spectrograph, 104
Spectrometer, 97, 99, 104
Spectroscope, 104
  direct vision, 111
Spectrum, *see also* Spectra
  absorption, 316, 366, 369
  analysis, 321
  arc, 316
  band, 315, 370
  black body, 329
  cadmium, 347
  continuous, 314, 326, 329
  electronic bombardment, 312
  emission, 314
  energy, distribution of, 329
  enhanced, 316
  flame, 311

  helium, 315, 357
  hydrogen, 315, 359
  line, reversal of, 318
  line, self-reversal, 318
  line, structure of, 176
  lithium, 343
  magnesium, 316, 338
  mercury, 315
  of incandescent solid, 329
  prismatic, 227
  rational, 227
  single line, 314
  sodium, 315, 317, 346
  solar, 316, 320
  spark, 316
  stellar, 319
Spherical:
  aberration, 48, 79, 82
  wave-front, 22, 135
  waves and amplitude, 135
Spherometer, 170
Spin:
  electron, 361
  momentum, 362
  nuclear, 365
Spiral, Cornu's, 201
Star, measurement of width of, 157
Stark, 320
  effect, 320, 323
Stationary:
  states, 350
  waves, 137, 306
Stellar spectrum, 319
Stigmatic image, 50
Stokes, 299
Stop, 79
Structure:
  fine, 177, 361, 362, 363
  hyperfine, 364
  single line, 176
Straight edge, diffraction, 203
Strain in glass, detection of, 281
Sugar solution, analysis of, 289
Sun, spectrum of, 316, 320
Superposition, principle of, 124
System, band, 376

Tear, 305
Telescope, 76
  and parallel rays, 76
  crosshair lines, 86
  exit pupil, 77
  eyepiece of, 76, 79
  eye point, 77
  eye ring, 77
  field of view, 79
  limit of resolution, 211
  magnifying power of, 77, 82

objective, 76, 155, 171, 207, 211, 214
  reflecting, 215
  resolving power, 214
  with Huygens' eyepiece, 85
  with Ramsden eyepiece, 81
Term notation, 349, 364
Term, spectral, 343, 361, 401
Terms and energy levels, 358, 366, 368, 369, 370
Theory of:
  dispersion, 306
  light, corpuscular, 3, 4, 8
  light, elastic solid, 298
  light, electromagnetic, 298
  light, quantum, 9, 335
  relativity, 399
Thermionic emission of electrons, 363
Thick lens, 61
Thomson, 384, 385
Tint of passage, 287
Tolansky, 174
Tomaschek, 397
Total reflection, 4, 27
Tourmaline, 249, 255, 257
Transmission grating, 224
Transverse vibrations, 247, 299
Triplet series, 345, 347, 363
Trouton, 397
  and Noble experiment, 397

Uniaxial crystal, 249
Urey, 356, 357

Vectograph, 269
Vector:
  electric, 305
  light, 305
  model of atom, 359
Velocity of light, 2, 10, 20
  and aberration, 12
  Anderson, 17
  Bergstrand, 18
  Bradley, 12
  Cornu, 13
  Essen, 19
  Fizeau, 12
  Foucault, 14
  Galileo, 10
  Houston, 19
  Michelson, 15, 16
  Newcomb, 15
  Pease and Pearson, 16
  Roemer, 10
  rotating mirror, 14, 15
  toothed wheel, 12
  tunnel experiment, 16
Verdet's constant, 291

Vibration plane, 260, 261, 264
  and plane of polarization, 264
  and principal plane, 261
  rotation of, 285, 292
Vibrational energy level, 371
Vibration-rotation band, 373
Vibrations:
  circular, 132, 278
  elliptical, 132, 278
  longitudinal, 247, 299
  natural frequency, 307
  transverse, 247, 299
Vision, 71
  and position of image, 72
Voigt, 23

Walsh, 333
Watts, 20
Wave equation, 117
Wave form, 116
Wave-front:
  continuous, 9, 337
  discontinuous, 9, 337
  plane, 22, 135
  spherical, 22, 135
Wavelength(s):
  comparison of two, 176
  definition of, 115
  measurement of, 152, 227
  of electron waves, 383
  table of, 101, 400
Wavelet, 23, 249
  spheroidal, 249
Wave mechanics, 382
Wave motion, 115
  on electromagnetic theory, 303
Wave-number, 341
Wave theory, 3, 8, 301, 379
Waves:
  cause of, 115
  characteristic of, 115
  composition of, 137
  electric, 302, 304, 306
  electromagnetic, 298, 299, 303
  electron, 381
  Hertzian, 302
  plane, 133
  plane, equation of, 133
  plane, reflection of, 24
  plane, refraction of, 26
  shape of, 136, 140
  spherical, 30, 38
  spherical reflection of, 32, 37, 38
  spherical refraction of, 31, 44
  stationary, 137, 306
  train of, 115
Wedge, quartz, 349

Whittaker, 399
Width of:
  fringes, 147, 173
  grating maxima, 225
  spectral line, 322
Wien, 335
  radiation law, 335
Wiener, 306
Wilson, 359
Wollaston double-image prism, 263
Wood, 237, 369

X-rays, 305

Yerkes Observatory, 214
Young, 6, 8, 170

Zeeman, 320
Zeeman effect, 177, 236, 263, 320, 323,
    324, 325, 326, 327
  anomalous, 327
Zone plate, 197
Zones, half-period, 190
Zernike, 229